THE WORLD OF
LEONARDO DA VINCI

*MAN OF SCIENCE, ENGINEER AND
DREAMER OF FLIGHT*

Dr. Hart has also written:

History of Science and Technology

THE MECHANICAL INVESTIGATIONS OF LEONARDO DA VINCI
JAMES WATT AND THE HISTORY OF STEAM POWER
MAKERS OF SCIENCE
THE GREAT ENGINEERS
THE GREAT PHYSICISTS

Textbooks

A STUDENT'S HEAT
INTRODUCTION TO ADVANCED HEAT
INTRODUCTION TO PHYSICAL SCIENCE
AERONAUTICAL SCIENCE (with W. Laidler)
INTRODUCTION TO MECHANICS

"Rhythm in the Workshop." Muscular energy in harmony with mechanical power. Note the store of gun-barrels and cannonballs in the rear. A pen-and-ink study of a large cannon raised on to a gun-carriage (from the Windsor Royal Library).

THE WORLD OF
LEONARDO DA VINCI

MAN OF SCIENCE, ENGINEER AND
DREAMER OF FLIGHT

IVOR B. HART
O.B.E., Ph.D., B.Sc.

"The great bird will take its first flight on the back of the great bird, and filling the world with stupor and all writings with renown, and bringing glory to the nest where it was born."
FROM LEONARDO'S NOTEBOOK "ON THE FLIGHT OF BIRDS".

MACDONALD: LONDON

For
DEB, BASIL and BETSI—
and as a Tribute to the Memory of
CHARLES SINGER
who started me on this Course of Study
nearly forty years ago

Made and Printed in Great Britain by
Purnell and Sons, Ltd.
Paulton (Somerset) and London
First published in 1961 by
Macdonald & Co. (Publishers), Ltd.
16 Maddox Street, W.1

PREFACE

My purpose in this book is to present a reasoned picture of Leonardo da Vinci as a man of science, a practitioner of civil, military and mechanical engineering, and a dreamer of aeronautical dreams, set against a background of the world in which he lived and worked. It is intended primarily for the general reader but it is hoped that the more specialist students of Leonardo da Vinci may find the documented references interspersed throughout the book of some use.

The first half of the book is devoted to a survey of the world of politics, culture, science and technology in which Leonardo developed his many-sided genius. It is my view that this background picture is essential to a true appraisal of Leonardo's notes and studies. Accordingly, much space is given to an historical account of the various factors involved in the making of the Renaissance, from the days of classical antiquity to the peaks of intellectual revelation in the Italy of the fifteenth and early sixteenth centuries.

No one person is wholly competent to assess Leonardo's entire range of contribution over the arts, science and technology. I have, therefore, in the second half of the book, concentrated primarily upon his work in physics and mechanics, thereby leading to his activities as an engineering consultant. This is followed by a consideration of his studies in bird flight, and of his life-long but largely futile schemes for a man-powered flying machine. The book ends with a discussion of Leonardo's influence on the science of his days, and on its development by those who came after him.

I.B.H.

ACKNOWLEDGMENTS

I have been fortunate in the co-operation and help of many expert friends. Mr. K. R. Gilbert, M.A., D.I.C., the Hon. Sec. of the Newcomen Society and an authority on the engineering of Leonardo da Vinci, has read through the whole of the manuscript and has guided me skilfully through many tricky paths of interpretation and historical accuracy. Mr. C. H. Gibbs-Smith, M.A., so well-known as an authority on Leonardo's aeronautics, has similarly helped me, particularly with Chapter IX, and has also read through the entire proofs of the book. The Very Rev. John P. Canon Murphy has given me the valuable help of his scholarship with English translations of essential material from Medieval Italian, and Mrs. R. Knowles, a scholarly neighbour and friend, has helped me similarly with German material. To Miss A. H. Scott Elliot, Keeper of Prints and Drawings in the Royal Library at Windsor Castle, I am deeply indebted for generous facilities for the first-hand study in facsimile of many of Leonardo's Note-books.

Equally with all other English students of Leonardo's work, I have found Jean Paul Richter's *Literary Works of Leonardo da Vinci* and W. McCurdy's *Note-Books of Leonardo da Vinci* essential books of reference; and I have, with permission, used passages both from these and from the late Irma Richter's *Selections from the Note-Books of Leonardo da Vinci*. I am most grateful to Miss Gizela Richter, the executrix of the late Irma A. Richter, and to the Oxford University Press, the publishers of her father's "Literary Works" on the one hand, and to Mrs. McCurdy, widow and executrix of the late W. McCurdy and to Messrs. Jonathan Cape Ltd., the publishers of his "Note Books", for their ready permission to do this.

Additionally, the proofs had been read by my old friend Dr. Dorothy Feyer, as well as by Messrs. Gilbert and Gibbs-Smith. Finally, I must pay a word of tribute to Miss A. E. Smith, who has laboured so efficiently through the task of converting so much almost illegible scribble into readable typescript; and to my publishers, Messrs. Macdonald & Co., Ltd., for their patience and helpfulness over the many problems of publication.

THE ILLUSTRATIONS

With regard to the illustrations, I must first of all register my warmest thanks to Mr. T. D. Jones, the Director of the Department of Arts and Sciences of the International Business Machines Corporation of New

York, who has not only given me ready permission to reproduce illustrations freely from the excellent brochures and handbooks relating to the Leonardo Exhibition held by the I.B.M. in New York some years ago, but has also provided me with some of the original negatives for these illustrations.

A large number of the illustrations are copies taken, with the permission of the Director, from the reproductions by the Photographic Department of the Science Museum.

I am also grateful to Her Majesty the Queen for Her gracious permission to reproduce some six illustrations from originals in the Royal Library at Windsor; to the Oxford University Press for similar permission in respect of various illustrations taken from their publications; to the Mansell Studios for permission to use certain photos by Anderson and by Alinari; to T. Werner Laurie Ltd., for permission to use an illustration from *The Sons of Vulcan* by Thomas Hibben; to W. & T. Avery Ltd., for permission to use three illustrations from *A Short History of Weighing* by L. Sanders; to Mrs. Dorothea Singer for allowing me to use illustrations from the works of her late husband and my former teacher, Dr. Charles Singer; and to my friends Mr. C. H. Gibbs-Smith and Dr. L. Reti for the use of illustrations from their own writings.

The ready co-operation of all concerned has been a warming and pleasurable feature in the task of preparation.

Additional acknowledgments are included where relevant, in the captions to the plates.

I.B.H.

Lynwood,
  Thorpe, Surrey.

CONTENTS

CONTENT

LIST OF PLATES

PART ONE

LEONARDO'S ITALY—
THE BUILD-UP OF THE RENAISSANCE

I

LEONARDO THE MAN

I. LEONARDO AND HIS NOTEBOOKS

Leonardo da Vinci was a product of the fifteenth century. He was born in the small Tuscan village of Vinci, near Florence, on 15th April in the year 1452 (Plate 1). He was certainly a love child and almost as certainly unwanted—the product of a brief and illicit adventure between Ser Piero da Vinci, a young and lusty lawyer of twenty-three, and a simple peasant girl of the neighbourhood in which he lived.

Yet this was the child whose subsequent genius has become one of the high-lights of the human story. Leonardo da Vinci ranks as an outstanding figure in the history of civilisation. For some long period after his death in 1519 circumstances which will be discussed later in this book limited his tremendous reputation to the field of art—but notebooks, which he had compiled during his lifetime and which were lost and forgotten for long after his death, gradually came to light. It has been largely on the basis of the accumulated study and research upon this material during the past hundred years that Leonardo da Vinci has come to be recognised as a genius in many branches of culture and knowledge outside art.

In his memory, the year 1952, the 500th anniversary of his birth, was made the occasion of a world-wide tribute on a remarkable scale. In numerous centres of culture—London, Paris, Milan and New York are but a few examples—special exhibitions were arranged in his honour. In Italy a commemorative stamp was designed and issued to mark the occasion, and in London the Royal Academy of Art not only assembled an impressive collection of his pictures, cartoons, sketches and notebooks but also arranged a series of public lectures by experts in the various fields of Leonardo's activities.

It is difficult to find a parallel to such a world-wide range of tributes in respect of any of the many other great men whose stories and achievements belong quite properly to the history of human progress. There is, however, in all this, one unusual feature that calls for special remark. Those whom the world has recognised and extolled as men of genius have, in general, been men of positive achievement. But the genius of Leonardo da Vinci has, in some respects, taken a very different form. Generally speaking, the world's famous artists, philosophers, teachers and men of science have left behind them either their works of art or their books, their teachings or their records of discoveries and researches; great engineers have produced their gigantic designs and structures for the good of posterity; great statesmen have practised the gift of good government for the benefit of the nations for whom they are responsible; great soldiers have impressed their indelible stamp of masterly campaigns upon the pages of history. But Leonardo da Vinci falls into none of these categories. Although he was one of the world's greatest artists, unfortunately only a few of his paintings have survived; and in the sense of a link between teacher and taught, he was neither a teacher nor a writer. He held no academic appointment and he published no consistent schemes of research.

When we refer to Leonardo da Vinci as a profound student of science, engineering and technology in their manifold aspects it would seem relevant to infer that he had made a positive contribution to research and development in these fields. It is a freakish fact, however, that although his work was quite brilliant it had no permanent effect on the science of his successors, and no very marked influence on their technologies. Living at a period when publication, though perhaps difficult, was nevertheless not impossible, he published nothing. Instead, he scribbled and sketched thousands of pages of notes—a feverish and disordered activity of a lifetime—notes that teemed with scientific discussions based on acute observation and experiment; notes that swept through a wide range of problems in art, science, philosophy and engineering.

Leonardo's notebooks, for so long lost and at last salved, can well be described as a vast scrap-heap, the study of which shows their writer to have displayed an ingenuity and a capacity for original thinking on a variety of matters far ahead of the days in which he lived. It is these notebooks, as well as the few paintings and the numerous cartoons and sketches that have survived, that place him in the forefront of the world's greatest intelligences.

2. THE CRITERIA FOR GREATNESS

Let us be a little more specific about this problem of the estimation of Leonardo's claims to lasting fame. We should use this term sparingly, since lasting greatness is indeed a rarity. By what criteria is it proper for the judgment of history to assess an individual life-record as being outstandingly great?

It is suggested that there are three such criteria. Firstly, there should be an intrinsic specialised knowledge in some field or fields of intellectual activity beneficial to mankind; secondly, there must be some record of positive achievement within that field of activity; and thirdly, there should be evidence of a lasting influence produced by the work of the individual concerned, not alone in a purely contemporary sense but of a sufficiently permanent character to claim for it an influence on posterity.

Now, how does the record of Leonardo da Vinci respond to these criteria? It must again be stressed that he held no professional appointment in the academic sense. He was a freelance artist, open to accept a commission from anybody—although, indeed, having accepted it, there was no guarantee that he would ever carry it out. He lived vaguely under the intermittent patronage (and at times with even more intermittent financial reward) of various regional rulers in a country swayed by internecine intrigue and warfare. In times of peace he was from time to time employed in variously assorted duties that ranged from court engineer, architect and artist to that of a master of ceremonial. In periods of war, or even of the threat of war, he was used as an adviser on military engineering.

We have mentioned that, although he published nothing, he yet wrote notes extensively. There is, in fact, some evidence that he had hoped one day to co-ordinate his notes for the purpose of publication. In one of the anatomical manuscripts housed in Windsor Castle, for instance, he writes: "Let no man who is not a mathematician read the elements of my work"; whilst, more explicitly, there is the following oft-quoted passage with which one of his notebooks (now housed in the British Museum) opens: "Begun at Florence at the house of Piero di Braccio Martello on the 22nd day of March, 1508. This is a collection without order, drawn from many papers that I have here copied, hoping later to put them in their right order, according to the subjects which they treat. I fear that I must repeat myself frequently; do not blame me for this, reader, because the subjects are numerous and the memory is unable to have them all present and say: 'I shall not write this because I wrote it before.' And if I wished to avoid falling into this fault, it would be necessary in every case when I wanted to copy that, not to repeat myself, I should read over all that had gone before: and all the more since the intervals are long between one time of writing and the next."

There is here implied not only the intention to collate the notes but also that these notes are to be read by the general public. Indeed, as a thread throughout his notebooks one senses the atmosphere of that of the teacher addressing the taught; of the philosopher and thinker expounding his views to the reader and giving him instructions regarding the carrying out of a variety of investigations and experiments.

But as we have already indicated, these notebooks were lost and forgotten for very many years after his death; and even of his paintings relatively few remain.

We may take it, then, that Leonardo da Vinci fully intended that his writings should ultimately see the light of day. Unfortunately, he never got beyond the stage of notetaking. Although the wish was there, he never translated it into action. Instead, he wrote more notes and yet more notes. Critics have declared that he lacked the concentration of purpose in this, as in his incompleted works of art, to pass on his energies to the detailed treatment of a specific subject. But it would possibly be more correct to say that, whatever may have been his powers of concentration, the encyclopaedic vigour of his mentality created for his pen a continual and ever-ranging curiosity which compelled him to a never-ending stream of comments and impressions which he was powerless to resist.

In art, on the other hand, both his specialised knowledge and his achievements have long been acknowledged. With Michelangelo, his work could be regarded as the culmination of the Florentine school of Renaissance art. In his own day, when a mission in art was needed, he both preached it and practised it—and at all times since his work has been a source of inspiration to artists all the world over.

But Leonardo has far more title to fame than in respect of his art alone. We freely acknowledge nowadays that as an intellect he was rarely, if ever, matched in the history of civilisation. Few minds, if any, were so completely receptive, so observant, so curious and interested in all that was going on around him, so objectively speculative as to the meaning of it all and so much imbued with the modernist outlook in scientific method as expressed by the appeal to observation and experiment. His range of interest was quite extraordinary in scope. The mere turning-over and scanning of his notebooks is a breathtaking experience in their manifold range. In art he practised painting, sculpture, architecture and music, and, because he claimed that no artist could properly practise his art without them, he was an avid student of anatomy, of physiology, of botany, of optics, of mathematics and of mechanics. Indeed, all branches of natural, physical and mechanical science came extensively into his ken. Moreover, he was keenly interested in the study of bird flight, and one of his life ambitions was to achieve the conquest of the air by artificial means.

Throughout his career, too, he was intensely concerned with problems of mechanical, hydraulic, civil and military engineering, and his notebooks abound with evidence of a knowledge, skill and insight into the work of the engineer that went far beyond the empiricism of his day and led him into speculations on the laws of motion, the conceptions of force and power, and the problems of power transmission of a kind that are reminiscent of the topics one finds today in the average textbook of applied mechanics without which no engineering student can pursue his studies.

It will be seen from the foregoing, therefore, that the genius and greatness of Leonardo da Vinci do not follow the normal pattern. In their separate ways, the claims to a high place in history for such men as Aristotle, Caesar, Shakespeare, Newton, Napoleon and Einstein, to quote a few examples, are quite obvious. In the case of Leonardo da Vinci they have needed some explanation and justification, resting, as we have indicated, largely on the evidence of his notebooks. Now notebooks are "rough and ready" things, and in the case of Leonardo da Vinci it would be quite easy to be diverted from a true judgment as to their superlative merits by taking much of the contents too literally. Many of the notes bear the stamp of haste and spontaneity. They are mixed up with the varying hour-to-hour and day-to-day moods of the writer. Some are crude, some make nonsense. There is much in them of errors and flaws for the purist to condemn. The style of their expression is more that of "the man in the street" than that of an intellectual. But, inasmuch as they are just notes—day-to-day records—and because they display, in their aggregate, a depth, a range, a sense of vision and a true spirit of scientific enquiry, their overwhelming intrinsic merit is beyond dispute.

3. SOME REFLECTIONS ON LEONARDO'S PERSONALITY

How far do the notebooks reflect the personality of the man as distinct from his cultural and scientific qualities? It is important that we should enlarge on this aspect of Leonardo as an aid to our judgment. There is an inescapable individuality about all notebooks. Every student, every notetaker, develops his own characteristic scheme of abbreviations and his own tricks and habits of writing and sketching. So far as Leonardo is concerned, we shall consider these in greater detail when we refer to the story of the loss and recovery of his notebooks; but, for the purpose of our immediate theme, there is, among the thousands of pages, one special record that gives us a glimpse of how Leonardo regarded himself. Perhaps the biggest collection of his notes is that which has come to be known, on account of its size, as the *Codex Atlanticus (Codice Atlantico)*. It was acquired by the Ambrosian Library at Milan in 1636. It contains 402 sheets and more than 1,700 drawings and sketches.   Folio 319 of this collection contains a draft or copy (incidentally, not in his own handwriting) of a letter which Leonardo sent early in the year 1481, when he was twenty-nine years of age, to Ludovico Sforza, the ruler of Milan.   This letter was, in fact, an application for employment and patronage.   It was known to Leonardo that Ludovico Sforza was seeking a sculptor whom he could commission to produce an equestrian statue in honour of his father, Francesco Sforza.   But he also knew that Ludovico was, at the time, in great political trouble and was being seriously threatened with encirclement by rivals all round him—from Venice to the east; from the Pope's armies in Rome to the south; and from the King of France to the north.

Playing upon his needs, it is evident that Leonardo's letter to Sforza shaped his tactics of approach accordingly.   Although he was primarily an artist, the letter refers to his prowess in this direction only in the last paragraph.   The rest of the letter is taken up with his claims to a range of abilities in practical engineering mainly directed to the art of war, though a penultimate paragraph is reserved for some extensive claims in architecture and civil engineering.

The letter reads thus:

"Having, most illustrious sir, seen and considered the experiments of all those who profess to be masters in the art of invention of the apparatus of war and, having found that their instruments do not differ materially from those in general use, I venture, without wishing injury to anyone, to make known to your Excellency certain secrets of my own, briefly enumerated as follows:

"1. I have a process for the construction of very light bridges, capable of easy transport, by means of which the enemy may be put to flight and pursued: and of others, more solid, which will resist both fire and sword and which are easily lowered or raised.   I know also of a means to burn and destroy hostile bridges.

"2. In case of the investment of a place, I know how to drain moats and construct scaling ladders [Plate 2] and other such apparatus.

"3. Item: If, by reason of its elevation or strength, it is not possible to bombard a hostile position, I have a means of destruction by mining provided the foundations of the fortress are not of rock.

"4. I know also how to make light cannon easy of transport, capable of ejecting inflammable matter, the smoke from which would cause terror, destruction and confusion among the enemy.   [Note here a fifteenth-century anticipation of smoke-screen and poison gas.]

"5. Item: By means of narrow and tortuous subterranean tunnels, dug without noise, I am able to create a passage to inaccessible places, even under rivers.

"6. Item: I know how to construct secure and covered wagons for the transport of guns into the enemy's lines, and not to be impeded by ever so dense a mass, and behind which the infantry can follow without danger. [There is here a possible vision of the modern tank.]

"7. I can make cannon, mortars, and engines of fire, etc., of form both useful and beautiful and different from those at present in use [Plate 3].

"8. Or, if the use of cannon happens to be impracticable, I can replace them by catapults and other admirable projecting weapons at present unknown; in short, where such is the case, I am able to devise endless means of attack.

"9. And, if the combat should be at sea, I have numerous most powerful engines both for attack and defence; and ships which are both gun-proof and fire-proof; and also powders and inflammables.

"10. In times of peace, I believe that I can compete with anyone in architecture and in the construction of both public and private monuments and in the building of canals.

"I am able to execute statues in marble, bronze and clay; in painting I can do as well as anyone else. In particular, I will undertake to execute the bronze horse in the eternal memory of your father and of the very illustrious house of Sforza and, if any of the above-mentioned things appear to you impossible or impracticable, I will offer to make an attempt at it in your park, or in any other place which your Excellency may please to choose, to which I commend myself in all humility."

Now this is an extraordinary letter and it will be agreed that it throws an interesting light both on the writer as an individual and on the scope of his activities and interests in Florence, where he was educated and trained. It may be argued that the letter lacks modesty. A sufficient reply to this is that we have here an artist who puts his art last on his list of qualifications. Leonardo was seeking patronage and employment and his letter needed the right tactics to gain what he sought. He aimed at striking the imagination of the recipient in terms of his urgent military needs as well as of his less urgent call for a sculptor. Certainly as an application for employment it would have intrigued the modern psychologist, and it was successful in its purpose. In a later chapter we shall discuss the technological picture as it existed in the fifteenth century, but it may here be said quite definitely that Leonardo's claims, as envisaged in this letter, go far beyond this picture in a variety of directions. Nevertheless, it is a fact that included in his sketches and notes are very definite records of a host of ingenious ideas covering the whole range of his claims (Plate 4). As to whether he could, or would, or did pass from the sketches and ideas contained in his notes to actual accomplishment or even attempt at achievement is a different matter. He was much too busy with more notes and more ideas for this to be possible.

What does the world owe to Leonardo da Vinci? To what extent has he merited our gratitude? However great may be the mentality of a man, however important the intrinsic value of his work and of his writings, unless these have been offered to the world for the edification of mankind, unless something of his wisdom and his understanding has been passed on to civilisation, mankind owes him nothing. All the evidence goes to show that Leonardo's many-sided studies in technology, unlike those of his contemporaries, were either, on the one hand, founded on scientific principles or, on the other, were empirical exercises that led him to formulate or speculate upon scientific principles and that these principles were often far in advance of his time. But the fact remains that these studies were unknown to those who, both in his own day and in the times that followed, might have profited by their wealth of information and suggestions to enable them to quicken an advance and a progress in scientific and technical knowledge that was thus otherwise halted. The loss of his manuscripts was indeed a tragedy but for which the course of scientific history may well have been much earlier enriched. The great pioneers of research who lived after him had, therefore, to traverse afresh the ground he had, in fact, covered, and only today are we beginning to realise the true extent of the world's great loss. To quote one example, Dr. Charles Singer, one of the foremost authorities on the history of anatomy and medicine, tells us in his *Evolution of Anatomy* (pp. 90–91) that, having begun to dissect in order to improve his art, Leonardo soon became interested in the structure and working of the body (Plate 5). "His scientific preoccupation at last exceeded his artistic, and his anatomical notebooks . . . have revealed him for what he was: one of the very greatest biological investigators of all time. In endless matters he was centuries ahead of his contemporaries. Had he produced the anatomical textbook which he had planned in collaboration with the Pavean Professor, Marc Antonio della Torre, the progress of anatomy and physiology would have been advanced by centuries."

4. HIS FAILURE AS A CAREERIST

Here, then, was a man of great intrinsic qualities of curiosity, intellect and capacity for observation—a man who displayed fertility in constructive ideas in a variety of fields, with, fortunately, an outstanding ability to illustrate his ideas with masterly sketches supported by notes. Yet he nevertheless lived a life of little positive success in the day-to-day meaning of the term. From time to time one hears of genius going either unrecognised during the lifetime of the individual concerned or at least becoming recognised very late in his day— destined to pass his years in poverty and obscurity—yet blossoming perhaps ultimately into a glory of fame and recognition. But at least such recognition is usually founded upon the actual accomplishments of genius—there, for all to behold, if it be in the field of art, or to read, if it be in the field of letters. But this cannot be said of Leonardo da Vinci in any other of his many-sided interests outside his art. In his art, however, in spite of a waywardness and a seemingly dilatory temperament that made him unreliable in the matter of successfully concluding contracts and commissions in painting and sculpture, he did, in fact, gain recognition as an outstanding genius among his contemporaries, many of whose works have become the cherished possessions of the great art galleries, palaces and the art connoisseurs of today.

As a careerist, however, Leonardo must be counted as practically a failure. Perhaps he lacked the little bit of luck that so often makes and marks the difference between success and failure in the material sense. But there was surely more to it than just the matter of luck. Living either in or on the fringe of the courts of the rulers, under whose none-too-lavish patronage he was variously employed, his status and his lot were probably neither too happy nor too specific. As a young man he was gifted with a handsome and a muscular physique and endowed with a love of life and jest. He had the ability both to produce good music and to fashion the musical instruments for the purpose, and one might well have imagined him as the "jolly good fellow" of the court circles around him.

But in a variety of ways he must have lacked that "something". Leonardo's early upbringing was to some extent responsible for this. His mother was of peasant stock. His father belonged to a world of thrift, industry and tradition derived from a long line of lawyers whose reputation and standing meant very much within the village of Vinci but not so much outside it. The Vinci family had been notaries, often in the service of the Florentine republic, with a legal record that went back into the thirteenth century. They were also minor land-owners and farmers. They lived, in fact, what today we would speak of as a solid and a stolid middle-class life. Leonardo was accepted in this family a few years after he was born, partly because his mother, Caterina, was herself getting married and partly because his father, Ser Piero, was then still childless. Leonardo's stepmother welcomed him and treated him well, and this period of his young life must have been reasonably happy. But it was incomplete. Not only was there that background feeling of not quite belonging—accentuated when, subsequently, other children came to the household—but there was also the lack of a formal education. He did, in fact, learn to read and write, and he was grounded in the elements of mathematics (mainly arithmetic, with some geometry), and he obtained perhaps even a bare notion of some of the rudiments of Latin, the inadequacy of which was to prove a great handicap in his subsequent and adult reading and study. But, on the whole, he was left much to his own devices at a time when human relationships and the benefits of disciplined and formal education should have meant so much.

On the other hand, he rapidly developed an innate love of nature which compensated greatly for his lack of human companionship. The village of Vinci was ideally and beautifully set for this development. Dominated by Monte Albano and (to his child mind) a seemingly mysterious but fascinating series of crags, slopes and mountain streams on the one side, and the rich green valley of Lucca on the other, his imagination and his interest were continually aroused, and, without doubt, the seed was sown for that perpetual urge to a study of nature and natural phenomena that was to endure throughout his lifetime. Here, too, in his fascination for the bird life that hovered about the mountain slopes were probably born those life-long dreams, which are shown so clearly in his notebooks, of a man-made machine that would one day emulate the birds in their passage through the air.

It was from this atmosphere and this free and quiet communion with nature that Leonardo was transplanted, at the age of sixteen, to the wealthy merchant city of Florence, with its busy craftsmen and traders. Here, under the stimulus of a growing humanism, there had been gathering the intellectual momentum of a Renaissance that was to sweep across Western Europe. One phase of this was that the intellectuals of Florence were imbued with an urge to imitate and emulate the classical past, with its ancient art, its literature and its philosophy.

But so far the Renaissance had not reached down to the mass of the people. It was confined, perhaps inevitably, to those whose education and social level could absorb its influence—and, indeed, intensified rather than diminished the social and intellectual gap between these relatively few and the main population. It was a curious situation. The Renaissance was not to achieve complete fulfilment until it could break from the shackles of the past and fulfil its own independent mission in terms of the future. This, however, it could not do without first reviving the lost artistic and intellectual glories of the Greek and Roman eras, and this, therefore, became the predominant intellectual occupation of the time. Leonardo's personal position in this was peculiar. On his father's side he could just about claim a footing among the ranks of the social and intellectual élite of Florence, but his lack of formal education made it almost impossible for him to keep pace with the level of life and living about him. The press of humanist doctrine and practice was tyrannical in its intellectual demands. It involved a persistent study of the classics; it required a day-to-day mode of living patterned on the lines and the teachings and the habits of the great Latin scholars, lawyers and statesmen; it even called for the use of Latin in ordinary conversation—and it dramatised all this with a wealth of classical quotations. Such standards were not only beyond Leonardo but were contrary to his nature and temperament. His instinct was to look forward rather than backward. But he did what he could.

To appreciate the nature of the language problem with which Leonardo da Vinci found himself confronted in his anxiety to read and master the writings of the ancient philosophers, we must recall that the history of the confusion of tongues described by Moses in the Bible was typical of what happened in Europe. When the Romans established an expanding empire by conquest, they hoped to make their language the legal, religious, civil and administrative cement binding the conquered peoples to them and to each other. But by the time, in the fifth century, that the empire of the Caesars had become, like Babel, a vast ruin, the Latin tongue had been injected with a growing mixture of the idioms of the invading barbarian languages, producing differences and divergencies from land to land according to the varying origins of the invaders, whether from the heart of Asia, the eastern extremities of Germany, or the lesser-known regions of the North. Thus began the languages of modern Europe, still basically derived from the Latin of the days of Livy and Cicero. In an endeavour to maintain tradition, classical Latin was still spoken and understood by the upper classes of society, but the people as a whole used a rustic language, a *lingua Romana*, of differing dialects according to place and population. These diversions were naturally magnified with time until, by the fifteenth century, classical Latin was far removed from the "vulgar" speech of the people. One had to be "brought up" with it to speak and read it with familiarity, and this, as we know, did not happen to Leonardo. He persisted in his endeavour to master it, but the effort was a continual burden. The easy possession of the Latin tongue was a hall-mark of social status. It had "snob value", and its absence kept Leonardo out of the inner social circles of the courts in which he served. He must have felt this very keenly, and perhaps more so at some periods in his career than at others. But for him there was additionally involved the urge to study the actual writings of the ancients. He wanted to understand Plato and Archimedes, Aristotle and Galen, and the others, and in this he persisted throughout his life.

In his younger days it sufficed that he could live and work with his master, Andrea del Verrocchio (1435–1488) (Plate 6), as an art apprentice, and in the shelter of those developing years there emerged that tremendous spirit of curiosity and enquiry which, harnessed to the developing genius of his great art and his capacity for thinking out all kinds of practical problems and devices, enabled him to reach a measure of competence and belief in himself that brought him, as we have seen, his appointment to the court of Ludovico Sforza at Milan. Yet neither there nor elsewhere subsequently could he ever be regarded as having commanded a position of responsibility or as having acquired a status that would have deemed him a man to be reckoned with in the world of affairs. Not on these counts could the name of Leonardo da Vinci hope to survive.

5. HIS INTELLECTUAL AND CULTURAL CONTACTS

We have indicated that there was in Leonardo's personality and qualities something that failed to make for leadership and success as a careerist. Indeed, for many periods in his life he was in some financial straits. But it is, after all, not infrequently the lot of genius to go hungry whilst displaying either artistic or intellectual brilliance. As we have already said, Leonardo was soon being talked about as a painter of supreme ability, and later, both in Florence and elsewhere, as one of the great artists of his time. And it says much that all through his life his name was linked with a succession of distinguished men of his day. As a youth, during his apprenticeship to Verrocchio, he came under the influence of Benedetto d'Abbaco (b. 1432)—who was also known as Benedetto d'Aritmetico. d'Abbaco had set up the Florentine Scuola d'Abbaco, and here Leonardo studied mathematics. But d'Abbaco was also interested in industry and commerce and, accordingly, gave a practical twist to Leonardo's interests. It was probably at this period that Leonardo began to read widely, largely from books borrowed from friends and fellow pupils at the Scuola. Here, too, he met and was influenced by the Greek scholar Giovanni Johannes Agiropulo (1416–1486), a fugitive from Constantinople after its fall in 1453. At a time when it was the vogue for all the intellectuals of the time to learn Greek and Latin, Agiropulo's lectures at the Studium Generale of Florence were very popular. In particular, his translation of Aristotle's *Physica* and the *De Coela* into both Latin and the Vulgate (which was the vernacular of the people of Italy) introduced Leonardo into fields of interest that were to develop profoundly for him in later years.

During this period, too, that great Venetian-born student of manifold interests, Leon Battista Alberti (1404–1472), was attracting considerable attention. He was a cleric in the Metropolitan Church of

Florence, and, in addition to his interests as painter, poet, musician, architect and philosopher, he wrote extensively upon scientific problems over a wide variety of fields. These Leonardo read avidly, and he refers to them on a number of occasions in his notebooks.

But the greatest influence on Leonardo at this time was that of Paolo Toscanelli. He was one of the most illustrious of the Florentine physicists and geographers of the fifteenth century. He was a "stay-at-home" geographer in that he never left his native city, but, on the one hand, travellers and adventurers sought him out from all parts of the world and, on the other hand, from the records of their travels, combined with his own speculations, there sprang his conviction of a westward route to India. This he conveyed, it is claimed, by correspondence in 1474 to Christopher Columbus at Lisbon, and the famous explorer was thus inspired, years after Toscanelli's death, to that great adventure that was destined both to change the face of the world and to affect its subsequent history. There is no doubt that Leonardo came to know and to be influenced by Toscanelli. And so he dreamed his dreams of distant lands and their peoples, of variations in land and sea formations, of maps and map construction, of heavenly bodies and their movements, all adding to the growing quota of his interests and impressions at this most formative period of his career.

At the age of twenty Leonardo had become enrolled as a member of the Painters' Guild of St. Luke, and, although he continued to live with Verrocchio, he was working independently under the fleeting patronage of Lorenzo the Magnificent. There was now developing a wide sweep in his interests from art to science and engineering. Anatomy and perspective were for him essential studies as an artist, whilst architecture, another of his deep interests, and the problems of civil and military engineering to which he felt himself drawn, led him insensibly and intensively into various problems in the fields of mechanics and hydraulics. His essentially modernistic outlook had already begun to develop, and this brought him into critical judgments and disagreements with some of those teachings of the ancient philosophers with which he had become familiar from Agiropulo's lectures.

Leonardo felt that the blind acceptance of classical authority that had become characteristic of his day and age in Florence and elsewhere, whether it be in the name of Plato, Aristotle or Ptolemy, or any other of the great thinkers and writers of classical antiquity, was wrong. "Anyone who in discussion relies upon authority uses not his understanding but his memory," he writes in the *Codex Atlanticus*. The test of experiment (he called it "experience") was, for him, a supreme criterion. So he says: "Many will think that they may reasonably blame me by alleging that my proofs are opposed to the authority of certain men held in the highest reverence . . . not considering that my works are the issue of pure and simple experience, which is the true mistress."

In subsequent phases of his career Leonardo developed personal friendships with other great philosophers of his day. In Milan, for instance, there was his close association with the distinguished mathematician, Fra Luca Pacioli, a man of tremendous importance and prestige (Plate 7). He was a minorite friar who lectured on mathematics at Rome, Pisa and Venice, later to become the first occupant of a chair in mathematics founded by Ludovico Sforza. He died in 1510. His *Summa de Arithmetica, Geometrica, Proportione et Proportionalita* was published in Venice in 1494 and was the earliest *printed* textbook on the subject. It was founded on the writings of the thirteenth-century mathematician Leonardo of Pisa. Da Vinci had already studied this book when he first met Pacioli soon after the latter's arrival in Milan, and the two soon became close friends. Leonardo did, in fact, give material assistance to Pacioli in the preparation of his next book, *De Divina Proportione*; and when later Leonardo left Milan to return to his native Florence, Pacioli went with him.

Another contact of importance to Leonardo in these Milan days was that of Fazio Cardano (1445–1524), whose natural son was the famous mathematician Jerome Cardan. Fazio was both a learned jurist and a "hobbyist" mathematician, and in fact his hobby was of sufficient magnitude and importance to prompt him to undertake, in 1480, the editing of the hitherto unpublished work, *Perspectiva Communis* by John Peckham, Archbishop of Canterbury. The *Perspectiva* was a treatise on Optics, which Leonardo studied with intense interest.

Then, too, there was Donato d'Agnolo, who, under the name of Bramante (*c.* 1444–1514), achieved a considerable reputation as both painter and architect. He, like Leonardo, had developed a considerable interest in mechanics and science, and this naturally brought the two together. Of his later years, perhaps Leonardo's most fruitful friendship was with the gifted young anatomist, Marc Antonio della Torre, born in 1483 (when Leonardo was thirty-one years of age). Della Torre was descended from a noble family of Verona. His father, Jerome della Torre, had studied medicine at the University of Padua, and here, in due course, the son had followed him. His subsequent career took him from Padua, first to Venice and then to Pavia. He soon became an anatomist of unusual ability. His outlook was modern, and he had very little patience with mere book study. Instead, he practised dissection and firsthand study of the human form and organs whenever opportunity offered. It is tragic that his life was cut short in 1512, in his thirtieth year, from fever. It is clear, however, that at Pavia a close friendship had sprung up between him and the much older da Vinci. Apart from a mutual liking, their common interest in anatomy enabled each to help and influence the other. Leonardo's natural ability in the sketching of anatomical detail was of considerable importance to della Torre. Indeed, Leonardo's anatomical drawings are accepted for their accuracy of detail and their vivid portrayal as a contribution of positive value to the evolution of anatomical knowledge.

6. HIS BRILLIANCE AS A THINKER

We have enumerated only some of the many names of importance in the cultural field of Leonardo's times with whom he had come into contact and by whom he was influenced and aided in the development both of his personality and of his natural and acquired abilities and interests. As we have seen, these latter developed an increasing momentum that filled his life to overflowing. There was more in the day than his tremendous appetite, curiosity and deep ability could cope with. Little could be brought to the stage of completion, but most of it could be and was recorded in note after note and in notebook after notebook, either in brief phrases or in more extended form, but usually, fortunately, with quick and vivid sketches made naturally possible by his artistry. Much of his genius lay in the spontaneity of these notes and (in the light of recent study) in their intrinsic qualities of originality, of insight and vision, and of the essentially modernistic outlook of his procedures. To these must be added the experimental basis of his conclusions and his extraordinary flair for the design of mechanical contrivances in a host of directions.

But the notebooks were lost and their contents were for so long unknown. On the other hand, on the positive side there was, before everything else, his incomparable art. This at least was both supreme and undeniable. Inheriting as he did the glorious traditions of the Italian Renaissance, and living as he did in the full crest of the wonderful wave which had so effectively transformed the outlook of the Western world, the whole objects, aims, hopes and achievements of the Renaissance seem to have been epitomised in his being. As a painter and a sculptor he preached a mission of universality in art which brought into his range the whole of creation which, as we know now, resulted initially in involving him in those scientific and philosophic studies which literally engulfed his life.

It is when we add to this positive achievement the recognition of those qualities of mind and spirit that have emerged from an intensive study of his recovered notebooks that the true greatness and genius of his mighty intellect and his personality claim our admiration and our recognition. In no other individual in history is this universality of brilliance so consistently maintained.

Small wonder, therefore, that he has been singled out for all time as one of the very select band of the world's greatest personalities.

Plate 1—The village of Vinci at which Leonardo was born.

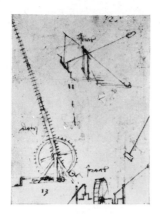

Plate 2—"I know how to construct scaling ladders."

Plate 3—"I can make cannon, and mortars, and engines of fire." Studies of mortars and cannon. Note the mortar firing from a boat at the bottom of the Plate (Windsor Royal Library).

II

LEONARDO'S CULTURAL SETTING — THE BUILD-UP OF THE RENAISSANCE IN FIFTEENTH-CENTURY ITALY

I. THE MEANING OF THE RENAISSANCE

Leonardo's life was lived during that period of intense cultural activity and expansion referred to by historians as the Renaissance. It was a momentous era in European history—an era of great change in man's outlook on life, on Nature and all its problems, on everything fundamental. The Renaissance, as the term implies, was a re-birth of something vital that had ceased to live. That something has been variously indicated by the terms culture, learning, the practice of thinking abstractly and objectively—in sum, all the ingredients which make up what matters in civilisation.

But the Renaissance, in its full purpose, had to mean much more than a mere recovery of lost wisdom and of a lost habit of thinking. It had to go forward—to look ahead and to develop from the regained intellectual ground a new outlook and a new purpose, with new procedures and techniques for thinking and investigation. Only thus could the world be set afresh on its feet and be ensured of that progress without which civilisation must remain stagnant. It is a sad commentary on the period leading to the Renaissance that the process of cultural recovery was such a very long one. We have, in fact, to go back to classical antiquity—that is to say, to the days of the Greek and Roman civilisations—to find the real basis for the heritage of the fifteenth century. This is a long time. The implication is of a very long gap in the processes of culture. Both the Greeks and the Romans gave much to the world in art, in science, in philosophy, in law, in administration and good government. Circumstances, unfortunately, brought these contributions first to a state of decline, and then, following the collapse and the over-running of the Roman Empire by invaders from north-eastern Europe, to a period of more or less complete intellectual silence. We speak of this period as the Dark Ages, and it was the centuries of intellectual sterility of this period from which was to emerge the dawn of hope, largely through the medium of a gradual

recovery of the lost and forgotten writings of the ancient world. From
the twelfth to the fourteenth century the pace of this recovery gained
momentum. By the fifteenth century the full tide of the Renaissance
had swept over Italy, to be carried over in its various and varied aspects to the other countries of western Europe.

An essential preliminary to the understanding of the gradual recovery of the lost manuscripts of the ancient teachers was the necessity
to be able to read them. Greek and Latin had to be learned afresh;
and as the wisdom of these ancient writers and thinkers was unfolded
to a growing following of scholarship, enthusiasm for their literature
spread over Italy. Initially, therefore, the Renaissance was in the
world of letters—of the poets, the essayists and the historians of the
old world. But art was quick to follow, and inevitably science came
in the wake of these; and finally, caught up on its practical aspects,
there came a growing awareness of the applications of science to a
medieval technology.

This, then, was the world and the atmosphere and the intellectual
climate of Leonardo's life. Our purpose here is to give, in some detail,
a picture of his own contributions, through his notebooks, to these
interests. It is fitting, however, as a preliminary, to paint a background
to this picture by describing, in turn, some of the principal factors in
the advent of the Renaissance from the various aspects involved—
cultural, political, scientific and technological.

2. THE CULTURAL LEGACIES OF ANTIQUITY—GREECE

In considering the state of knowledge at any given time we must
bear in mind that two factors are involved. There is, first of all, the
legacy of the past, and there is, secondly, the contribution of contemporary investigation and research. History is conventionally
referred to in terms of three broad divisions—ancient, medieval and
modern. What we have to discuss from the cultural angle is the broad
transition from ancient to medieval times and the circumstances which
were to bring that "new look" on life and living, and on nature and
natural phenomena, that was to inaugurate the modern period of
history.

The earliest people to initiate true thinking in its modern sense
were the Greeks. They came from Aryan stock who invaded Greece
about 1500 B.C. Keen of intellect, temperamentally of an inquiring
nature, they were naturally well fitted for the task of inaugurating
the era of abstract thinking for the world.

They organised their social structure into three classes—the nobles,
the common people, and the slaves (captives of war and their des-
cendants). The same was also later true of Rome. The normal unit

of a Greek community was the city-state, which was sometimes governed by a democracy, sometimes by an oligarchy, and sometimes autocratically by a "tyrant". These cities, small in themselves (Athens, the largest of them, had a population of about a quarter of a million, half of whom were slaves), became the nursery of a Greek civilisation that was characterised by a spirit of the freedom of the individual combined with a sense of service to the community. Athens in the period of its greatness was a democracy of free citizens.

Many great names were connected with this era, and we can but single out a few. There was the great statesman Pericles, who in the fifth century B.C. guided Athens through some thirty years of supreme greatness. Then there was Socrates (469–399 B.C.), the great propounder of the basic principles of human conduct. Poor, ugly and brave, he devoted his life to the search for genuine truth and righteousness. He made many enemies but trained many followers. Greatest among these latter was the philosopher Plato (429–347 B.C.) (Plate 8), and in the discussions between these two, master and pupil (preserved for posterity in the famous Dialogues), were laid the foundations of thinking in a clear and disciplined manner. Plato, in his *Republic*, devised a new scheme of life for mankind—an ideal state or Utopia, ruled with justice and wisdom. His influence upon history has been profound. Equally with others who preceded him (Thales of Miletus, Pythagoras of Samos, Hippocrates of Cos, and Democritus of Abdera are but a few examples among many), he interested himself in the mathematical and physical sciences, and speculated upon the structure of matter and on the framework and purpose of the universe. These aspects of his teachings were incorporated in his work, *Timaeus*. This was one of the few important works of antiquity to survive in medieval Europe and its influence was accordingly very great.

Plato founded a school at Athens, known as the Academy, and here his most famous pupil was Aristotle (b. 385 B.C.) (Plate 9), whose teachings (or, more correctly, what passed for his teachings) were to become the predominant factor in the intellectual life of the succeeding eighteen hundred years. In particular, he did much to develop the biological and mechanical sciences, and, since his influence persisted to the times of Leonardo da Vinci, we shall later discuss his teachings in detail.

By this time the geographical influence of Greece had extended considerably. Its Macedonian king, Alexander the Great, tutored in his youth by Aristotle, had pursued his brilliant, meteoric career, destroying the vast Persian Empire, which, under Darius and Xerxes, had previously so sorely harassed the Greeks; and he even penetrated into India. In the other direction, he also overran Egypt; and to commemorate his victories he founded a city on the southern shores of the

Mediterranean Sea, named Alexandria in his honour. Its success was immediate, and in a very short time it became a populous city and a flourishing port

Alexander died prematurely in 323 B.C. at the early age of thirty-two, and his Greek Empire was divided up amongst his more powerful officers. Egypt fell to the lot of one Ptolemy Lagus, a great general but also a lover of learning. He freely encouraged philosophers and students to gather round him to form what was called the School of Alexandria—a nursery and a university of Greek learning, housed in a magnificent block of buildings comprising a library, a school of science and an observatory. From here, during the next two centuries, came a succession of distinguished thinkers, among them Euclid (a compiler of the geometry of his predecessors whose influence was unbroken for 2,000 years); the geographers Aristarchus and Eratosthenes; Archimedes of Syracuse (virtually the father of mechanical sciences); Hipparchus the astronomer; and, in some respects the most important of all, Claudius Ptolemaus or Ptolemy (who lived and worked in the first century A.D. under Roman rule). Ptolemy's influence on the Middle Ages in the field of cosmology ranks alongside that of Plato and Aristotle. What we speak of as the Ptolemic System was set forth by him in his *Megalis Syntaxis*. Translated later by the Arabs under the title of *The Almagest*, it was the only complete systematic work on astronomy which the ancient world produced. We shall refer to it further in Chapter IV.

But by now Greece and its former possessions had been subjugated by the Romans, whose new and powerful empire began to extend over much of the then known world. Our story must therefore pass from the Greek to the Roman phase of the history of culture.

What, in effect, was the legacy of Greece to civilisation? We have emphasised her great achievements in philosophy, mathematics and science; but neither in art, in literature nor in politics can we lightly ignore Greek influence. In the architecture of the Parthenon and the Great Temple of the Acropolis at Athens; in the sculpture of Pheidias (perhaps the greatest artist of antiquity); in the dramas of Aeschylus, Sophocles, Euripedes and Aristophanes and in the lyric poetry of Pindar; in the historical writings of Herodotus and Thucydides; in the statecraft of Pericles and the constitutional law of Solon, to quote but a few, we find a range and a depth of culture and scholarship, and a record of the practical means whereby a civilised community could live an individual and a communal life based on spiritual ideals and values. This was no mean gift to civilisation.

3. THE RISE AND FALL OF ROME

The Roman conquerors of Greece were really related to the Greek peoples both by blood and language. They were another branch of the same initial Indo-Germanic or Aryan group. They were called the Latins, and they reached central Italy about the same time as the Hellenic Aryans entered Greece. From a combination of Latin farming settlements grouped round a central temple on a sacred mountain there rose the city and the city-state of Rome, and from this simple city-state of Rome there grew, by a fantastic miracle of expansion, the mighty Roman Empire, whose achievement at the height of its power affords one of the greatest stories of civilised peoples.

The rise of the Roman Empire found its culmination in the golden age of imperialism in the second century A.D., from the death of Domitian in A.D. 96 to the accession of Commodus in A.D. 180. But from thence onwards the story of the Roman Empire was very different and the era of its decline had begun. Commodus ended a debauched and cruel reign by being murdered, and this was characteristic of a number of bad rulers who followed. The first signs of fracture came in the third century A.D. Between A.D. 211 and A.D. 284 there were no less than twenty-three emperors, of whom twenty were murdered— all in the space of seventy-three years! And amid an increasing cracking of the economic system, a growing depravity developed. With affluence, the upper classes had become "soft". With a growing self-indulgence came degeneration, lust, extravagance and cruelty that brought with it the threat of a serious decline in the population. In a land of superstitions, this aroused in the people a sense of impending doom. The empire had, after all, been founded on the inspiration of the "gods of their fathers", the worship of whom had been incorporated in the structure of their constitution. But now the Romans were losing faith in their gods.

It was in such an accumulation of circumstances that the Christian Church was able to rise in Rome and to develop both its doctrine and its organisation throughout the empire. The Christian Church rose as heir to the Jewish tradition. At first, to those in authority the activities of the early apostles and evangelists merely seemed eccentric but gave no cause for alarm. Gradually, however, it began to emerge that this new religion was not so innocuous after all. It began to show signs of exclusiveness and of intolerance to the other religions of the empire.

The reaction of an alarmed central authority to this now dangerous state of affairs was to institute large-scale persecutions and attempts at suppression—attempts which ended in failure because, as far as the *people* were concerned, it was the *Church* and not the *empire* which gave promise of life and hope. The failure of this policy of persecution must be regarded as an element of the greatest significance. It was bound to fail because Christianity offered a superior and a moral faith for the older and non-moral faith of the gods.

Perhaps the biggest attack on the Church was by the Emperor Diocletian at the very beginning of the fourth century A.D. Its failure and his own ill-health led to his abdication in A.D. 306 and caused his successor, the Emperor Constantine, in A.D. 313, to accept the formal recognition of Christianity as a lawful religion. From that time the Church never looked back, and by the end of the fourth century it had, in its turn, suppressed paganism completely and had become the only lawful religion of the empire.

But another factor was reaching a culminating point in the downfall of the Roman Empire. With its military resources necessarily weakened by an essential dispersal of its strength in carrying out the "holding" duties in distant possessions, the strain on the system of defence grew greater—and now barbarian hordes from Germany and the East, beginning at first with destructive raids across the frontiers, were penetrating in depth and strength, ultimately to bring the whole rotting social structure down in ruins.

The robber armies crossed the Danube in A.D. 375; they rushed the frozen Rhine in A.D. 405; and by A.D. 410 Rome itself was sacked and destroyed.

Only in the East did the Roman Empire survive, centred on the new and powerful fortress capital at Constantinople. Nevertheless, both in the West and in the East the Church succeeded in remaining strong. But the basic conditions of its strength were different in the two areas. In the East, on the original pattern of Constantine, it stayed subservient to the emperor as a department of the state; but in the West, where imperial authority had completely disappeared, the Catholic episcopate became sole heir to the power of Rome (Plate 10). The Bishop of Rome, the eternal city, took over the title of Pontifex Maximus, added civilian authority to divine authority and assumed the task of winning back the lost provinces of the West to the obedience of the Pope. Missionary preachers and monastic embassies were sent out to each area of western Europe, and, in their turn, each of the barbarian chiefs of Gaul, Britain, Spain and Italy were wooed and won over to the civic and spiritual sway of the new papal monarchy.

Of all the early Popes, the greatest and most successful was Gregory I (A.D. 590–604), with whose achievements we may regard the end of the ancient period of history and the real beginning of the Middle Ages.

4. THE CULTURAL LEGACY OF ROME

Let us now consider what the Romans contributed to the cultural evolution of mankind (Plates 10 and 11). In the intimate contact between the governed and the governing peoples that followed their conquest of the Greeks there came an inevitable blending of a dominant characteristic of each race, namely: the Greek ability in analysis and generalisation on the one hand, and a Roman gift for government and administration on the other.

Upon this union was founded Roman law, the enactments and principles of which were developed at their best during the Antonine period of the second century. They were to become a model for later legal codes throughout western Europe.

In philosophy, however, Rome had relatively little to contribute. The Roman was more a man of affairs and action than a philosopher. He was concerned rather with the next step than with the ultimate goal. So he could make excellent roads and aqueducts and viaducts and buildings because these were immediate necessities, but he was not ready to speculate creatively upon scientific matters. Nevertheless, it would be wrong to assume that philosophic discussion was non-existent. The chief philosophers of this period were the Epicurean Lucretius (*c.* 95–55 B.C.), who wrote *On the Nature of Things,* an excellent and widely read discussion on the material and mental worlds in terms of the interaction of atoms; and the Stoic writer Seneca (3 B.C.–A.D. 65), whose best-known work was his *Natural Questions.* This was a critical discussion of natural phenomena and their relationship to the destiny of man. Seneca's attitude had much in common with the then growing cult of Christianity and so was favourably regarded by the Church.

Another Roman writer was Varro, whose encyclopaedia of the sciences not only provided a broad picture of what was then known but was also a pattern for many a subsequent treatise on what he called the nine "liberal arts" or disciplines—grammar, dialectic, rhetoric, geometry, arithmetic, astronomy, music, medicine and architecture. As we shall see later, these, with the exception of the last two, became the traditional pattern of organised study throughout the Middle Ages.

Lastly, mention must be made of the *Natural History* by Pliny the Elder (A.D. 23–79), a monumental, if somewhat confused, compendium of current knowledge whose theme is that nature exists for man.

With the building up of an expanding empire, it will be understood that the geographers of Rome were important. Their incentive in the main was utilitarian—to supply the needs of military expeditions and extended travel. The Graeco-Roman historian Polybius (204–122 B.C.), however, explored and described the coasts of Africa, Gaul,

Spain and Italy with a commendable appreciation for the need to determine positions and distances with accuracy. Later we have Strabo (b. *c.* 63 B.C.), whose travels ranged far and wide and who speculated shrewdly on the possibilities of unknown lands beyond the confines of the expanded Roman Empire; whilst a century later the more utilitarian geography of Pomponius Mela pictured a spherical world with land forms entirely surrounded by sea. He described five zones, ranging from torrid in the middle to frigid at the two extremes.

For a complete synthesis of the geography of Roman times we have, however, to turn to the Graeco-Roman Claudius Ptolemaus (second century A.D.), to whose influence throughout the centuries that followed we have already referred. His *Geographical Outline*, written in Greek, contained maps of all the known parts of the world ranging from China and India to Norway. He refers to Britain as Albion, and his maps are marked with parallels of latitude centred on the North Pole and with lines of longitude. The book was undoubtedly scientific in spirit and concept.

Meanwhile, what of Roman art and literature? Roman literature has ever been a vital force in the history of mankind. It was a reflection of the best qualities of the Latin race, and it found expression both in the rhetoric of its orators and in the writings of its historians, essayists and poets. There is, in fact, a very live record of six centuries of Latin literature to which we can here offer but the briefest reference. It began, not unnaturally, with the study and imitation of the Greek writers whom it succeeded. According to Greek allegory, Clio, the Muse of History, was first in rank among the Muses, and the great exponents of this art were Herodotus and Thucydides. Early among their Roman successors was Livy (59 B.C.–A.D. 8), supreme both as a literary writer and historian of the Augustinian age. Although he could not be regarded as a critical historian, the Roman character became live under his pen and the Roman record glorious. Shortly after his period came both Tacitus (A.D. 55–120) and Plutarch (d. *c.* A.D. 120). Plutarch will always be remembered for his biographies of forty-six distinguished Romans and Greeks. His *Lives* was written in Greek and has been used as a source-book of historical knowledge even in modern times. Tacitus and Plutarch may both be regarded as the last of the Latin historians in the classical tradition. After their day history and biography fell into a decline.

In the more specific field of literature the name of Cicero (b. 106 B.C.) occupied a high place. He lived and wrote in the first century before Christ and was distinguished as an orator, statesman and essayist. Other literary writers included Quintilian, whose book on the theory and practice of Education, when brought to light in the fifteenth century, was to influence the educational movement of the Renaissance; Tertullian, the lawyer turned Churchman; and Lactantius, one of the Latin Christian Fathers, whose gracefully written book, *The Divine Institution*, is, in fact, far better as a piece of literature than as a theological exposition.

Passing from prose to poetry, the debt of civilisation to Rome is at its peak in the masterpieces of Virgil (70–19 B.C.) and Horace (65–8 B.C.)—names known to the schoolboys of centuries. Dryden referred to the *Georgics* of Virgil as "the best poem of the best poet". His *Aeneid* is the great epic poem of Rome in terms of its ideal ruler Aeneas. It tells of his glories and of his vicissitudes; of his deeds in war and peace; of his passage, in vision, to the other world across the River of Forgetfulness, viewing both the punishments of Hell and the rewards of the Elysium Fields. "He touched human things with the Virgilian magic. . . ." "The *Aeneid*," writes Mackail, "is the voice not only of Rome but of mankind."

Of Horace we will merely say that his *Odes*, his *Satires* and his *Epistles* have become a permanent part of the international heritage of literature. Finally, we must note the work of Ovid in the generation that followed (43 B.C.–A.D. 18). Ovid, more than any other of the Latin poets, was most copied and lauded in the later Middle Ages. Poetry was his delight. His was the gift of story-telling in verse, with grace, fluency and lightness of touch. Many others there were, of course—but the quality and the grace had reached its peak and the best had been told.

Finally, we must offer a brief but necessary word on Roman art and architecture. Some have claimed that, intrinsically, Roman art and architecture were negligible—that what there was was either Hellenic or a product of Greek inspiration. But there are reasonable claims for the view that a Roman imperial art did develop, admittedly influenced by Greece, but nevertheless with a life of its own. It is to be found, for example, in the statuary and the triumphal columns and arches (Trajan's Arch by Benevento in A.D. 114 is a striking instance— Plate 12) and the relief motifs that are dedicated to the Roman story. There are also reasonable claims in support of a reality and independence in Roman imperial architecture that was both massive and magnificent. The Romans took great pride in the elaborate planning of their public buildings. Two glorious examples were the Flavian Amphitheatre or Colosseum at Rome (A.D. 80) and the great central halls of the Imperial Baths of Caracalla.

It is almost certainly because of its obvious decorative link with Roman architecture that we find monumental sculpture as so vital a form of Roman art. Public monuments and memorials to great rulers

and to great events were all done on a grand scale, as in the great
Arch of Constantine (A.D. 315), with its fine scheme of reliefs above the
arches and of statuary above the columns. The equestrian statue at its
best is also very specifically a Roman heritage. Alexander the Great
had one in Athens and so we must assume an Hellenic precedent, but
a fine Roman example was the bronze statue of the Emperor Marcus
Aurelius (A.D. 161–180) at the Capitol (Plate 13). Andrea Verrocchio's
equestrian statue of Bartolommeo Colleoni in 1488 was almost certainly inspired by it (Plate 22). On the other hand, apart from examples
of decorative design and some illuminated manuscripts, the influence
of ancient painting on modern art was almost negligible.

5. THE ADVENT OF THE DARK AGES IN WESTERN EUROPE

Following the breaking down of the Imperial Roman Empire under
the repeated onslaughts of the barbarians, there ensued in western
Europe a degeneracy into a long and unhappy interval of intellectual
darkness, into which the light of improvement was not again to penetrate until about the tenth century.

By the end of the fifth century barbarian chiefs were reigning in
every conceivable city area in western and central Europe. Some of
them were little more than independent brigands making a very flimsy
show of allegiance to the King Emperor. In Italy the Latin tongue
became distorted by a blending with the tongues of the invaders
and only a remnant of the more senior clergy and scholars preserved
any sort of ability to both speak and write in Latin. These, in the
main, were to be found among the monks and missionaries and in
the surviving monasteries. The Church at least continued to hold fast
through these periods of turmoil and destruction, and Christianity
continued to spread even among the barbarians. Meanwhile, it will
be remembered that the Greek-speaking eastern portion of the Roman
Empire had shown a stability that was sorely lacking in Rome. The
same fifth-century disasters which destroyed the imperial power in
Rome brought Attila and his Huns as far as the walls of Constantinople, but the city stood firm and the Eastern Roman Empire remained
intact. In the sixth century, when the Dark Age of scholarship had
descended in the West, the Eastern Empire under Justinian (A.D.
527–565) was able to extend its dominion by reconquering North
Africa from the Vandals and much of Italy from the Goths. They even
obtained a foothold in the south of Spain. Constantinople now became
a new focus of learning, and, to encourage this, Justinian founded a
university there. He ordered the closing of the traditional schools at
Athens and thus brought an influx of scholars from Greece, and with
them came most of the manuscripts of the old Greek Masters. Never-

theless, there was little originality in the work of these émigré scholars. They were caretakers rather than creators of learning.

Two writers must, however, be mentioned, whose stars of learning shone in isolation in a fading world of thought—Boethius and Cassiodorus. They were, in a sense, the products of a vogue known as Neoplatonism, which had emerged from the early philosophic rivalry between the Stoics and the Epicureans in the days of Lucretius and Seneca.

Neoplatonism was founded in the third century A.D. by one Ammonius Saccas of Alexandria. His teachings were oral and were shrouded in mysticism, somewhat on the pattern of the Pythagoreans of Ancient Greece; but his Roman successor, Plotinus (A.D. 204–270), brought the doctrine out into the open. One of its central teachings was derived from Plato's conception, developed in his *Timaeus*, of the relationship of microcosm to macrocosm—of man to the universe. In one form or another, this doctrine of microcosm and macrocosm persisted throughout the Middle Ages, and we shall discuss it further in Chapter IV.

But it is a curious thought that St. Augustine, who was much influenced by Neoplatonism, was himself responsible in considerable measure for much of the mental stagnation of the centuries that followed. His main preoccupation was with the inward contemplation of the spirit as against the outward and more earthly contemplation of the physical world. He was, therefore, inferentially opposed to the study of nature and natural phenomena. "Go not out of doors," was his dictum. "Return into thyself. In the inner man dwells truth." He was speaking figuratively and he may not have meant this to be taken too literally. But the effect of his great authority was profound. "And so," writes Singer in his *Short History of Science*:[1] "for a thousand years men responsible for the thought of the Western world did not go out of doors"—a great indictment on the mistakenly retrograde influence of one man.

It was in this stifling atmosphere of Church admonition that Boethius and his contemporary Cassiodorus were able to make their contribution to the flickering scholarship of the period. Of the two, Cassiodorus was the less original. His role was rather that of collecting ancient manuscripts and writing commentaries upon them. When he retired from public life in A.D. 540 he founded a monastery whose monks were enjoined to study and to copy these ancient manuscripts. His own writings included an encyclopaedia of the seven liberal arts which, in effect, helped to determine the educational curriculum of the Middle Ages. But to Boethius (Plate 14), the last of the true Roman

[1] C. Singer, *Short History of Science*, p. 151 (Oxford, 1941).

philosophers, the debt of the Middle Ages is more specific. He did much to develop the study of arithmetic but his ambition was to render the writings of Aristotle and other Greek writers into Latin. Imprisonment and sentence of death prevented him, however, from completing this task. Nevertheless, his was the main medieval source both for Aristotle and for Plato, and his reputation and his influence were immense.

Such, then, was the general picture of the Europe of the dark Middle Ages. With culture at its lowest ebb, not only were there now no scholars to produce fresh learning but there were also but few readers capable of even informing themselves of what their predecessors had done; and since, at the same time, there was almost a complete ignorance of Greek as a language, and less and less reliable Latin versions were to be found of what the Greeks had written, what little knowledge existed was confined more or less exclusively to the clergy and the monks, and these were mainly concerned with the applicability of these books to Church dogma and Church doctrine.

The monastic establishments at least provided sanctuary for these writings. Fortunately, in an age of tumult and bloodshed, the monasteries were held sacred to all parties and to all quarrels. So it was that in the libraries attached to these institutions the manuscripts of the ancients found repose and safety (and perhaps dust!), secure from external injury, until the time could come for them to be restored to the light and the study and inspiration of a future generation and age.

One small subsequent flicker of light in this story should be referred to. At the end of the seventh century Charlemagne became emperor of the West in Rome and encouraged some educational reforms by Alcuin, an English monk. Alcuin set up a sort of academy and his main mission was to transmit the culture and learning of the Carolingian world to the English monasteries which had developed a generation before him under the direction of the Venerable Bede. Bede, who knew Greek and had studied Pliny, had himself written extensively. But, like him, Alcuin was almost entirely alone in this small intellectual adventure.

But while the Dark Age of learning had settled deep in northwestern Europe, a fresh world of light was beginning to dawn in the East. A new religious force was blazing across Europe, carrying great political and military consequences in its wake, destined to influence and ultimately to reawaken the spirit of culture from its long slumber in the West. And so our story turns to the rise of Islam.

6. CULTURE TURNS EAST—THE RISE OF ISLAM

The advent of Islam was both sudden and unexpected—unexpected because Arabia and its desert was the shifting home of innumerable small and bickering tribes whose only common ground was the Arabic tongue. In their midst, in the pagan town of Mecca, was the great black stone called the Kaaba. This was the principal object of pilgrimage and worship throughout the country.

Naturally, however, not all the inhabitants of Arabia were Arabs. There were quite a number of Jews, mainly in the south; and, of course, in Syria itself there were some Christians.

Among the citizens of Mecca was one Abir-l-Qasim Mohammed. He was born *c.* 570, and at the age of forty he felt a call to religious prophecy. He began to speak of the Oneness of God and, from this, to develop that intense form of monotheism which has ever since been the main characteristic of the Mohammedan religion. Mohammed's doctrine, which he incorporated in a book called the Koran, now rapidly gained general and fervid acceptance. When he died in 632 his power had spread over the whole of Arabia. The Koran has little literary merit, but its influence was, and remains, immense. We may summarise its main characteristics as (1) its intense monotheism; (2) its freedom from doctrinal complications; (3) its complete detachment from a priesthood and from temple centres of worship; and (4) an insistence on the brotherhood and equality of all "true believers" of whatever colour, race or standing. A fanatical attitude to the rest of mankind almost inevitably developed, and all who were outside the faith were infidels and enemies who must either be destroyed or subjugated.

Under this prophetic formula all the hitherto warring tribes of Arabia were welded into a wild and conquering unity. When Mohammed died in 632 his chief disciple and follower, Abou Bekir, became Caliph (i.e. successor) and the banner of Islam was unfurled. Imbued with the will and the determination to subjugate the world to the will of Allah, the story of rapid conquest that followed is an amazing one. Divided Christendom was Islam's opportunity. The Byzantine army under the Emperor Heraclius was smashed and great cities like Damascus, Palmyra, Antioch and Jerusalem fell with little resistance; and wherever the conquerors went, large numbers of the subjugated peoples embraced Islam. Persia became the next victim—and, indeed, the eastward push was only halted by the Chinese. In other directions the Islamic surge overwhelmed Egypt, possibly destroyed all that was by then left of the great Alexandrian Library (since the Koran was fanatically regarded as completely sufficient for everybody), then pressed along the coast of North Africa as far as the Straits of Gibraltar, and by A.D. 710 had invaded Spain. Ten years later the Arabs had reached the Pyrenees, and, although they temporarily penetrated into France, this was the limit of their conquest. But one stronghold held fast. This was the Byzantine capital Constantinople, which between the years 672 and 718 successfully repelled repeated attacks both by land and sea. But in the space of twenty-five years the Arabs had accomplished what the Romans took centuries to do.

Such was the amazing story of Islam. It was an unwieldy and unstable organisation, since the Arabs had neither political aptitude nor experience, and it was due inevitably to break up. But at least for a considerable time there followed a period of rule under the line of Ummayad and Abbaside Caliphs, whose immense empire stretched from Spain to Samarkand and whose court at Damascus (the new capital that replaced El Medina) soon began to show a luxury and a wealth hitherto undreamed of by the Arab.

What was the influence of all this conquest on culture? It was not long before the early attitude of intolerant self-sufficiency became blunted. Contact with the obvious learning among the Nestorians, the Jews, the Syrians and the Persians now brought to the ruling Arabs an increasing curiosity and a desire to acquire some of this learning for its own sake. Schools sprang up in various centres—in Cordoba and Toledo in Spain, in Cairo, in Baghdad, in Meragha, in Bokhara and in Samarkand. At the express wish of El-Mamoun, Ptolemy's famous *Syntaxis* was rendered into Arabic in A.D. 827 under the title of the *Almagest*. What was happening was indeed, in its way, a forerunner in the Semitic world to the Renaissance which was to follow later in Christian Europe.

Thus it was that in the East the teachings of Aristotle, of Hippocrates, of Ptolemy, of Galen and others began to spread among those who could read; and on the foundation of this knowledge the Arabian philosophers began to make their own contributions to the mathematical, medical and physical sciences, and to the Arabic forerunner of chemistry known as alchemy.

Let us refer quite briefly to some of the main features of this new Arabian culture. It should be noted first of all that there were two geographical aspects of Arabian culture. In the West they had inherited and superseded the Latin civilisation of the Holy Roman Empire, whereas in the East it was the Hellenistic civilisation which had been inherited and the Byzantine Empire which was superseded. On the whole, the Eastern culture was the earlier and the more vital. One of its most noted exponents was Jebir ibn Hayyan—westernised as *Geber*—who lived and worked, probably in the ninth century, first at the court of the Caliph Haroun-el-Raschid at Baghdad and later

at Kufa. He was a noted alchemist of the Middle Ages, who understood and described the usual chemical operations of solution, crys-
tallisation, filtration, reduction and so forth. He was familiar with
many chemical substances and was the forerunner of a long line of
able men who, in spite of the mysticism with which they shrouded
alchemy, nevertheless materially advanced knowledge which may be
described as a medieval brand of modern chemistry.

Next we should mention the very able Arabic tradition in medicine.
Although this was largely in the hands of the Jews of the Arabic world,
one of its greatest exponents was the Persian-born Abu Bakr Muham-
med ibn Zakariyya (A.D. 866–925). A native of the town of Raz, near
Teheran, he became generally known as Rhazes. His voluminous
Comprehensive Book was translated into Latin in the thirteenth century
under the title of the *Liber Continens* and became one of the standard
medical works of the Middle Ages. It traversed the whole of medical
knowledge current in his day.

In philosophy, the greatest name in Islam is that of Abu Ali ibn
Sind, westernised as *Avicenna* (A.D. 980–1037) (Plate 15). He practised
as a doctor for many years. His *Canon of Medicine* became almost as
well known as the *Liber Continens* of Rhazes.

The most fruitful period in the history of Eastern Islam was, however, that covered by the tenth and eleventh centuries. This has been
referred to as the Golden Age of Islamic culture.

A great figure of this period was Alhazen (A.D. 945–1038), a native of
Basra in Mesopotamia. His main work was in optics, in which he was
outstanding in his day. His best-known book was translated into Latin
under the title of *Thesaurus Opticae*. A Polish writer, Witelo, published a
revised copy of this in 1260 under his own name, without acknowledging
its source. We shall refer further to Alhazen's work in Chapter IV.

Turning to Western Islam, the main centres of culture were in
Spain and Sicily, and from both of these areas it was able to reach
by infiltration and other means, to both France and Italy. In Cordoba,
Ibn Rashd, jurist, physician and philosopher, taught in the twelfth
century, and the Jewish writers, including the great Moses Maimonides,
were wielding a wide influence. At Cordoba, too, a library and academy
had been founded in 970, and similar establishments were to be found
at Toledo, Salerno and other places.

Moses Maimonides (1135–1204) was renowned as a religious teacher,
philosopher and court physician. His medical writings were characterised by their outspoken criticism of Galen, who was probably the
most influential physiologist and medical teacher of the second century
A.D. and upon whose work so much of the medicine of the Middle
Ages was based.

But the greatest philosopher of Arabic Spain was Ibn Rashd (1126–1178), known to the Western world as Averroes. His theories were heterodox and none too popular with the Mohammedan world in which he lived and worked. He was born in Cordoba, which in the ninth century had become an independent Caliphate. In particular, his discussions on the human intellect greatly excited the academic world of Western Christendom. These led him to the view that individual intellect in man does not survive death and that, therefore, there is no personal immortality. It will be appreciated that this doctrine was not in harmony either with Mohammedan or Christian orthodoxy. Nevertheless, Christian philosophers held both Averroes and Avicenna in high esteem. It is specially significant that, while Dante in his *Divine Comedy* (the influence of which on medieval philosophy and cosmology was so profound) places Mohammed in hell, he finds places for both Avicenna and Averroes in Limbo. But the Mohammedan world was not so considerate to Averroes: they disliked his theories so much that he had to leave Spain and seek safety elsewhere.

7. THE INTELLECTUAL TWILIGHT AND THE RISE OF UNIVERSITIES IN WESTERN EUROPE

Meanwhile, while Islam was making its own contribution to culture in the manner described above, Christian Europe was sunk in the intellectual depths we have referred to as the Dark Ages. The temporary flicker of Latin scholarship, led by the Venerable Bede and Alcuin during the enlightened rule of Charlemagne, expired in a new wave of barbaric invasions. And so, in western Europe, one may say that the period between A.D. 800 and 1000 was probably the darkest of the Dark Ages.

Central government had almost entirely collapsed, and pillaged abbeys and towns could find neither protection nor redress. Each separate locality had to try to stand on its own legs to prevent slaughter. It was out of this state of affairs that *feudalism* was born. Primarily a military system of defence, though with subsequent political and economic repercussions, it sprang up spontaneously and developed efficiently, and from its system of walled and fortified castles and its panoplied knights emerged the salvation of Europe. By the end of the tenth century the worst was over. Feudalism had done its work, and by the eleventh century western Europe had once more become a conscious, if heterogeneous, unit. A new note of hope was discernible, therefore, with the opening of the eleventh century, and in fact we may regard the period from A.D. 1000 to 1300 as being the crown of the Middle Ages.

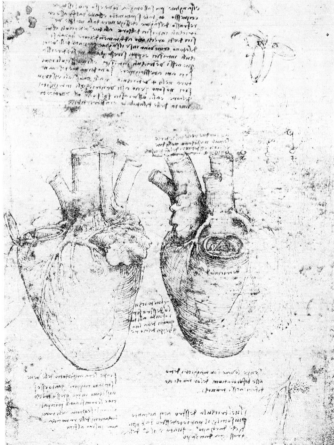

Plate 4—Various devices of armed combat. Note the archer with shield, the horseman with three lances, and the chariots with flails (Windsor Royal Library).

Plate 5—An example of Leonardo's anatomical studies—drawings of the heart (Windsor Royal Library).

Plate 6 — Andrea-del Verrocchio (1435-1488), tutor to Leonardo.

Plate 7 — Fra Luca Pacioli, friend and contemporary of Leonardo. From a painting in the Museo Nazionale at Naples, ascribed to Jacopo de' Barbari (Mansell Collection).

Plate 8 — Plato (Mansell Collection).

Plate 9 — Aristotle (Mansell Collection).

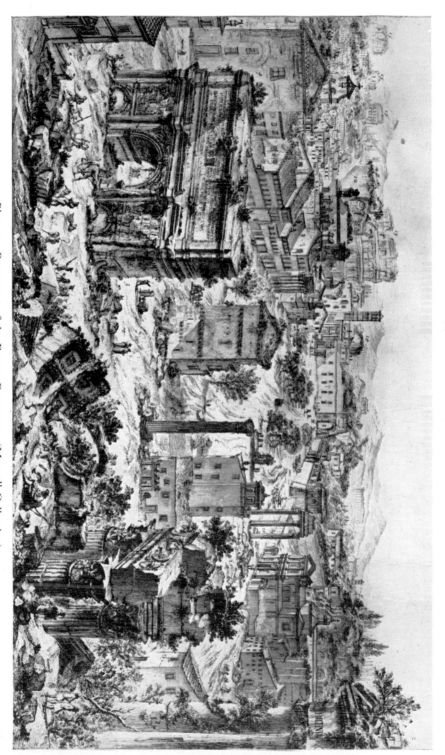

Plate 10—Panorama of the Forum Romanum (Mansell Collection).

Plate 12—Western face of Trajan's Arch, Benevento, A.D. 114 (Mansell Collection).

Plate 11—Roman Amphitheatre at Amman, Jordania—an example of culture in the Eastern Roman Empire.

Two broad factors were now emerging to influence the trend of thought and culture through the tenth, eleventh and twelfth centuries. One was the evolution of an educational scheme that culminated in the rise of universities of learning in various centres: the other was the gradual infiltration of the lively scholarship which had developed in the East across what might well be described, in the idiom of modern world politics, as the Iron Curtain between Islam and Christendom. Let us briefly review these separately.

The traditional educational scheme of the seven liberal arts had long been established. In the days of the Roman Empire its basis was rhetorical and its mainstay was grammar. The languages and the literature of Greece and Rome were regarded as presenting a mirror of human life, though, since these were pagan, the Church had to be persuaded to sanction their study. So, broadly, the seven liberal arts, comprising the *trivium* of grammar, rhetoric and dialectic, which were the arts proper; and the *quadrivium* of geometry, arithmetic, astronomy and music, which were the four disciplines, became in fact the hand-maidens of theology, and were designed primarily to serve its purpose. It was this which found its expression in the system of schools which developed.

The vehicles for this instructional scheme were, initially, the mon-asteries and the cathedral schools, pioneered originally by the Bene-dictine order. The ritual and the procedure of their daily routine called for some foundation of formal learning, and so, in the eleventh century, under the inspiration of Bishop Fulbert of Chartres, centres of in-struction were created for the purpose. To some extent these provided a training in the literary, poetical and musical practices of the monastic life; but they brought natural extensions of study in other directions— the observation of stars, the times of their rising and setting (a sub-stitute for the non-existent clocks); the practice of arithmetic as an aid to the running of the financial side of the monastic estates—and so on. It was in this connection that Gerbert, later to become the Pope Sylvester II, reintroduced the abacus, the calculating board of the ancients. Soon the Dominicans came into this educational picture. The standard of scholarship did not amount to much, but at least, within the framework of a monastic community, some elementary knowledge of the riches of Latin literature, both pagan and Christian, was becoming increasingly established.

But outside the intensely disciplined monastic communities there were the more secular clergy of the cathedral churches. Here, in a freer and less circumscribed atmosphere, were set up the cathedral schools. They existed at two levels. The lower was the Song School, at which music and the reading of Latin was taught for the conducting

D

of the church services. At a higher level was the Grammar School, where the normal curriculum of the liberal arts was taught. These made small beginnings but were to loom larger in scope and repute as the tenth century ended. The new eleventh century was born with a growing awareness of the need for the revival of the ancient wisdom and learning. Moreover, students were becoming both more vocal and more numerous. The itch to learn and to go, however far, where there was a centre of instruction, was beginning to produce both a student class and a teacher class as well as more schools to serve their needs. Thus, the School of Paris, which had made a particular feature of training in logic, was able to draw a stream of students from Italy and elsewhere, since logic had largely begun to replace rhetoric as a basic feature in education. So we find the cathedral schools of the eleventh century, equipped both with libraries and teachers, playing a rapidly increasing part in cultural development.

By the twelfth century scholars were beginning to develop a growing understanding of the legacy of learning of the Greeks and Romans. Some of this had been unearthed and studied from the dusty stores of the monasteries and libraries, and, as we shall shortly discern, some was being slowly acquired from Arabian sources. These latter included, in particular, the Arabic commentaries on the scientific and meta-physical works of Aristotle, the renewed study of which was opening up a new and vital chapter in the history of learning.

A characteristic of this period was the appearance of a succession of compendiums summing up what had previously been written in a variety of fields of study, mainly relative to the liberal arts, and form-ing the basis for further discussion. These became, as it were, the textbooks of the Middle Ages. They included Gratian's *Concordance of Discordant Canons*, a compendium on Canon Law which appeared about the year 1140; Peter Lombard's *Four Books of Sentences*, covering the field of theology; the *Historia Scholastica* of Petrus Comestor; and the grammar of the *Summa* of Petrus Helias—all of which appeared in the middle of the twelfth century.

Peter Lombard was representative of the best in teaching of his time. As an Italian he was familiar with the legal scholarship of Bologna in northern Italy, and this he was able to blend with the dialectic and theology of northern France when, about 1140, he went to Paris. He became Bishop of Paris in 1159 and died shortly after. But by this time the pattern of education had become fairly set. It was all a question of what funds were available to the would-be scholar, as to where he could go for his scholarship. The less fortunate would go to a cathedral school near at hand, where, nevertheless, he could at least be sure of the services of able teachers. But for the better favoured and the more adventurous there were now coming into prominence various focal points for scholastic organisations on a much wider scale, to which teachers of eminence had been attracted. These were the new universities. Paris, Chartres and Bologna were outstanding examples—Paris being famous for its courses in philosophy and theology; Chartres for letters and literature; and Bologna for its law. On the other hand, for those attracted to the newer fields of science, there was Toledo in Spain; whilst for the would-be medical student there were the famous medical schools at Salerno and Montpellier.

And soon other universities appeared including, of course, Oxford

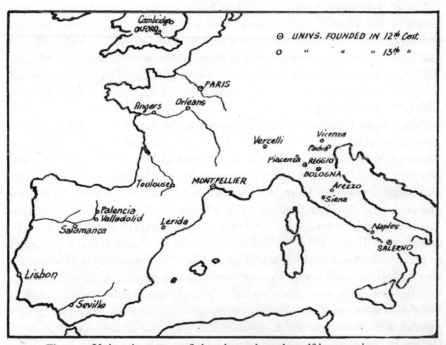

Fig. 1.   University towns of the eleventh and twelfth centuries.

and Cambridge in England (Fig. 1). The term *universitas* denoted in the Middle Ages the combined body of professors and students teaching and studying in a given city—but to this a charter was usually added in due course, conferred by king or papal legate on behalf of the Pope and formally constituting the *universitas* as a corporation, with defined statutes and privileges. In some cases houses of study were introduced for the benefit of various religious orders. These usually comprised a chapel, a hall, dormitory, library and tutors. Thus, for example, the Dominicans, who were the Order of Preachers, and the Franciscans came to be associated with the University of Paris and later with Oxford.

These houses of study were the forerunners of the constituent colleges that came to be formed within the universities. The Sorbonne in Paris, Merton College in Oxford, and Peterhouse in Cambridge are thirteenth-century examples of these colleges.

It was largely through these sources that the trends of theological discussion and the relations thereto of Aristotelian philosophy took the form and characteristics of dialectical argument known as scholasticism, and which gave the disputants the name of scholastics or schoolmen.

8. THE INFILTRATION OF EASTERN CULTURE INTO WESTERN EUROPE

Let us now turn to the second of the two great factors in the processes of the recovery of classical learning in western Europe during the three centuries from A.D. 1000 to 1300, which was to usher in the full tide of the Renaissance in the fourteenth and fifteenth centuries. This was the passing on to western Europe of the Islamic records of learning and, with them, the teachings of Greece and Rome upon which they were based.

What were the centres of contact with the learning of Islam available to north-western Europe? At the beginning of the period in question, the Moslems of Spain and North Africa were pressing hard on the main European bloc. They held all the islands of the area including Majorca, Corsica, Sardinia, Malta and Sicily, and had driven north through Spain to the Pyrenees. On the other hand, in the eastern Mediterranean the countries of north-west Europe had to contend with the Byzantine Empire, which, centred on Constantinople, reached out to the Dalmatian Adriatic and materially threatened the Italian Adriatic from Venice down to the south. Venice itself was a privileged link between East and West; and, similarly, following a later recession of the Moors southwards, Toledo in central Spain provided its link between Christian Europe and Islam. So also, with the recovery of the Mediterranean islands, Salerno in the south provided yet another source of contact with Islamic learning.

The key to this intellectual recovery was the extent to which personal contact became possible. The various elements in bringing this about were: (*a*) the contacts of trade; (*b*) the loose interflow of personnel of various types incidental to the Crusades; (*c*) the intermingling of the peoples of East and West along the changing frontiers—surprisingly friendly where one might have expected hostility; and, by no means least of all, (*d*) the journeyings of adventurous scholars into the various centres of Islamic learning for the specific purpose of acquiring the "new knowledge".

On the whole, during the tenth and eleventh centuries the intellectual contacts with Islam must have been difficult, but following the recession of the Moors south of Toledo consequent upon the advances of Alphonso VI of Leon in 1085 an easier situation developed. In Toledo, Arab, Christian and Jew intermingled freely, and under such conditions the earlier work of transmission of Arabic learning thus became possible.

Usually the services of Jewish translators were employed, especially since a number of important works were by Jewish authors. Through their agency most of the writings of Geber, Avicenna, Averroes, Maimonides and others became available in Latin and so helped to shape the pattern of scholasticism that was emerging among the rapidly growing universities of north-west Europe. Among the more important scholars of western Europe who were associated with this general task of transmission were Sabbatai ben Abraham (known as Donnolo the Jew of Otranto), who learned Arabic while a prisoner in Saracen hands and was thus able to study the new learning at first hand; Constantine the African, a native of Carthage, who naturally spoke and read Arabic and who subsequently became a monk at Montecassino in southern Italy; Adelard of Bath (*c.* 1090–1150), whose journeys into Spain and Sicily produced Latin translations of Al-Kwarizmi's *Arithmetic* and also the first Latin version of an Arabic translation of Euclid; Robert of Chester (*c.* 1110–1160), who translated the Koran and Al-Kwarizmi's *Algebra*; Domenigo Gonzales (*c.* 1140), who prepared Latin versions of Aristotle's *Physics* from Arabic; John of Seville (*c.* 1145), a converted Jew who was prolific in producing a variety of translations, mainly astronomical; and the very distinguished scholar, Gerard of Cremona (1114–1187), who, after learning Arabic in Toledo, undertook a prodigious series of translations, including Ptolemy's *Almagest*. Curiously enough, an earlier Latin translation of Ptolemy's *Almagest* has been made direct from the original Greek in Sicily, twelve years earlier in 1163, but it made little impression and was completely overshadowed by Gerard's version from the Arabic (later, in the fifteenth century, to be the subject of a special study by Georg Peurbach). Gerard also translated the voluminous *Canon* of Avicenna, a medical treatise which is still in use in the East to this day.

9. THE AGE OF SCHOLASTICISM

We have now traced the main channels along which the broad streams of the revival of learning were moving in the twelfth and thirteenth centuries. What frame of mind was this producing in the scholars of those days? We are speaking now of the period before printing had transformed the problem of the dissemination of literature. In the aggregate, many people were at work on the slow process of copying and reproduction and some of these were more careless and less conscientious than others. So, all too frequently, books, both devotional and learning, were indifferently copied, badly commentated, and often deliberately altered according to the whim of the copyist. The slow tasks of both the production and the reproduction of manuscripts were, of course, temperamentally best suited to those with a placid and settled way of life. These, in the main, were to be found in the monastic world, and it will be recalled that Casseodorus had, in the sixth century, actually founded a monastery in southern Italy for this special function. When to this we add the fact that more and more universities were coming into existence, and the number of schools in Europe was rapidly increasing, we can well understand that the quickly-growing student class thus created virtually brought into being a new trade of copyists on a large scale, both outside the monasteries and within.

What was the quality and the attitude of scholars and scholarship emerging from this growing accumulation of Latin translations of Arabic literature? Earlier in the period in question, before the tide of acquired translations was getting under way, the intellectual level was definitely below that of the thinkers of past ages. On the whole, the effect of Christian training was to regard any manuscript handed down from antiquity as the repository of some divine revelation. A work either confirmed this or its study was simply forbidden. As a consequence, the tendency was increasingly to regard such work as authoritarian, clearly at the expense of original thinking. In these earlier days Aristotle's *Elementary Logic* was the only part of his writings which was generally available and this, therefore, became the training ground for all thinking and the authority for all judgment. Not that this attitude was either immediately or completely acceptable to Church authority.

One of its great earliest exponents was Peter Abelard (1079–1142), virtual founder of the University of Paris as a focus for intellectual thought in western Europe. His advocacy of the dialectic methods of disputation on the Aristotelean pattern brought him into official disfavour. But the successors to Abelard were his own pupils and soon the dialectic method of summarising the pros and cons of an argument became the general practice in the lecture-room. Thus began the era of the schoolmen and the days of scholasticism.

We must note further that one of the great factors in the revival of learning during the eleventh and twelfth centuries was the recovery of most of the other writings of Aristotle. These included the *Physica*, the *Meteorologica*, the *De Anima*, *De Sensu*, *De Coelo*, *De Generatione et Corruptione*, the *Historia Animaleum*, in addition to other works spuriously ascribed to him. This was a new situation confronting orthodox

Christianity. Here was, in the aggregate, a complete survey of practically every phase and field of thought, worked out with a thoroughness in marked contrast to the fragmentary elements previously available in Plato's *Timaeus* and the *Logic* of Aristotle himself, his only earlier-known work. The appeal to the Middle Ages of this new and complete synthesis of knowledge was profound. "Aristotle the Dialectician", now became "Aristotle the Philosopher", and the authority of his writings was complete.

With the great weight and obvious authority of Aristotle's writings now confronting the Western world, it was becoming necessary to decide how far they could be acceptably related to Church orthodoxy. Aristotle was simply too big to be ignored. In 1210 the Provincial Council of Paris forbade the teachings of his natural philosophy but not of his ethics or his logic. But in 1231 Gregory IX set up a commission of theologians to "correct the works of Aristotle". The tide was clearly turning. Prohibitions officially renewed in 1263 were quite ineffective and by now Aristotelean studies became general. The pressing necessity for Christianity to come to terms with Aristoteleanism was smoothly achieved as a result of the labours and the writings of two great Churchmen—Albertus Magnus and St. Thomas Aquinas.

Albertus and Aquinas both recognised in Aristotle's science the products of natural reason, and in his theology those of divine revelation, but accepted that a complete separation of philosophy and theology was impossible—"for what is faith but a higher reason and reason but an imperfect faith?"

Albertus Magnus (1206–1280) was a man of remarkable erudition, who came to be known as the "Universal Doctor". He was a German Dominican, who taught both at Paris and at Cologne, and Thomas Aquinas was one of his pupils. He was a genuine lover of nature, who preferred to make his own observations and to base his judgments on what he saw and found, and he made notable contributions both to zoology and botany. For him, natural science was something specific and apart from the revealed truth of faith. This was the standpoint of the Arabian Jewish philosopher Moses Maimonides, and Albert was virtually a pioneer in this distinction between faith and reason as an approach to the problems of his day.

It was in this sense that he engaged in the task of somehow fitting Aristotle within the Christian structure. His great work was his *Summa Theologica*.

His pupil, St. Thomas Aquinas (1227–1274), was also a Dominican and came to be known as the "Angelic Doctor".

Aquinas had a great flair for the task of systematisation and this he brought to bear upon the whole philosophy of Aristotle. His approach, in a sense, was that of a natural theologian utilising reason to support revelation. In so doing, he sought to harmonise Aristotle with the Christian view. The result was a genuine achievement which made a great impression upon his time, and in so far as such a thing was possible the philosophical system of Aristotle was welded into a harmonious whole with Christian theology. This was not, in fact, completely possible. It would be more true to say that the two traditions were not so much capable of being welded as of being reconciled to each other; and although not everyone accepted it, it was a most useful and effective compromise. Those who did so were spoken of as the Thomists, but there were followers of the more rigid Augustinian tradition and outlook who were not so mentally accommodating. These, in the main, were the rival Franciscans, one of whom was William Lamarre, who wrote a *Correctory of Brother Thomas*. Another was the distinguished John Peckham, Archbishop of Canterbury; and yet another, after St. Thomas's death in 1274, was the great medieval philosopher, Duns Scotus Erigena.

Yet on the whole, in those thirteenth-century days the artificial blending of seemingly irreconcilable ideas made its appeal. It suited the medieval mind, which naturally gravitated towards the call of authority. Here were two such calls—the authority of the newly discovered Master Peripatician, Aristotle; and the demands of Church dogma. Both became necessary to the medieval mind and so, despite their fundamental differences, the attempt at their blending became inevitable. Inconclusiveness was more essential than basic consistency; and, for a time at any rate, the solution of the Angelic Doctor was found satisfying.

10. FROM SCHOLASTICISM TO HUMANISM

So we come to the fourteenth century, a century of adjusting relationships in a variety of aspects—social, political, theological and philosophical—adjustments that followed a succession of more and more worldly-minded Popes. As a reaction, this slackening in religious fervour produced in an extreme section of the Franciscans and the Cistercians a doctrine and a practice of absolute poverty.

Politically, too, this was a period of general upheaval conditioned by the sequences of fighting between England and France which came to be spoken of as the Hundred Years War, one effect of which was to lose for Paris its hitherto unique status as the main centre of European learning; whilst economically, a number of factors were compelling a lowering of standards—a decline in birth rate, aggravated by the Black Death of 1348–1349, less ground under cultivation, less trade and financial difficulties arising from the cost of war, a series of peasant risings, and so on.

In the field of philosophy the general tendency in the fourteenth century was for a disengagement between faith and reason, characterised by the standpoint that the natural and the supernatural were not only separate but were also without any point of contact. So there developed rival outlooks—one founded on fact and empiricism and the other on matters of belief and faith.

But there was yet one other tendency which saw its beginnings in the fourteenth century and which was to develop increasing momentum, to become a considerable factor in the fuller Renaissance of learning in the fifteenth century of Leonardo da Vinci. This was the movement, if we can so call it, spoken of as humanism. The gradual recovery of the literature of Greece and Rome was developing an emotional effect. This recovery, as we have seen, derived from various sources. Much of it came from the Latin translations of Islamic works of learning; much came also from the study of the actual original Latin manuscripts as they came to light in the monastic libraries in which they had lain through the centuries; and now some of it was beginning to be made available in Latin translations direct from the original Greek by a very small number of scholars who had mastered the Greek tongue and by a few Greek scholars who were increasingly drifting westward from Byzantine country. All through these centuries, then, a revival of letters was on its way. (See footnote 2, p. 224.)

But with it was a growing change of heart, conditioned in part by the reactions above-mentioned against the laxity of standards of those highly placed in the Church. This new tendency towards a more tolerant culture was well displayed at the time in the region of Provence. Here poetry and gentle living were blooming and naturalism was finding a free expression through the medium of lyrics—of such romances as that of Arthur and his Knights, of the tales of Lancelot and Tristram, and so on. A favourite of those days was Gollardi, with his songs of wandering students in the *Carmina Burana*, written in medieval Latin. Here the theme of love was handled with the freedom of the classical age of Bacchus and Venus. And so, whilst Christendom was still busy with its Crusades abroad, a preoccupation with naturalism and an enthusiasm for classical feeling was developing "at home". There was a growing, if veiled, sense of the natural humanity of man—veiled, perhaps, because in the background lay the uneasy menace of the displeasure of the Church.

One of the earliest pioneers in this process was Francesco Petrarch (1304–1374) of Arezzo in Tuscany, whose fame rests on his various contributions to the spirit of humanism which he helped to create. A poet in his own right (his *Rime* was one of the earliest in the language of his time), he modelled the Italian sonnet and other poetic forms with polish of both diction and melody. Moreover, he was a devoted hunter after and restorer of many works of classical learning.

Petrarch was, in fact, one of three great founders of the literature of Italian humanism in the fourteenth century. The others were Dante Alighieri (1265–1321) and Giovanni Boccaccio (1313–1375). Dante, to whom we shall have to refer again in our discussion on the scientific background of Leonardo da Vinci, differs from the other two in that, although his great poem, *The Divine Comedy*, was written earlier in the century and has had a greater prominence in the literature of the world, it was framed in a spirit of allegory, symbol and vision. With Petrarch and Boccaccio it was different. Both their poetry and their prose, written mainly in the vernacular of the day, abandon allegory and symbol and continue rather in the Provençal tradition, appropriately revised to the Tuscan idiom, with a more realistic treatment of emotion.

Boccaccio was a Florentine whose early years were spent in commercial training in Paris, but his heart was always in authorship. This he pursued for many years in Naples. Here was composed, among other works, the *Decameron*, on which his fame mainly rests. It was modelled on the pattern of the Provençal "Fabliaux". These were metrical tales, mainly of the thirteenth century, which embodied sarcastic or witty reference to passing events and were intended for recitation. From these Boccaccio borrowed freely. His *Decameron* tells of a party of gay ladies and gentlemen who retired from Florence to a villa at Fiesole during the plague of 1348 and who amused their leisure by the recital of the stories which go to make up the book—a diversion which lasted for the ten days which give the title to the work. The *Decameron* was a masterpiece of grace and liveliness, in places debased by a palpable grossness. But subsequent to his writing the *Decameron*, Boccaccio became the fortunate inheritor of a considerable fortune. This enabled him to do two things close to his heart—to study and master the Greek tongue and thus to read its classical literature in the original; and to organise an intensive search for a collection of the manuscripts of the classical writers. It was this work, organised mainly from Florence, that brought him into close personal contact and friendship with Petrarch. Here, too, in his last years, he lectured on Dante. He died in 1375.

What, then, was this new spirit of humanism which was now asserting itself? It was, in effect, a break-away from the enslaving Middle Ages conception that both the intelligence and the emotions were bound to a rigidity of life in order to earn the rewards of a future state of the soul, and the substitution in its place of a recognition of the goodliness of both man and nature, and of a zest for life and living which could give expression to that recognition. It was because this was found increasingly to be reflected in the great writings of the past that both the study of and the search for more and more of these great works of the ancients became an increasing cult of the period. And for Italy especially, there could be added that extra pride and stimulus of being descended from the great "Populus Romanus" of the classical past. It was but one inevitable step from this to appreciate, as did both Petrarch and Boccaccio, the need for a fresh study of the long-since-dead Greek language, to make available the further riches of Greek literature. So came the visits of enthusiasts to Byzantium, and the general hunt for fresh evidences of the manuscripts of the past. This extended well into the fifteenth century, and the prominent names associated with it included Guarino, Filelfo, Niccolo Niccoli and Poggio. The process became infectious and received the practical aid and blessing of wealthy patricians, merchant princes and despots. A thirst for learning had gone beyond the special class of recluses and professional scholars—it extended, in varying degree, to most of the intelligent people of the community.

Professional copyists, need it be said, were having a very busy time (Plate 16). They were of two types. There were the relatively few but more elevated *scrittori*, men of erudition, some of whom knew Greek; and the *copisti*, a bigger band of mere clerks, usually schoolmasters and other needy men of learning who copied manuscripts as a spare-time occupation to supplement their income.

But, as Charles Singer stresses, it was a backward-looking movement. It was a mighty resurrection of the spirits of the past. Nevertheless, it was a prerequisite of the Renaissance of the fifteenth century. It was the task of the Renaissance to set afoot the spirit of enquiry and experiment and to create an attitude of objective independence—a looking ahead, in fact. But this could only follow as a sequel to the work of reconstruction of the knowledge and the writings of the ancients and the finding therein of an inspiration and an example through their literature, their art and their science.

11. THE FULL TIDE OF THE RENAISSANCE IN LEONARDO'S ITALY

So we come to the full tide of the Renaissance in Leonardo's fifteenth-century Italy. It was a sweep which was accelerated by other factors additional to those we have so far enumerated. A general quickening of life and of a sense of curiosity, together with an awareness of happenings and possibilities "around the corner" were, so to speak, developing from such related factors as a growing prosperity through increasing trade, the opening up of new worlds, a sense of adventure, a complete revolution in the dissemination of literature and learning through the invention of movable-type printing, a more modernistic slant on the conceptions of the cosmos, a more rational philosophy, and a reaction from the cramping authority of the Roman Church, leading to the Reformation. All these factors were operating at the same time. Each was contributing its quota to the general result, and the aggregate effect was tremendous. The "looking-back", characteristic of the fourteenth-century, was giving place to a more modern "looking-forward" that was to give a final *finis* to the Middle Ages.

Let us review some of these factors separately.

Less and less fettered by Catholic tradition and beliefs, the fifteenth century was leading, gradually, to a reconstruction in the minds and thoughts of educated persons of the social, political, artistic and aesthetic picture of life as it was in classical days. Latin, as we have seen, was the first, and natural, channel for this. The language of most Western peoples was based on it; all Church rites, rituals and procedures were expressed in it; and most scholars of the day were rediscovering the ancient Roman literature in all its fullness and its beauty. Virgil and Cicero became the standards of diction and the cult of a growing leisure. But a Greek revival was soon to follow as a second stage in the Renaissance of the fifteenth century. When, in 1453, Constantinople fell to the Turks, one of the consequences was an acceleration in a previously slow flow westwards of Greek books and Greek scholars —and with them came the ancient world and words of Homer and Aeschylus, of Thucydides and Aristophanes, of Socrates and Plato.

And all this was happening in an expanding world. An excited people was learning that beyond the vast emptiness of the forbidding oceans and seemingly limitless plains were other worlds and other peoples and, indeed, other civilisations. Much earlier, the Mongol conquests of Genghis Khan and others had stimulated the geographical curiosity regarding what we would now call the Far East; and the detailed records of the journeys of the Venetian, Marco Polo, with his father and uncle to the Mongol Court in China about 1272, have achieved a just fame.

One of those whose imagination, two centuries later, was fired thereby was the Genoese mariner, Christopher Columbus. There is a copy of Marco's *Travels* in Seville, with marginal notes by Columbus. By now, too, the conception of a spherical world, established by the geographers of Greece and Rome and since forgotten, had been revived —first by Roger Bacon and Albertus Magnus and, more recently, by Cardinal d'Ailly (d. 1422), a copy of whose work, the *Imago Mundi*, came into the possession of Columbus.

We have already referred to the contacts between Columbus and the distinguished Florentine mathematician and cosmographer, Paolo del Pozzi Toscanelli. When Columbus sought the support of King Alphonso V of Portugal for his project of sailing westwards round the world to China, the latter sought the advice and opinion of Toscanelli. His famous journey of two months and nine days across the ocean in three small ships brought him, as we know, in 1492 to what he thought was India but what, in fact, were the West Indian Islands off America. The mainland was reached in 1497 by Amerigo Vespucci. So far as ocean voyages of discovery were concerned, the "hunt was up", and amid a succession of expeditions we should, in particular, record the journeys of Vasco da Gama (1464–1524), who, starting from Lisbon in July 1497, sailed round the Cape of Good Hope on 22nd November, ultimately to reach India itself at Calicut on 20th May 1498; Magellan, whose expedition of five ships left Seville in 1519—one, the *Vittoria*, returned in 1522, having circumnavigated the world for the first time (but Magellan himself was killed in the Philippine Islands); Cabot, another Genoese, who discovered Newfoundland; and Cortez, who in 1516 sighted the Pacific from the peak in Darien, and who entered Mexico in 1521.

It was a breathless rush. Trade, opportunity and adventure were all around the corner and a new chapter in history was being written. Soon, as we know, gold and silver was to flow into Europe from South America, furs and timber from the north, and spices from the east. The effect on the mind of Europe was stupendous.

Meanwhile, an invention of a new printing machine was now to make its impact on the world of culture and learning. It was made possible, first of all, by an improvement in the technique of paper-making. Originally a Chinese production, the art was passed on first to the Arab Moslems, through the agency of prisoners who were skilled paper-makers, and thence to Christian Europe. By the end of the thirteenth century it had reached Italy, and a century later Germany and the rest of Europe were producing good paper abundantly and cheaply. Thus it was possible to utilise the invention of movable type printing in 1438 by Johann Gutenberg of Strasburg. He conceived the idea of making metal letters separately so that they might be used over and over again. Gutenberg and his colleagues thus printed the first Bible in 1455. In Italy the first printing press was started in 1465, another in Paris in 1469 and Caxton's first English press in 1474. Indeed, within fifteen years of the foundation of Rome's first press in 1465, one was to be found in practically every town of consideration in Christian Europe. So began a new weapon for the dissemination of culture whose influence was rapidly to become enormous. The day of the copyist was over.

An immediate result was the appearance of Bibles all over the world. Another was the availability of a host of books for schools and universities. It will be of interest to note briefly the general character and range of the earlier types of literature that first came off the presses of the fifteenth and sixteenth centuries. Not surprisingly, the Bible and other sacred writings had top priority. Next came the works of the medieval theologians. Then followed successively the medieval treatises on civil and ecclesiastical law, medieval medical texts, and then the writings of classical antiquity—the literary works first, and the scientific writings a bad second. All these were printed in Latin. Greek was still a scarce accomplishment and came much later. Until it did, the Greek writers of antiquity had to be read in translations that were mainly in Latin but occasionally in the vernacular. Meanwhile, contemporary writings were printed only to a very limited extent.

To be more specific—the three standard books on the liberal arts which had been copied and used generally throughout the medieval period were the somewhat crude encyclopaedias of Martianus Capella in the fifth century, of Cassiodorus in the sixth century and of Isidore of Seville in the seventh century. To these we should add the *Arithmetic* of Boethius in the sixth century. It is interesting to note that as many as eight different editions of Martianus were printed between the years 1499 and 1599, seven editions of Isidore's *Origins* between 1472 and 1577, and innumerable printings of Cassiodorus up to 1580. Boethius' *De Arithmetica* was printed almost continuously from 1488 onwards. Another great favourite of the printing presses was a Universal History written by Orosius in A.D. 417 called *Seven Books of Histories against the Pagans*. It was a compilation compounded of the Bible, Livy, Tacitus and others and its theme was that of the divine punishment of paganism. It was used as a textbook in schools—as was also a grammatical work *On the Eight Parts of Speech* by the fourth-century writer Aelius Donatus.

It must not, however, be supposed that these were the exclusive products of the early printing presses of the fifteenth and sixteenth centuries. Pliny's *Natural History* (in continuous use in the manuscripts of the Middle Ages) was printed at Venice in 1469; Varro's *Res Rustica* (on farming) at Rome in 1472; the writings of *Lucretius* at Brescia in 1473; the medical writings of *Celsus* at Florence in 1478; and so on. It is also of interest to note that Euclid appeared first in Latin at Venice in 1482, then in Greek at Basel in 1533, and subsequently in English at London in 1570. (See footnote 2, p. 224.)

In all this activity statistics show how far Italy clearly led the way. From the middle of the fifteenth century, when presses were first set up, to the end of the century, no less than 2,789 books had been published in Venice and 972 in Rome, whereas outside Italy the corresponding figures were 789 in Paris, 298 in Strasburg, 137 in England and 126 in Spain and Portugal.

Meanwhile, other factors were contributing to the new outlook. Trade was prospering in a new social order in which both nationalism and capitalism were now, as a consequence of a growing return to central power in the various countries of western Europe, rapidly replacing the feudal system of old—the system derived from the "client-patron" relationship under which the strong patron could guarantee the lower orders from both violence and economic distress—at a price! Now, with nationalism and capitalism, there came into existence a professional class to administer the law and general policy of money circulation that could regulate both taxation and commodity prices. The new worlds of Columbus and Vasco da Gama opened up new sources of wealth and trade; and if they produced an inevitable monetary inflation, they at least carried with them increased incentives both to producers and traders. In Germany the Hanseatic League was co-ordinating the trade of the north, and the ships of England, Holland, Portugal and Spain were journeying to and from the new worlds; whilst in Italy the commercial wealth of Venice and Florence was becoming a dominant factor in a general era of prosperity.

One consequence of this prosperity was an increasing and a more informed leisure and, with such leisure, an increasing sense of revolt at the restrictive pressures of the Catholic Church against the drift towards freedom of thinking on theological and philosophical issues. Impatience against restraints was bringing men like the German Martin Luther (1483–1546) into a growing conflict with the Church of Rome that was quickly to culminate in the well-known Reformation movement which swept across the whole of western Europe. Luther taught that man's place in the domestic surroundings of his home and his fellow citizens was entirely consistent with his ability to pursue a life of religious faith.

This was the fundamental principle underlying the Reformation movement that successively separated England, Scotland, Sweden, Norway, Denmark, North Germany and Bohemia from Rome. And it was entirely consistent with the general setting of the times. It was, in fact, another and an inevitable phase of the general Renaissance—a fifteenth-century widening of both cultural and political horizons. In addition to the rich poetry and prose of the past that was now at hand for everybody to enjoy, there had developed a sense of nationality and political thought such as was once preached and practised in both Greece and Rome. The city-states of classical antiquity were not, of course, national states, but they were self-contained communities and commonwealths. These were the inspiration of the famous Niccolo Machiavelli (1469–1527), the great political contemporary and acquaintance of Leonardo da Vinci, whose dream was for a united Italy and who expressed his ideals of an independent national state in his book *The Prince*. So, too, a century later, was the Englishman Thomas Hobbes (1588–1679) inspired during the English Civil War to write his *Leviathan*.

Two interesting points relating to the Great Reformation should be mentioned before we pass on. One is that, although the movement was a definite protest against the dogmatic attitudes of the Church of Rome, the Reformers very quickly showed in their turn an equal intolerance and dogmatism of their own. The other point relates to the influence of the Reformation on Education. Its "short-term" influence was quite bad, simply because so many schools, equally with all other Church property and endowments, were confiscated and closed. It was on this score that Erasmus (1404–1536), a great pioneer of education, disapproved of the Reformation. The "long-term" effect was, however, wholly good. Luther realised the necessity for education, if only to ensure that as many as possible could read the Bible; and as soon as the German Church was severed from Rome in 1521 he translated the Bible into German and opened up Protestant schools all over the country.

The other relates to the philosophical field. We have noted the dominant influence of Aristotle, as his writings became more and more available. But what of Plato? We have, in fact, to record that in Italy there was a distinct revival of Platonism in the fifteenth century, and, indeed, it extended well into the sixteenth century. The inherent charm and wisdom of Plato's *Dialogues* had much to do with this, and the man most responsible for making it available was Marcilio Ficino (1433–1497). Under the patronage of Lorenzo the Magnificent, Ficino founded the "Florentine Academy" and modelled it on the earlier Academy of Plato. Ficino, aided by his distinguished pupil Pico della Mirandola (d. 1494), translated into Latin a number of the works both of Plato and of the neo-Platonist Plotinus, and attempted to reflect their teachings in a Christian setting.

We have already referred to the relationship between the humanistic outlook and the fourteenth-century literary revival associated with Dante, Petrarch and Boccaccio. These were contemporary writers portraying their period—but now, in the fifteenth century, contemporary writing was discarded in favour of a literary trend that was a frank imitation of the great writers of classical Rome. Indeed, this hero-worship of the great men of ancient Rome was extended to many activities of day-to-day life—public orations, letter writing, and even

Plate 13—Bronze statue of the Emperor Marcus Aurelius at the Capitol, Rome (Mansell Collection).

Plate 14—Claudius Ptolemaus and Boethius—portion of a fresco drawing by Raphael in the Royal Academy, Venice, showing philosophers of different periods, e.g. Ptolemy is of the first century A.D. and Boethius of the sixth (Mansell Collection).

CI·PTOLEMAEO·ALEX· FL·BOETIO·

Plate 15—Impression of Avicenna (A.D. 945–1038) lecturing. (By permission of the Oxford University Press.)

Plate 16—Professional copyists—a scribe at work. From a fifteenth-century MS. at Paris, written by Jean Mielot (from Hart, *Makers of Science*—Oxford University Press).

Plate 17—An impression of Leonardo as a young man. The original is in the Uffizi Gallery, Florence, and is described as by a "Tuscan Master" of the fifteenth century.

social occasions. So men of genius, who might well have shown themselves capable of much literary originality, were lost in the inferiorities of imitation. It was a great price to pay for what perhaps was an essential prerequisite for future progress, and it was not until Lorenzo de Medici and Politian diverted these activities by writing their own more contemporary Italian poetry that the potentialities of a new era of literature became apparent. Their example was soon followed and to such effect that one such work, the *Orlando Furioso*, by a writer named Ariosto, has been described as the purest example of Renaissance poetry.

So the tide of the new literature set in, and in the wake of the Renaissance of letters came the turn of art. But there was this great difference. Unlike literature, there was no classical tradition to entice the artist from reflecting the originality of his own day. Little of ancient art had come to light during the fourteenth and fifteenth centuries. Such classical stimulus as was needed as a spur and an example could, therefore, only reach the fifteenth-century painters, sculptors and architects through literature. In art itself, imitation therefore had less scope, and originality had more free play.

There was one possible exception to this for a time in the field of architecture, because among the recovered writings of the past was the *De Architectura* of Vitruvius. This had been a most important work in Roman times, and Vitruvius was an important figure in the world of engineering and architecture of his day. It is unfortunate that the copyist and imitative spirit in literature, to which we have referred, found sufficient extension in the case of Vitruvius to prompt architects to work his mechanical formulae of construction into their own designs. The effect was to produce a pseudo-classic and artificial style that unfortunately spread over much of western Europe—but even in this field the true spirit of the Renaissance was bound to break through.

So we come to the full glory of sixteenth-century art, with its polish, its perfection and its spirit of free individuality in all its branches—in the paintings of Raphael, Titian, Correggio and our own giant of study, Leonardo da Vinci; in the sculpture (following the earlier fifteenth-century Donatello) of Michelangelo, Giambologna, Cellini and Sansovino; and in the architecture of Bramante, Omodeo and Lombardi. These stood as high in the elegant ranks of Renaissance art as did the exquisite poetry of Ariosto in the field of literature. The Renaissance was in full spate.

E

III

LEONARDO'S POLITICAL SETTING—
THE CITY-STATES OF
FIFTEENTH-CENTURY ITALY

I. THE POLITICAL COMPLEX OF THE RENAISSANCE PERIOD

Apart from his last few years, Leonardo spent the whole of his life in various parts of Italy. At the age of sixty-three, when his health was failing, he accepted an invitation from Francis I of France to take up residence in the Castle of St. Cloux, near Amboise, and it was here that he died on 22nd May 1519. But apart from this, the main centres of his activities were his own native Florence and the cities of Milan and Rome, with a brief intervening period in Venice. In those days Italy was not a unified political unit. The nationalist movements that had produced a united England, and France, and the Netherlands and Spain, had failed to produce a united Italy. That was only to come in relatively recent times. The political complexities of western Europe were great enough even between the countries we have mentioned—but in respect of Italy they were exceptional. Nevertheless, without some understanding of these complexities we cannot properly appreciate the extent to which external political factors influenced the life and movements of Leonardo da Vinci. His political backgrounds may have been of less significance than was the cultural and scientific atmosphere in which he lived and worked, but they did determine where he lived and the conditions under which he worked; and so we must survey them briefly.

We must first hark back to the feudal system in Europe and its breakdown. Inherent in this system was the existence of the great mass of population in the role of serfs. These were the underdogs of the whole system, and at the other end of the scale were the feudal potentates—and massed on the side lines, so to speak, with continual efforts to break through, was the Church.

Theoretically, as we have previously noted, the feudal system was born out of a real need, in which overlord and people provided mutual services and protection. But, in practice, there inevitably appeared between them various levels of "middlemen" who were little other

66

than rapacious "underlords", whose abuses of their powers and functions tended largely to nullify the value of the system. It was here that the Church could and did intervene to compel feudal potentates, small and great, to curb the rapacity of their retainers and to restore ill-gotten gains—though it must be admitted that some members of the church were not above "cutting in" on these to their own gain. The accumulation of wealth by the Church was, indeed, one of the preoccupations between the eleventh and fourteenth centuries that helped to bring it into disrepute. Priests were always on the hunt for legacies. Penitent sinners were exhorted to bequeath their lands and property to the Church as a price for their salvation. In many countries as much as a quarter of the land became Church property. Small wonder, therefore, that kings and princes alike were at odds with the Church. Where feudal lords were expected to provide military support and funds, their lands were found instead to be supporting abbeys and monks and nuns.

Moreover, these lands, as Church property, automatically came under the foreign domination of papal Rome. It was all part of a general struggle between princes and papacy. The Pope claimed the right to appoint and invest the bishops—but so did the kings and princes. Moreover, the Church not only claimed exemption from taxation by the states but even claimed the right to levy a tax of one-tenth upon the property of laymen, over and above what these unfortunates had to pay to their own princes and kings.

In this general struggle between Pope and monarch the dice were usually loaded on the side of the Church. The threat of excommunication, of absolving the subjects of a recalcitrant monarch from allegiance to him, of refusing to recognise his successor, of withholding such priestly functions as marrying and burying the dead—these were deadly and effective weapons against the medieval mind. They were most effective in the twelfth century, but, in the end, they were overdone. The realm and the sphere of lay-life could stand so much of this intrusion and no more. The Church even had its own law courts. A wide variety of matters relating to wills, marriages, cases of alleged heresy, sorcery or blasphemy, and all matters relating to priests, monks, students, widows and orphans, were regarded as the business of the clerical court. And when, as frequently happened, the Church was headed by Popes of questionable morality and standards of conduct, the cumulative effect, both on the public conscience and the hostility of lay rulers, ended, as we have seen, in the Great Reformation. There was even one earlier period, referred to as the Great Schism, when rival factions appointed rival Popes at one and the same time! This was when, following the period of the papal translation from Rome to

Avignon, Pope Gregory XI returned to Rome in 1377. For many Churchmen of French origin and sympathies this return was un-popular, and when Gregory died in 1378, at the same time as the Italian Urban VI was elected to succeed him in Rome, a rival "anti"-Pope, Clement VII, was elected at Avignon. It was an extraordinary situation. Each Pope duly cursed and excommunicated the other; Europe was split into two camps; and, as we know, the Wycliffites and other non-conformists made the most of their opportunity.

But amid all this another potent factor in the breakdown of the feudal system was the growth of the medieval towns. In a genuinely feudal organisation there was no real place for a town and its citizens. Their requirements and their mutual interests called for an organisa-tion and a scheme of administration far removed from the simple for-mula of a collection of serfs controlled by a feudal lord. As the cities grew, trade and manufacture developed, and many of the burghers became steadily wealthier. And if, in fact, the feudal overlord of the town found himself in urgent need of money, he now had to meet this need by borrowing from the burghers. But the terms were now theirs and not his, and time after time these terms meant giving them a charter of formulated rights and liberties. Indeed, in many cases such charters were purchased by the burghers direct from the ruling king or prince himself.

So cities developed, both in wealth and organisation, and in either quasi or complete independence. Such, for example, were Venice, Florence, Genoa, Lisbon, Paris, Bruges, London, Antwerp, Ham-burg and Nuremberg. All were trading cities, with travellers coming and going. They formed two broad groups in terms of the main trade routes with Asia. The northern one came up the Volga and thence to the Baltic coast. By the beginning of the fifteenth century some eighty cities were united in the great Hanseatic League for the control of their trade. The southern route came up the Red Sea or the Persian Gulf and thence overland to the ports of the eastern Mediterranean and so on to Venice, Genoa and the other great towns of northern Italy. And here in these cities the inhabitants rapidly acquired a high degree of skill both as traders and as craftsmen. Such towns, with much of the adjacent surrounding country, grew sufficiently wealthy to enable their citizens to purchase almost entire independence. They were known as free cities. Instead of being serfs performing tasks on the lands of the overlord, the townsmen now paid rent and did their own tasks for themselves. The traders of the city would form their merchants' guilds, and the craftsmen their crafts' guilds. Thus Leon-ardo, as we have seen, joined the Printers' Guild in Florence when he was twenty-one years of age.

The final step in the organisation of these city-states, reminiscent of the Greek city-states of classical times, was the formal institution of democratic self-government by the setting up of *communes*. These were organisations, often formed in defiance of their feudal superiors, many of whom had to be fought in open combat. The object was to set up a republican form of government in the city, with an obligation that no citizen would be permitted to remain if he did not join the commune. The cities of northern Italy were powerful examples of these new city-states; and within them there developed a keen sense of citizenship, a love of freedom, ideals of equality and of public and social service strongly reminiscent of the age of Pericles.

But the new freedom of the city-states was not wholly a story of virtues. As with the Greek city-states of old, there were vices also. Party faction was inevitable, but with this went party bitterness and, all too often, open strife. And as, equally inevitably, there were in the countries around and beyond the eager eyes and hearts seeking extensions of power and control, the mutual support which was so often necessary as between the city-states was seldom available. On the other hand, the mutual jealousies often meant that one city might be prepared to enter into partnership with a more powerful neighbouring national monarchy against another city-state. Warfare and accompanying disturbances of trade and amenities, and a recurrent sense of anxiety and lack of freedom from security, were therefore of sporadic recurrence in a land crying out for tranquillity.

In Italy there was yet one other tendency that followed the pattern of ancient Greece. Faction and disunion within the city's bounds provided the opportunity for the personalities of the moment —men, frequently both able and popular—placed at the head of the city's organisation, to become little more than autocratic tyrants. These, in fact, dominated city after city in Italy until, in the fifteenth century, Venice alone could still be regarded as maintaining fully its republican institutions—and later Venice, too, was to succumb to the dictates of a despotic oligarchy.

Generally speaking, it was the policy of these ruling despots to disarm their subjects. Although the object was to eliminate factions among the people and to secure their own personal safety, this in general was a popular measure. The bogey of military service was avoided at a stroke. But in its place came the practice of employing mercenary armies whose cost had to be met by taxation. As a consequence the people became "finance-conscious", and trade and business received a great impetus. On the other hand, in course of time, the mercenaries and those who led them became increasingly conscious of their own power, and by the beginning of the fourteenth century a new factor was brought into

Italian life—the Condottieri came into existence, frequently dictating their own terms to their nominal masters.

When one such mercenary, Francesco Sforza, entered Milan in triumph in 1450 (two years before Leonardo da Vinci was born), he virtually produced a new era in the history of despotism. Ruling despots learnt to rely less and less on paid armies and warfare, and more and more on diplomacy and bribery. The literary exponent of the philosophy and technique of this theory of rule was Machiavelli, whose cynical writings on the principles of statecraft by the application of intelligence to the expediencies of craft, corruption and diplomacy have become permanently associated with this period of Italian history.

Nevertheless, it must broadly be accepted that, with all the difficulties of internal faction and dissention and external strife, the city-states of Italy did present to the world an example of democracy and autonomy on the Greek model in which could be nurtured not alone a spirit and a sense of freedom but a home of culture where art and literature, science and philosophy could be given full rein and encouragement. Whatever may be said of the tyrants politically, they were, on the whole, liberal patrons of learning in the Renaissance Italy of the fifteenth century. Such, for example, included the Medici family in Florence, the Sforzas in Milan and the Borgia family in Rome.

To sum up, following the twelfth- and thirteenth-century eras of the free burghs of Italian history, the fourteenth and fifteenth centuries became the Age of the Despots; and it was during this latter period that the Renaissance in learning flowered to full fruition. Within it individual talents were encouraged and diffused, and an example and an incentive to learning and culture for its own sake was handed on to the other nations of Western Europe. By the time the powers of the Despots had given way, in the sixteenth and seventeenth centuries, to what for Italy was virtually an age of foreign domination, the sweep of the Renaissance had passed on to France, to Spain, to Germany and to Great Britain.

It is here necessary, however, to clear away one possible source of misunderstanding in relation to the development of what we have called the city-states. Geographically, they had become, so to speak, minor countries. In the days of the later national unity of Italy in the nineteenth century they would be referred to as provinces. As a city-state, in the narrower sense of the term, developed successfully, so its power and geographical bounds increased. Not only did the surrounding countryside naturally merge within its jurisdiction and rule, but so also did the lesser towns and cities in its broad proximity. In effect, therefore, Italy comprised, by the middle of the fifteenth century, several city-states of quite appreciable dimensions (see map, Fig. 2). In the south was the Kingdom of Naples (including the two Sicilies, the islands of Sicily and Sardinia, and the mainland "toe" of Calabria); the states of the Church (including the Patrimony of St. Peter, with Rome as its capital, Umbria, Urbino and Perugia); the city-state of Siena; then, further north, Florence, Modena, Genoa (including the island of Corsica); and still further north, stretching from west to east across the Plains of Lombardy, were the House of Savoy, the Duchy of Milan and the Republic of Venice.

We have referred to the external hazards confronting the city-states in Italy in respect of the hostile threats of neighbouring countries. It was an ever-changing pattern—a kaleidoscope of uncertainty which were in a sense an anachronism in the European scene. It was an anachronism of perpetual disunion that was to persist because of jealousy of city against city, and of ruling family against ruling family. Instead of the city-states of Genoa, Venice, Milan and Florence joining hands with each other and with the papal states to withstand the threats of France and Spain and Austria, they preferred to carry on with their intrigues and wars against each other. For, unlike Italy, there had now generally emerged in Europe a principle of *nationalism*. This was, in effect, a consolidation of the power of monarchy in alliance with democratic popular assemblies, expressed in terms of a natural geographical and ethnical unit. There came to be recognised the unity of an English people and nation, a French people and nation, a Spanish people and nation—and so on. This consolidation into a national and monarchist unit was encouraged and hastened by the great wars of the times—as, for example, between the English and the French and between the Spaniards and the Moslems, who for so long had invaded their lands. These were no longer wars between feudal aristocracies— they were shared with the common people with a growing sense of common interest and a burning sense of national patriotism. A king was a popular figure because he was a national leader against a national foe. Thus it was, for example, that the long wars of the Spaniards against the Moslem Moors ended with the conquest of Granada late in the fifteenth century, leaving in their wake a strong and a unified Spain.

Amid this European "family" of nations, the failure of Italy to emerge as a unified nation made its city-states fair game for their covetous and powerful neighbours. From Germany, in particular, numerous attempts were made to acquire a governing stake in the wealth and prosperity of these cities—and all the time the special place, standing and power of the papacy (the natural enemy of the kings and emperors and therefore well disposed to the city-states) added to the general complex of these political and military manœuvres.

Fig. 2. Italy in the fifteenth century.

Indeed, yet another complication was the fact that all the time there were hostile Mongols and Turks operating on and threatening the eastern front of Europe. To all these difficulties and threats the some-times varying, sometimes combined, but always determined, resistance of the Italian city-states and the papal forces were long effective through-out the fifteenth century, though they were finally overrun and par-celled out between France, Spain and Austria. But, in fact, so too was Germany, and it was not until the nineteenth century that unity and nationhood could come to both Italy and Germany.

2. THE CITY-STATE OF FLORENCE

Let us consider in more particular detail the city-state of Florence, in which Leonardo da Vinci, the subject of our main study in this book, spent the first thirty years of his life and to which he subsequently returned for yet another term of years.

Between the beginning of the fourteenth century, when Clement V had moved to Avignon, and the middle of the fifteenth century, when Nicholas V had moved the papacy back to Rome in 1447, the city-states had reached a degree of self-government greater than at any other period in their history. By the mid-century Italy comprised five principal units—the Kingdom of Naples, the Duchy of Milan, the Republic of Florence, the Republic of Venice and the Papal States (Fig. 2)—and, in the main, unity of confederated action and mutual support between them determined and secured, for Italy as a whole, a broad period of tranquillity and prosperity for the next forty-five years that coincided with the main cultural achievements of the Renaissance.

At their heads, as we have seen, were the tyrants who had established themselves as either captains of the people or leaders of the Church, or heads of the two great opposing parties of those days—the Guelphs and the Ghibellines. These self-made princes sustained themselves in power by seeking and obtaining the favour of the people by such devices as both freeing them from the requirements of military service and by disarming the nobles. As their hold grew and their sense of tenure became firmer, they assumed titles and advanced and sustained dynastic claims for their heirs and successors. Their strength lay more in the power of the purse than of the sword—in financial inducements at home and political intrigue and finesse abroad. These were usually found more effective than internal coercion and external wars—though at home there was always the hidden threat of terrorist action behind the smile of inducement.

Thus ruled, for example, the family of the Medici in Florence. Under them the city-state waxed in power and in the prosperity that came with increased trade. They encouraged the erection of beautiful buildings, patronised the arts, gave a measure of delegated authority to the merchants, and obtained the co-operation of the nobles by converting them into courtiers, diplomatists, men of affairs and seekers after favours.

To appreciate the broad steps of political evolution in Florence we should go back to the beginning of the fourteenth century. We have referred to the general division over Italy of two factions—the Guelphs and the Ghibellines. These arose from acute discord between two great family units of the early thirteenth century. Now one and now another of these two parties gained ascendancy in Florence. Broadly, we may regard the Guelphs as the democrats holding the allegiance and support of the "people"; and the Ghibellines as the protagonists of the "aristocrats". Even when, in the course of time, the terms "Ghibelline" and "Guelph" had become mere labels whose origins were lost in the past, practically the whole of Italian society remained violently riven in the partisanship of one or the other fold. Trivialities of custom and practice were perpetuated to differentiate the one party from the other, whether it be in the banners and heraldic colours displayed, or which side of the caps the feathers were worn, or even, almost incredibly, whether fruit was cut at the table crosswise or straight down! The ding-dong nature of the conflict between them actually brought one period when the city was divided into two almost autonomous republics—one, the *commune* headed by the *podesta*, and the other the *popolo* headed by the *capitano*; but this was a fleeting anachronism of party strife. Later, there was a period of domination of the Florentines by one Walter of Brienne, Duke of Athens, who in 1342 seized power. He was an astute and ambitious "foreigner", half French and half Levantine, who successfully induced the populace to acclaim him as Lord of Florence. Once in power, he disarmed the citizens with the aid of an imported French bodyguard and ruled with both cruelty and oppression. The inevitable sequence of unsuccessful plots against him culminated in his final overthrow in 1343. It was a very brief but violent period of misrule, the rebound from which produced a series of measures and enactments that converted Florence into a thoroughly democratic and commercial republic. Its scheme of administration provided for the representation of most (but not all) classes and interests *within* the city walls. Political rights were therefore excluded from the subject towns and villages outside the city itself.

Florence, city of traders, naturally divided its citizens as between wholesale merchants and shopkeepers. Their respective interests produced respective political groups, but their common interest was commerce. All the arts and crafts were organised in guilds, and many of these became as powerful and wealthy as, for example, the great city guild companies of the City of London today. The power, of course, lay with the wealthier wholesale merchants and traders, and these naturally assumed the control of foreign policy.

As one would expect the external policy of the state was dominated by commercial considerations. The main elements in this policy were, firstly, a need to acquire direct access to the sea (which meant a rivalry against its neighbour, Pisa); secondly, to prevent its southerly neighbour Siena, from interfering with its main trade route to Rome (which involved a series of quarrels with Siena for supremacy); thirdly, a pro-Guelph bias in its general politics, since this carried with it the promotion of its banking business with the papacy and its vast funds and states; and, fourthly, a need to extend its territories northwards in Tuscany to ensure the safety of its main land routes to North-West Europe.

The remainder of the fourteenth century saw Florence through a kaleidoscopic series of "ups and downs"—internal dissensions and uprisings against those in power, and external wars with Milan in 1351, with Pisa in 1362, and with the Holy See (which was anxious to annex the city of Florence to itself) for three years from 1375 to 1378, and once again with Pisa at the turn of the fifteenth century. This time the campaign involved making overtures to the King of France for support, with the bait of accepting the anti-pope Benedict XIII (of the Great Schism). Pisa was besieged and the mouth of the Arno blockaded. It surrendered in 1406 and Florence gained its sea-port at last—and with it a new and direct maritime trade; and as a few years later the Genoese expressed willingness to sell the Port of Leghorn, south of Pisa, to the Florentine republic for 100,000 florins, a new trade boom lay ahead and all was well.

It is in this setting that we now meet the name and family of the Medici—a name with which so much of Renaissance Florence became associated. The founder of this distinguished Florentine family's political fortune was Salvestro, who enjoyed the rank of *gonfalonier* (chief) of the republic from 1378 to 1381, when he was banished in a popular uprising by supporters of his opponents, the Albizzi family. Salvestro's son, Giovanni de' Medici, remained in Florence and occupied himself in commerce with great success and wealth, and became *gonfalonier* in his turn. He died in 1429, and one of his two sons, Cosimo, now comes into the Florentine scene.

Cosimo de' Medici was born in 1389 and was trained to commerce in his father's house, carrying on the tradition with great success. He, too, was caught up in the feud with the Albizzi family and, like his father, suffered a term of exile in Venice as one of the exigencies of this feud. He returned, however, within a year, in 1434, amid the acclamations of his fellow-citizens. From that time onward for the next three hundred years, the history of Florence remained associated with the house and family of Medici.

Cosimo's rule had all the triumphs and vicissitudes of the times from the political angle—but from the point of view of culture it was one sustained story of triumph. The richest private citizen of Europe, he surpassed many sovereign princes in the munificence of his patronage. He gathered round him some of the most learned men of the age. We have already referred to his encouragement of the study of Greek culture, its languages, its letters and its philosophy, and to his establishment of the Florentine Academy under the directorship of the Platonic philosopher Marsilio Ficino. His administration dominated the republic although, technically, he was a private citizen. He exiled those who opposed him, and saw to it that at the five-yearly elections the magistrates were appointed to his nomination. He was involved in a series of wars. One, in 1437, was against the Visconti and brought a great military victory by the Florentines at Anghiari in 1440. This battle was later to be the subject of a number of wonderful sketches and cartoons by Leonardo da Vinci, intended for a great work of art, in competition with Michelangelo, but unfortunately it was never completed.

Cosimo died in 1464. He was succeeded by a very infirm son named Piero, who died five years later, in 1469, and it was *his* son, famous grandson of a famous grandfather, who succeeded him to initiate a brilliant era of government for Florence. He has appropriately been named Lorenzo the Magnificent (*Il Magnifico*). Born in 1448 (four years before the birth of Leonardo, who was, therefore, contemporary with him), he was given all the advantages of education available from the many distinguished men of languages, literature, art and philosophy, who had made Florence their home. With this he combined a love of sport and exercise and an early ability in the business affairs of his house. He was sixteen when his grandfather died, and was scarcely ready for full public life when his ailing father died shortly after. This, however, his natural abilities soon remedied. He obtained a powerful ally in the famous Orsini family of Rome by marrying Clarice, the daughter of *Giacobbe Orsini*, in 1469.

Early in his official career, in 1472, he was confronted with a revolt of the inhabitants of Volterra, a neighbouring subject city within the Florentine republic. He showed considerable military skill in taking the city. Subsequently, he visited Pisa, re-established its Academy and did much to build it up as a seat of learning, at considerable expense to himself.

In 1478 he and his brother Giuliano were the victims of a plot for their overthrow, to which Pope Sixtus IV and Salviato, Archbishop of Pisa, were undoubtedly partners. Giuliano was murdered, but so far as Lorenzo was concerned the plot failed. The actual murderer, Gerrardo Bandino, was hanged, and the sight of this was the subject of one of Leonardo's cartoons showing the dead Bandino dangling from a noose. He had, as is well known, a queer attraction for the bizarre and presumably found this study irresistible. The Pope, need it be said, was inflamed to rage at the failure of his treacherous plot. He excommunicated Lorenzo and the magistrates of Florence and formed a league with the King of Naples for the invasion of Florence. The subsequent campaigns were pursued with varying fortune until Lorenzo's personal success in persuading Ferdinand, King of Naples, to withdraw from the papal alliance and the death of Pope Sixtus in 1484 brought an era of peace.

So far as Leonardo was concerned, these seemingly unending sequences of hostilities aroused an intense curiosity and interest in the problems and the mechanisms of war weapons. His personal attitude to the Medici was detached and he professed no desire to be a fighting participant in anything, for anybody. But we have seen what a natural bent he had for mechanical problems and for thinking out, on paper, mechanical devices. The possibilities for military operations were irresistible and the extent to which he carried this we have noted in his famous letter to Ludovico Sforza. Inasmuch as all these many ingenious ideas and devices were sketched out seemingly without either expert military advice or help, or presumably experimental verification, one cannot but be astonished at their range and seeming pertinence. We shall, however, be considering this further subsequently.

Florence had become a great and beautiful and a busy city (Plate 21). Its population was well over 100,000. It included some 150 churches, monasteries and other religious houses, and its main streets contained over 200 shops. Its fine woollens and silks found ready markets all over Europe and the Near East. The woollen Guild had nearly 300 booths and shops in the city, and the silk weavers over 80.

The city was built at the foot of a hill on the banks of the Arno, with five magnificent bridges spanning the river—each with houses and shops similar to those on London Bridge in medieval England. Its fine buildings and libraries were centres of arts and letters. Florentine bankers and merchants were to be found all over the world—often in the advisory service of foreign governments. And crowning all this was the banking house and family of the Medici—as powerful and colourful in their international negotiations and transactions for the bolstering up of rulers, for the making and breaking of new states, for the granting or withholding of crucial loans required for every adventure of large-scale importance, as was the House of Rothschild in the nineteenth century.

3. LEONARDO AND VERROCCHIO IN FLORENCE

When Leonardo, as a youth of sixteen, first came to the house of his master, Verrocchio, from the relative quiet and solitude of the countryside of Vinci, one can understand his sense of wonder and bewilderment at the gay, busy and colourful scenes of activity around him. Buyers of the products of the weavers, the dyers, the cabinet-makers and the jewellers; merchants and traders mingling with the characteristically slender and beautiful Florentine women—it must all have been a wonderful sight to his young and naturally curious gaze. Much of what he saw was artistic and lovely—a reflection of the culture of the period—and much was the bewildering reflection of the day-to-day activity of a wealthy city of many people attending to their worldly needs—the meat, wine, oil, vegetables and dairy produce pouring in to a host of shops in carts coming from a countryside of countless thousands of farms and vineyards (Plate 24).

Leonardo soon found that the intellectual atmosphere of humanistic culture was dominated by the recovered picture of the gracious world of Roman letters and rhetoric. Florentine society was powerfully influenced by the literature and the politics of the mood and the moment of its ruler, Lorenzo the Magnificent. This mood, as we have seen, was definitely towards the promotion and encouragment of all forms of art and literature and philosophy pertaining to the classical world. Equally, however, it was a mood of external glamour, both of pomp and pleasure. Processions and pageantry, both lay and clerical, were of almost daily occurrence. The devotional round went hand in hand with the amenities of communal festivals. There was a due blending of the asceticism of Church ritual with a gay propitiation of the memory of the pagan gods of Ancient Greece and Rome. Even the games had a ritual character, and soon Leonardo was busy with his notebooks and sketches, recording scenes and impressions with vivid strokes and lines and pungent notes (Plate 18).

Actually, both games and pageantry interested Leonardo greatly, both as an artist, and as an athlete. He was gracefully and powerfully built himself and was a frequent participant in many of the ball games of the period. But whether in games or the daily round of life's major domestic happenings—birth, baptism, marriage or death—the itch of pageantry was irresistible to the Florentine world, with its love of processions and colour, both in flowers and clothes and also in music, all accompanied by a dramatization of gesture and an elaboration of procedure. And when Verrocchio, as sometimes happened, was called upon by Lorenzo for aid as pageant-master, he could always count on and eager and willing helper in his pupil, Leonardo (Plate 17).

Particularly magnificent was the pageantry of colour and feasting when the Medici were called upon to show hospitality to distinguished visitors. Leonardo found unfeigned delight in his seventeenth year, in 1469, when the city was visited in state by an embassy from the Sultan of Egypt. It was a veritable Arabian Nights tale come to life—a procession of gifts that included a lion and a giraffe, coloured fleeces, fine muslins and elaborate feasting. And again, in 1472, when Galeazzo Maria Sforza of Milan and his French princess, on a golden palfrey, visited the house of Lorenzo amid the fanfares of trumpets and the colours of a procession of gaily clad pages, cavaliers, huntsmen and falconers—all displaying the potential might and the luxury of the city-state of Milan, from whence they came. Lorenzo, on his side, did full honours to the occasion in every way amid the serene splendour of his great and palatial residence in the Via Larga. Here were set forth a sequence of pageants and miracle plays amid the harmonies of soft music. Among the guests was the yet childish but already secretive and thoughtful princess, Caterina Sforza, who was to make her cruel mark on a subsequent world and who was destined to return to Florence to end in peace a life of storm and passion.

But they were not all days of pageantry and colour in Florence. The daily round of work made its demands, and for Leonardo this meant his workaday life as a pupil and apprentice of Andrea Verrocchio. Actually, Verrocchio's *bottega* was hardly a studio in the modern sense of the term. It reflected the fact that the fine arts had not, at this time, found their separate place above the "handicraft" practitioners of the artistic crafts. Men like Botticelli, Pollaiuolo and Verrocchio, who became established as painters and sculptors, were usually first trained in the craft of the goldsmith. It was in a sense a period of transition. Among the "best" families it was still not yet "good form" for a son to become an artist. Even at the beginning of the sixteenth century, when the names of Leonardo and Michelangelo and Raphael had achieved European fame for their art, Baldassare Castiglione conceded in his *Cortegiano* (a sort of guide book for courtiers) that "while the complete courtier should try his skill in art, the artist's profession is not fit for a nobleman". And, in fact, the well-born Michelangelo incurred the anger of his father when, against his parental will, he became a pupil of Domenico Ghirlandaio.

It was almost certainly an excellent thing for Leonardo that his master, Verrocchio, was a man who had graduated to art through sound and solid craftsmanship. This meant not only that before he had become creative in his work he was content to acquire a complete mastery of his tools, his materials and his techniques—it also meant that at his *bottega* he was always content to accept commissions for a wide variety of artistic activities—paintings, statuary, goldsmith's work, fine mechanical contrivances, musical instruments and *objets d'art* in general—even repairs to existing works.

Verrocchio was much more the sculptor and goldsmith than the painter, and there was no lack of variety in his commissions, especially from Lorenzo himself. These included the work on the beautiful tomb of Cosimo's father Piero in San Lorenzo, and the erection of a great ball of gilded copper on the dome, surmounted by a cross. He also executed a bronze statue of "David" (Plate 19) for the staircase of the Palazzo Vecchio, and a year later he was at work on a silver altar for the Baptistry. These were outstanding examples. His masterpiece (unrivalled in the whole world with the possible exception of Donatello's "Gattamelata" at Padua) was undoubtedly his equestrian statue of the Venetian General Colleoni (Plate 20). But he was continually engaged on tombs, busts, armour, items for pageantry—a silver hind for Guiliano's helmet, or breastplates for a Sforza, the casting of a church bell for the monks at Vallombrosa, decorative work of cunning devices of clasps and cups for garden ornamentation and so on. Yet he was always in financial straits and difficulties—frequently when his patrons came to grief financially. It is said that he died at the early age of fifty-three from a fever contracted whilst working on a great equestrian statue (perhaps the "Colleoni") out-of-doors in inclement weather.

For a person of Leonardo's almost ubiquitous interests here were unending opportunities for his abilities to expand. There were other apprentices, too. Pietro Perugino, six years older than Leonardo, was a fellow pupil—a stolid, plodding peasant-type who won through to a successful mediocrity. Later they were joined by the younger Lorenzo di Credi—as an artist, shallow in creation, but uncannily successful in the imitation of the works of others—including Leonardo himself.

Between Verrocchio and Leonardo there was a great bond of understanding and sympathy. Verrocchio was some seventeen years older, but in spirit and interests they were similar. Both were coming to a realisation that there were more than tools and techniques needed for the mastery of art—one required a theoretical knowledge of human forms, the principles of perspective, the laws of mechanics; and there was also the need for mathematics—and particularly the study of geometry. With a master who felt such needs in common with his pupil, we may well appreciate that the *bottega* was a welcome meeting ground for others with similar tastes and appreciations. Here came Verrocchio's

Plate 18—Costumes of Florence in the fifteenth century, *c.* 1450–1470. (By permission of the Dept. of Arts & Sciences, I.B.M. Corporation of New York.)

Plate 19 Verrocchio's bronze statue of "David", for the staircase of the Palazzo Vecchio (Mansell Collection).

Plate 20—Verrocchio's equestrian statue of General Colleoni at Venice (Mansell Collection).

Plate 21—A panorama of Florence.

Plate 22—Ludovico Sforza (I.B.M., New York).

Plate 23—Study for an equestrian monument — one of a sheet of four studies (Windsor Royal Library).

neighbours, the brothers Pollaiuoli—Antonio and Piero di Jacobo—who were making their mark as painters and sculptors of the realistic school; Sandro Botticelli, gracious painter, who lived in the Via Nuova, in the house of his father, a struggling tanner; the elderly Paolo Doni Uccello and Domenico Ghirlandaio, almost contemporary with Leonardo in age—and many others. We have already discussed some of the other intellectual contacts by Leonardo during these Florentine years. Much of the talk was of art with its multiform problems and related interests—but for Leonardo there was much more. In art he had become moulded into a perfectionist in his twenties, but his interest had become stimulated in so many fields, at first related to his art, but now the subjects of study for their own sake, that time had become his master enemy. Every fresh artistic problem brought in its train a welter of scientific problems, many of them far-reaching and fundamental—problems of light and shade, principles of perspective, the physiology of the eye, muscular and mechanical movement, animal and plant biology, the flight of birds, and all the time the dream of artificial flight by man.

Much has been written of the sequence of commissions started but not fulfilled—and, indeed, the total of his surviving completed works at Florence is very scanty. On the other hand, by the time Leonardo was thirty-one, in 1483, when he left Florence for Milan, he had amassed a wealth of study that embraced not only theoretical argument and sketches and plans of practical projects, but also records of experiments covering a wide field of pure and applied mechanical science as we know it today. These included applications to hydraulics, military engineering and architecture, for all of which his reading must have been prodigious—and much of it under considerable difficulty, since, as we know, his Latin was laborious. Clearly he was an avid borrower of books. There is one note on the inside cover of one of his notebooks (Manuscript F) which reads thus:

Horace has written: of the speed of the heavens.	Concave mirrors Books of Venice Vernacular and Latin vocabulary Bohemian Knives Vitruvius Meteorologica Archimedes: de centro gravitatus Allesandro Benedetti's "Anatomy" The "Danto" of Niccolo della Croce	Aristotle's "philosophy" Messer Octavius Pallavicino for his Vitruvius

F

Albertuccio and Morliano
De Calculatione
Albert—De coelo et mun-
do—by Fra Bernardino

Clearly, Leonardo had cast his net far and wide. Indeed, one authority on his notebooks has set forth in alphabetical order a list of no fewer than seventy-two names of the classical and Middle Ages writers with whose works he had become acquainted.[1]

When, therefore, Leonardo departed from Florence in 1483 to take up a new life in Milan at the invitation of its ruler, Ludovico Sforza, at the age of thirty-one years, he could be said to have become not only an established artist but a man of ubiquitous knowledge in the fields of science and engineering. He was glad to go. Florence had become for him a city of intellectual frustration. The dominant cultural influence was that of Lorenzo's Platonic Academy, headed by Marcilio Ficino and graced by the gentle scholarship of Pico della Mirandola (destined to die at the early age of thirty-one). The Academicians had brought the culture of Plato and Aristotle to Florence but had set it on too high a pedestal. A sense of superiority over those less acquainted with the glories of Greece had brought an arrogance and an intolerance that was in no way improved by the "hair-splitting" techniques of argument that had crept into their discussions, reminiscent of the days and the methods of the scholastics. From these Leonardo was shut out, and the knowledge of this both humiliated and irritated him. They expressed for him his failure to obtain the recognition by his native city to which he felt entitled by a consciousness of both his ability in art and his growing mastery of the science and engineering outside art that he knew to matter so much in life. "I know well that because I have not had a literary education there are some who will think in their arrogance," he wrote later, "that they are entitled to set me down as uncultured—the fools! They will say that because I am uncultured I am not able adequately to express myself on the subject of which I wish to treat."[2] He is equally outspoken in a further note: "They go about puffed up and pompous, in fine raiment and bejewelled, not from the fruits of their own labours but from those of others; my own labours they refuse to recognise. They despise me, the inventor, but how much more are they to blame for not being inventors, but trumpeters and reciters of the works of others."[3]

Let us follow Leonardo to this next phase of his life in Milan.

[1] O. Werner, *Zur Physik Leonardo da Vinci*, pp. 22 and 23 (Erlangen, 1910).
[2] *Codex Atlanticus*, 119 r.
[3] Ibid, 117 r.

4. THE DUCHY OF MILAN

The Duchy of Milan was one of the richest of Italy's "splinter" states. Politically, it was always more or less in trouble. It was geographically the farthest north, and stood guardian and sentry in the Plains of Lombardy, between the ambitions for conquest by the rulers of France, Germany and Austria beyond the bastions of the Alps to the north, and the mutual jealousies of the other city-states to the south. Fortunately, the French were also much preoccupied in wars with England, but "in between" there was always danger. Milan was a natural *bon bouche* for European rapacity.

To appreciate the political position when Leonardo first went to live there, let us go back a century or so to survey briefly the chain of events leading to the establishment of the Sforzas as the reigning family of the Duchy.

We have referred to the origins of the despot families, of whom the Visconti and the Medici were outstanding examples, as having developed from the two main opposing factions of the Ghibellines and the Guelphs. Early in the fourteenth century these factions were involved in claims for the signory of Milan. At first this was held by the Guelphs, but invasion by Henry VII of Luxembourg gave the Ghibellines their opportunity, headed by the Visconti family. There then followed the well-known sequence of "ups" and "downs" in the fortunes both of the city and of the Visconti, one member of whom, Azzo, actually bought the city, in hard cash, from Ludwig of Bavaria in 1328. Later, in 1349, following the murder of his successor, Lucchino (by his wife!), Giovanni Visconti, Archbishop of Milan, assumed the lordship of the city and began a masterful control that soon extended the power of the Visconti to Genoa and much of northern Italy, as far as the frontiers of Piedmont in the west and Verona, Mantua, Ferrara and Venice in the east.

When Giovanni died in 1354 his heritage was at first divided between three brothers. One, Matteo, was conveniently murdered with the connivance of the other two—Bernabò in Milan and Galeazzo in Pavia, further south. Galeazzo at this time was perhaps the wealthiest person in Italy and he lived magnificently. His daughter, Violanti, married the English Duke of Clarence, and his son, Gian, a daughter of King John of France. Gian succeeded his father in 1378, and by successfully plotting against the life of his uncle, Bernabò, achieved his ambition to unite the joint domains of the Visconti family. He thus became one of the most powerful despots of Italy. His appetite for power seemed insatiable, and now, partly by force and partly by intrigue, he subdued the lesser despots—the Della Scala family in

Verona, the Carravesi in Padua, the Estensi in Ferrara, and the Gonzaghi in Mantua. Thus he pushed his way across Lombardy almost to the doors of Venice.

Gian Galeazzo now looked south and, at the turn of the century, began to attack the Tuscan city-states. Pisa and Perugia were both subdued and Florence was seriously menaced. Then, miraculously, in 1402 he was seized with a sudden and virulent attack of plague and so treachery and conquest were defeated by disease.

Seven years before, prompted by titular ambitions, he had bought from the Emperor Wenceslaus the titles of the Duke of Milan and Count of Pavia. But now, with his death, the allegiance of the mercenary troops he had used for his conquests was diverted by his generals to their own ends; and they either helped or sold themselves to the various Lombard cities previously seized by Gian, and the uprooted petty tyrants reappeared—the Estensi at Ferrara and the Gonzaghi at Mantua, and so on.

Nevertheless, the subsequent record of the Visconti maintained the family tradition of violence and cruelty. Giovanni, the elder of Gian's two sons, whose short rule of lust and cruelty ended in 1412 in assassination, was followed by the younger son, Filippo, who carried on with the family ambitions to regain the cities lost on his father's death. A series of campaigns followed, distinguished only by the emergence of generals of unusual military ability. One of these was Francesco Sforza, son of a peasant, who had risen by sheer merit to become a general. This was the family whose name now comes to be linked with the future story of Milan. Francesco Sforza had married Bianca, a natural and only daughter of Filippo. He received Pontremoli and Cremona as a dowry and was promised succession to Filippo. Shortly after the latter died in 1447 he acquired his master's heritage and wealth.

By this time Milan had once more re-established its status as a republic. It was, nevertheless, a very short-lived republic. By a subtle play upon the sympathies of the people, whose cause he pretended to support, and with the help of Cosimo de Medici in Florence, whose friendship he had meticulously courted, it was not long before Francesco was able both to lead the people and to assume for himself the title of Duke of Milan. He made his triumphal entry as such on 25th March 1450.

Francesco Sforza's first task was to consolidate his position politically, both with the people of Milan internally and by alliances and friendships externally. Politically, rather than give rein to his instinct for the further usurpation of power, he espoused the cause of a confederated Italy as an ideal and assured himself the protection of a "balance of power" by entering into close alliances of friendship with Cosimo de Medici of Florence and with Louis XI of France. At home he embarked on a number of projects. He rebuilt the fortress of Porta Giovio, erected a Great Hospital and constructed a canal connecting Milan with the River Adda. He ruled wisely and on the whole with humanity. He recognised the cultural expansion of the times and filled his court with Italian scholars and Greek exiles. His own daughter, Ippolita, became renowned as a Latin scholar.

Francesco Sforza died in 1466. He left five sons, of whom two call for a special mention as vitally concerning the succession to the Duchy. One was Galeazzo Maria, the eldest (b. 1444), and therefore the immediate successor: the other was Ludovico (surnamed il Moro—the Moor), who was three years younger.

There is little to say of Galeazzo's reign. He was sadistic, dissolute and cruel; but his mother, Bianca, had carefully educated all five of her sons in the arts and the humanities (a distinguished humanist, Francesco Filelfo, was one of their tutors) and Galeazzo adopted a policy of the encouragement of scholarship. But his many acts of cruelty caught up with him and he was assassinated at the porch of the cathedral on 26th December 1476 by three young Milanese noblemen, in imitation of the killing of Julius Caesar by Brutus and Cassius "in the brave days of old".

His son, Gian Galeazzo, was a boy of seven at the time of his nominal accession to the Duchy, but Ludovico the Moor had long been ambitious to assume the title. He had, in fact, so far ingratiated himself with his brother as to persuade Galeazzo, in 1471, to make him his subsequent heir in the event of the Duke's son, Gian, dying without issue. The young Gian's mother, Bona of Savoy, had assumed the regency on behalf of her son, but in the battle of wits and intrigue between herself and Ludovico she was supplanted in the regency. Thus, il Moro was now well on the way to achieving his full ambition. In all but name he was the ruler of Milan. Gian Galeazzo was a weakling, but he did in fact live to marry Isabella of Aragon, by whom he had a daughter. However, a year later, in 1494, he died suddenly—with a reasonable suspicion that his uncle was involved in its cause. Thus Ludovico il Moro was free at last to receive the ducal crown of Milan (Plate 22).

5. LEONARDO AT MILAN

When Leonardo came to Milan in 1482 in the service of his new master, Ludovico was still nominally a regent, although *de facto* Duke of Milan. He had taken with him a gift to Ludovico from Lorenzo, a silver lute which Leonardo had himself fashioned, in the likeness of a horse's head. It emitted notes of great purity and sweetness and pleased

Ludovico very much. Leonardo was now established as a member of the court household at a fine salary (which, in practice, he sometimes did and sometimes did not receive!), and seemingly all was well.

In fact, however, peace was threatened and hostilities were imminent with the republic of Venice. It will be remembered that Leonardo had framed his famous letter to Ludovico, with its many claims to military knowledge, with this threat well in his mind. Certainly such purely artistic projects as the equestrian statue of Ludovico's father, which originally brought Leonardo to court, were compelled to wait awhile. Nevertheless, in these early days Leonardo must have been full of hope for a life and a future in which his manifold interests, both artistic and scientific, might be allowed full licence.

Like the Florence he had left, he found Milan to be a city of wealth and luxury. It had a population of some 300,000 persons. Its streets sprawled out into the plains around—fertile plains well watered by the streams coming down from the "near distant" Alps. Its activities were many—including a thriving woollen industry. But a new industry had appeared recently with the planting of some mulberry trees which quickly thrived and multiplied—and the spinning and weaving of Milanese silk was soon quickly to create such a demand as to bring employment to no fewer than fifteen thousand work-people. The sowing and growing of rice was another successful experiment made possible by the richness of the well-watered soil of the countryside around the city—indeed, Galeazzo Maria Sforza had himself tried it out with encouraging success in his own ducal parks, and it soon became practicable to afford complete fiscal protection against the importation of rice from abroad (Plate 25).

But the major industry which had given name, fame and prosperity to Milan from as far back as the thirteenth century was the manufacture of arms. More than a hundred workshops were busy with the forging and hammering and shaping and filing of both armour and handweapons; and in the Via degli Armorai were concentrated shop after shop, with their crowded display of armour both for knights and their steeds, and of lances, pikes and halberds. It was an impressive sight and helped to reflect the inevitably military atmosphere which had become so natural to the city.

The defensive structure of the city's boundaries added considerably to this impression of a vast fortress. The walls of the city, with their seven great gates, were interspersed with fifteen heavily fortified towers—and within one of the gates, the Porta Giovia, towered the duke's castle, formidable with moats and a vivid red colouring to the high walls that offered an ugly challenge to the otherwise green and peaceful countryside without.

The streets showed a variety of colouring, and the houses, built in soft brick terra-cotta, displayed a mass of decoration that tended to soften the defiance of the city's walls and embattlements. The predominant architectural influence was Gothic and there was a tendency to mural decoration—wreaths, arabesques of flowers, symbolic animals and the like which, against the background of the surrounding scene, lent an air of conflicting aggressiveness and gaiety that reflected the general characteristics of the people.

The Milanese in fact exhibited a mixture of busy trade and craftsmanship and commerce with an indolence and an over-indulgence in the pleasures of the table. Cultured leisure was reserved for the retinue of court philosophers, poets and men of learning and the few citizens who were drawn to their teachings. The great architecture of the Renaissance, which had reflected itself so nobly in Florence to give it spaciousness, beauty and grace, was so far absent in Milan that where here and there examples were to be seen as a sudden intervention in the uniformity of Gothic lines, the effect was almost startling—and even these, in many cases, were due to the enterprise and tradition of Florentine interests. Such, for example, were the fine portico fronting the Bank of the Medici, and a chapel built for Portinari, an agent of the Medici—both the work of the architect Michelozzo. Generally speaking, "outside" expertise, whether in culture or business, was frowned upon. The Milanese were prepared always to indulge themselves without stint or regard to cost for themselves but not for strangers. On the relatively few occasions when an expert artist or architect was invited to Milan on a commission for some project, every conceivable obstruction would be put in his way by the masons and other craftsmen involved, until, in complete frustration, the artist would give up. Such, for example, was the fate of the distinguished Filarati who came to build a hospital, the *Ospedale Maggiore*, and, despite the goodwill of Francesco Sforza, had to abandon it to Milanese architects for transformation into the Gothic style. And Leonardo was himself to find that, from time to time, weeks and months passed with his salary unpaid. A comparatively rare example of a tolerated artist, because he was poor and therefore cheap, was the famous architect and painter Bramante, whom Sforza was content to pay less than half the amount (5 ducats a month as against 12 to 15) that was normally offered to singers and musicians. Bramante came to Milan some three years ahead of Leonardo. Yet this great architect, who was later to crown a distinguished career by building the great St. Peter's in Rome, had to content himself in Milan, in the main, with minor commissions in fresco painting.

It would be wrong to infer from the foregoing remarks that there

was anything mean or niggardly in the general appearance and
structure of the city. On the contrary, it was both capacious and, in
its way, splendid, with its castles and churches, and with its streams
and canals bordered with lovely houses and gardens. But the beauties
of Renaissance Italy were the exception rather than the rule. Rather
was it the splendour of strength (and perhaps of fear) derived from a
sense of the power and the domination of the tyrant. The streets
were wide and airy and bright, and here and there were occasional
examples of the art, grudgingly conceded, of the Tuscan masters—
Filarete, Brunellesco, Michelozzo, San Gallo, Bramante and Leonardo
himself. And all around, amid orchard and vineyard, and wheat-
land and woodland and meadow, were the lesser cities of the Duchy,
interspersed over the plain of Lombardy and stretching out in varying
directions to the Apennines, the Alps and the sea.

In due course, at any rate, Leonardo must have become aware of
this characteristic attitude of the Milanese to "outsiders" and to the
external influences imposed on their way of life. He had, of course,
left Florence full of hope and anticipation. If we speak of his new patron,
Ludovico il Moro, as his employer, the term must clearly be understood in a very loose sense. He is alleged to have been "appointed"
on a salary, and, as this was indeed the custom of the court in respect
of its patronage (and one must remember that he had come with the
primary duty of creating the equestrian statue in the memory of
Francesco Sforza), it may well be so. But Leonardo was, nevertheless,
free to accept individual commissions apart from his occasional court
duties. Undoubtedly, in the terms of his famous letter, he had hoped
to be employed in the role of military engineer. This had hitherto
been held by an ageing and none too efficient Bartolommeo Gadio and,
it turned out, so far as a formal appointment was concerned, Leonardo
was " passed over" in favour of one Ambrogio Ferrari. But, in any
case, the urgency of such duties was quickly fading—for Ludovico
was by now substituting diplomacy and argument for arms, and so
Leonardo was free to alternate between his many sketches and studies
in preparation for "the horse", his duties as a master of ceremonies
for the many fêtes and carnivals at court, his occasional "outside"
commissions as a painter, and his beloved notebook studies and indoor
experiments in the various fields of science and engineering that were
his continual interest.

Leonardo probably found matters progressively difficult in his first
few years. His personal tastes were a blend of the temperate with the
elegant. The grossness of the table common to Milanese households
was foreign to him; but the lesser elegances of the person came naturally to him—the quieter moods and modes in both clothes and

surroundings, exaggerated only (and necessarily) in his ornate planning for the masques and masquerades and festivities of the ducal court.

There are, unfortunately, only scanty records of the earlier years of Leonardo in Milan. Quite early he must have found his position financially one of increasing difficulty, and to help him eke out his resources he fell in with the usual custom of his fellow-artists in "teaming-up" and sharing both lodgings and studio. His own name and reputation as a painter helped him in this materially and he soon found himself established in association with Ambrogio de Predis, a young man of twenty-eight, who had begun to establish himself as a painter to the Sforza family. If Predis had the lodgings and the studio, he knew that Leonardo had the genius and the reputation. Both profited by the combination and, indeed, it was not long before the Fraternity of the Immaculate Conception contracted with them for an altar-piece. Ambroglio de Predis was to paint the altar wings and "Maestro Leonardo" the central panel. The result was the radiant "Virgin of the Rocks", two versions of which have graced the world of art—one in the Louvre in Paris, the other in the National Gallery in London. But they were completed after many years of haggling and bargaining over payments by the Fraternity of a kind with which, alas, Leonardo was to become frequently familiar in his great career as an artist.

The making of the two pictures was interspersed by years of other commissions—portraits and studies—and always with the continual preparation and planning for the great equestrian statue and the attendant studies and researches in equine anatomy and mechanics, and in the science and techniques of bronze-casting on a scale commensurate with the vast dimensions intended in the finished statue. But also he was busy throughout this period both with his notes and personal studies, and with self-disciplinary exercises in the practice of expression and the extension of his vocabulary. He used, among others, a dictionary of the time called *Vocaboliata*, by Luigi Pulci, and worked through some thousands of words and synonyms. "As iron rusts when it is not used," he wrote,[1] "and water gets foul from standing or turns to ice when exposed to cold, so the intellect degenerates without exercise."

Following a devastating outbreak of plague, we find him, in 1485, proposing plans to Ludovico for the reconstruction of the city on a basis of improved sanitary principles. The outbreak was a virulent one, from which a very frightened Ludovico fled to strict isolation—even state documents had to be heavily perfumed before he would

[1] *Codex Atlanticus*, 289 v.

see or handle them. Leonardo planned the diversion of the population into ten townships of four thousand houses each along the banks of the River Ticino "to distribute the masses of humanity, who live crowded together like herds of goats, filling the air with stench and spreading the seeds of plague and death".[1] Leonardo's scheme envisaged the emptying of all privies and garbage into underground conduits— "*vie sotterraini*"—for discharge into canals and thence into the rivers. Needless to say, his plans never got beyond the paper stage. Ludovico, in any case, was not prepared to find the money.

Between the years 1487 and 1490 he was busy with architectural projects including the planning of the completion of Milan Cathedral. It was this work which brought him into consultation with men of learning in the university and libraries of the neighbouring Pavia. At this time Leonardo had ceased to live with the de Predis brothers. Ludovico had now provided him with a ground-floor studio and an upper living-room in the old part of the castle, the Corte Vecchia. He worked on "the horse" in the studio, and conducted his own private experiments in mechanical and other investigations in the upper room.

His visits to the ducal library of Pavia were for him a source of unfeigned delight. The library was one of the finest in Italy. It was housed in a great hall in one of the towers of the ducal castle, approached by a fine broad marble staircase. Its shelves contained priceless parchment manuscripts, illuminated in rich colour and held to their places by silver chains. "Look up Vitelone, in the library at Pavia,"[2] he writes, Vitelone being the thirteenth-century Polish physicist Witelo, who interpreted the Arabic writer on optics, Alhazen, to the Western world. And following this study, Leonardo developed his own extensive notes on optics. His notebook C, devoted so largely to this, opens with the note: "On 23rd April 1490 I began this book and made a fresh start with the horse"[3] (Plate 23).

It was at Pavia, too, that Leonardo held many a discussion with the famous Fazio Cardan, lawyer, mathematician and physician. Cardan held the Chair of Mathematics at Pavia University and, as we have previously mentioned, had translated John of Peckham's *Perspectiva Communis* into Latin. It was this which inspired Leonardo to embark on his own work on perspective, and indeed his notes on this subject come nearer to the conception of a complete book ready for publication than anything else he wrote.

We should also refer to the opportunity afforded to Leonardo at Pavia, and indeed readily taken, of the first-hand anatomical studies at the Medical School. He readily availed himself of permission to

[1] *Codex Atlanticus*, 65 v. [2] Ibid, 225 v. [3] MS. *C*, 15 v.

practise the dissection of dead bodies for the purpose—both of animals and human beings.

A period followed of ever-increasing gaiety and splendour and ceremony at the court of Ludovico—his own marriage with Beatrice d'Este, and that of Anna Sforza (sister to Gian Galeazzo) to Alfonso d'Este—and later, in 1493, the ceremonial departure of Bianca Maria Sforza to be the bride of the Habsburg Emperor Maximilian. All these made their claims on Leonardo's ingenuity as a master of ceremonies. But the latter event also carried with it the culminating glory of enabling Leonardo at last to display both to the Imperial Ambassador and a wondering and admiring public the huge finished model, 26 feet high, of the equestrian monument to the memory of Francesco Sforza. It was erected in the courtyard of the Castello and it was viewed with the wildest excitement and pleasure by streams of people. Yet it was never to reach the final stage of conversion to bronze. In November 1495, under pressure of military need, the bronze originally intended for casting by Leonardo was sent by Ludovico to Ferrara to be made into cannon. As, unfortunately, the model was completely destroyed some years later, in 1500, by the invading Gascon archers of the French Louis XII, we have now only the many and varied notebook studies from which to appreciate the nature of its design; and the same applies to a later commission for an equestrian statue, never completed, in honour of Gian Giacomo Trivulzio, a former general of Ludovico, who later quarrelled with him and entered the service of his master's enemy, Louis XII of France.

The next few years found Leonardo busily preoccupied with many projects in architecture and engineering, interspersed by his work on what was to prove his greatest artistic achievement—the painting of "The Last Supper" for the refectory wall of the Dominican Convent Church of Santa Maria delle Grazie on the joint commission of Ludovico and the monks. For some months he was absent from Milan planning extensive works for the improvement of the irrigation and canal system of the Lomellina and adjacent regions of the plains of Lombardy, including a giant project for a canal to link Milan with the sea.

It was at this period too, that Leonardo met and formed a close friendship with the distinguished mathematician, Fra Luca Pacioli. Pacioli was much impressed both by Leonardo's great achievements in sculpture and painting and by his fundamental interest in mathematics and mechanics. The two helped each other materially on the work and calculations connected with their respective tasks, and when later, in 1499, under the stress of political events, Leonardo decided to leave Milan to return to his native Florence, Pacioli left the city with him.

Leonardo at this time was much engrossed in problems of mechanics. In the *Codex Atlanticus* we read the following note[1]: "On the first of August 1499, I wrote on motion and weight." And another note[2]: "What is percussion, what is its cause? What is rebound? Aristotle, Third of Physics, and Albertus [Magnus] and Thomas [Aquinas] and others on the rebound, in the Seventh of the Physics; De Coelo et Mundo."

Such notes prompt the query as to what sort of reading Leonardo had available to him at this time. A note in the *Codex Atlanticus*[3] provides this answer:

List of books in Leonardo's possession before leaving Milan

Book on *Arithmetic* (Abbaco)
Flowers of virtue (a medieval bestiary)
Pliny (*Natural History*)
Lives of Philosophers (Diogenes Laertius)
The Bible
Lapidary
On Warfare (Robertus Valturius)
Epistles of Filelfo
The First, the Third, the Fourth Decades (Livy)
On the preservation of health (Ugo Benzo of Siena)
Cecco d'Ascoli's *Acerba* (a fourteenth-century encyclopaedia in verse)
Albertus Magnus (Aristotelian philosophy and science)
Guido on Rhetorics (probably the *Retorica nova* by Guidotto of Bologna)
Piero Crescentio (on agriculture)
Cibaldoni's *Miscellanea* (a Latin version of a treatise on health by the Arabian Rhazes)
Quadriregio (The Four Realms—a Religious Scientific Poem by the Dominican Federigo Frezzi)
Aesop (Fables)
Donatus (a short Latin syntax)
Psalms
Justinius (History)
On the Immortality of the Soul (dialogue by Francesco Filelfo)
Guido (probably a book on astronomy by Guido Bonatti)
Burchiello (sonnets)
Doctrinale (a vernacular translation of "Doctrinal de Saprenci" by Guy de Roy)
Driadeo
Morgante } by Luca Palci
Petrarch
Jehan de Mandeville (book of travels)
On honest recreation (by Bartolomeo Sacchi)
Manganello (a satire on women)

[1] *Codex Atlanticus*, 104 r.   [2] MS. *I*, 130 v.   [3] *Codex Atlanticus*, 210 r.

The Chronicles of Isidore (a history to A.D. 615 by Isidore of Seville)
The Epistles of Ovid
The Jests of Poggio
Chiromancy
Formulatory of letters (by Miniatore Bartolomeo)

But political complications and dangers were developing for Milan and Ludovico, whose policy at this time was proving disastrous. Europe in general during the years between 1485 and 1500 had been full of trouble. The movement towards nationalism had reached a point of culmination. The Wars of the Roses had seen the defeat of the powerful war-lords and the ushering in of the House of Tudor with Henry VII to the throne of England. In France there were also great changes. Louis XI had brought together in unity all the French duchies and kingdoms under one central government and ruler, and as France "felt her feet" and her power, she too began to look farther afield. At the same time, the Emperor Maximilian I had by the end of the fifteenth century extended his power to cover the Netherlands, the various States of Germany, and much that was left of the old Roman Empire.

France and the Empire of Maximilian were, therefore, the two major elements in the power politics of Europe—and both were manœuvring for further extensions and supremacy. The potential prey was England in one direction and Italy in the other. It was to this end that, for example, Maximilian was prompted to aid Perkin Warbeck in his futile bid for the English throne. Louis XI had aided Ludovico when the latter needed help in his plans for power over his nephew Gian Galeazzo, and later allied himself with Louis' successor, his son Charles VIII. Charles inherited his father's ambitions but lacked his political ability. His aim was to acquire the throne of Naples, the natural enemy of Ludovico and Milan.

Ludovico's handling of his difficulties were none too well contrived. A visit to Milan was planned for Charles and his army and it turned out badly. The French soldiery were never popular with the Milanese and they behaved very badly towards their hosts upon whom they were quartered. Ludovico, unfortunately for himself, chose this moment to vacillate in his loyalties and to succumb to the temptation of turning to those Italian states who were hostile to France. His machinations included a plot with the Turks against Venice (Milan's old enemy), and with the Germans and Swiss against France.

Complications were to develop that lent fear to Ludovico. Charles had died and was succeeded by Louis XII. Now this Louis happened to be a grandson of a Visconti—the former ducal family from whom Ludovico's father, Francesco Sforza, had seized and usurped the title to Milan. Louis XII lost no time in proclaiming himself the rightful heir to the Duchy and with this end in view entered into a league of alliance with both the Pope and the republic of Venice. In the summer of 1499 the Venetians and the French launched their attack on the Duchy, and town after town fell to the invaders. Early in September Ludovico fled to the Tyrol to seek the protection of Maximilian, and by October Louis XII entered Milan in triumph.

But by now Leonardo had had enough of the city and its political uncertainties. What with the wanton destruction of the equestrian statue by Louis' soldiers, the absence of his patron Ludovico, and the dangerous uncertainty of his own future, Leonardo decided to leave Milan. One of Louis' nobles, the Comte de Ligny, who had claims on an estate in Naples originally owned by his late wife, sought the help of Leonardo to enlist financial support for these claims from Venice, and this probably helped to determine Leonardo's first destination in leaving the city. With Fra Luca Pacioli and a favourite pupil, Andrea Salai, he departed for Venice in December 1499.

6. LEONARDO IN VENICE

The republic of Venice differed from the other city-states of Italy in remaining more consistently faithful to the democratic tradition. From her small beginnings as the refuge in her estuary and lagoons of those who founded the city, she had grown by the fourteenth century to a position of power and equality as one of the major states of Italy. Her constitution as a commonwealth had emerged gradually, and sometimes painfully, to maturity and stability. At its head was the Doge, at first supported by a popular assembly which came to be known as the Grand Council. However, the usual individual and group ambitions of various powerful members of the community gradually produced constitutional changes. These were designed to oust the people from an effective share in the government, on the one hand, and to reduce the position of the Doge to one of ornamental and nominal rule, on the other. In 1297 an enactment virtually confined the Grand Council to a relatively few privileged families, and in 1311 the hereditary rights of these families were assured by a constitution which set up a Council of Ten. This constitution was, in fact, to endure for nearly five hundred years until the republic came to an end in the year 1797. But during all those years her citizens were both prosperous and intensely loyal to their republic. During the whole of their formative years Venetians consistently "minded their own business". They concentrated on the development of their maritime trade with the east and on the whole refrained from any attempts at conquests on the mainland.

Maritime consideration did, in fact, cause their first main intrusion in Italian affairs. Between the years 1352 and 1381 Venice found herself in serious competition with Genoa for the supremacy of the Mediterranean. The fleet of each in turn blockaded the other. Ultimately Venice was not only victorious but in 1406 was able to extend her dominion by the absorption of the cities of Verona, Vicenza and Padua.

Under the distinguished Dogeship of Francesco Foscari between the years 1423 and 1457, her growing strength and power brought her into the larger politics of Italian alliances. A culminating point was reached in the breaking of her long ties with the Eastern Empire on the fall of Constantinople in 1453, by which time the Venetian republic was able to rank as one of the five major states of Italy. This carried with it the inevitable sequence of grouping and re-grouping of alliances and, as we have seen, brought her, at the close of the fifteenth century, into hostilities against Milan.

We should also add, however, that later, in 1486, when Diaz rounded the Cape of Good Hope, the supremacy of her oriental trade was lost; and with it came a decline in her commercial fortunes from which, slow though it was, she was never to recover.

Leonardo travelled to Venice via Mantua. Here both he and Pacioli were graciously received by the Duchess Isabella Gonzaga, one of the d'Este family and a kinswoman of the Comte de Ligny, to whom we have already referred. Although Ludovico was her brother-in-law, she felt it expedient to propitiate the French and to invite de Ligny to visit Mantua. She also asked Leonardo to paint her portrait—and, in the meantime, he drew a very fine chalk profile of her which is now housed at the Louvre.

Leonardo stayed briefly in Mantua to see how the fortunes of Milan might turn out. As we know, in the early days of February Ludovico crossed the Alps and re-entered Milan. But in April the news came through that, betrayed by his Swiss mercenaries, he was once more attacked by Louis. So Milan was again in the hands of the French. Ludovico was finally overthrown and sent to die at Loches, in France. Milan was, in fact, to remain in French hands for the next twelve years.

The turn of events now brought Leonardo, with Salai and his friend Pacioli, to Venice. Actually, his ultimate destination was to be his own native Florence. This is evident from the fact that before leaving Milan he had arranged, in December 1499, for his savings, amounting to 600 florins, to be deposited on his behalf at Santa Maria Nuova in Florence (a loan institution used by his father)—and, indeed, he was back in that city by April 1500. Meanwhile, however, he was welcomed in Venice, and although his stay was brief it was a very busy one. The Venetian Senate was then heavily and none too success- fully involved in war with the Turks, and, following the defeat of Admiral Grimani at Lepanto, took advantage of Leonardo's arrival to consult him regarding the defences on the River Isonzo against the menaces of the enemy at their frontiers. After inspection and con- sideration, Leonardo recommended a scheme for the inundation of the countryside as being effective, even at the expense of injury to the land. He had, however, many other preoccupations. He was very busy with Pacioli on his own studies in mathematics and cosmo- graphy and also, of course, in the city that knew Marco Polo, in geography.

Venice was then, as it is now, one of the most beautiful cities of the world. Here sky met sea and east met west, making her rich in colour and in kind. The culture of the Renaissance and her many native artists and architects, combined with their greater Eastern contacts, caught the city in a special way, to make it, with its lagoons and canals and bridges and churches and streets, unique in Italy and, indeed, in the world.

But as a power she was doomed to a long but steady decline. We have referred to the fall of Constantinople and the economic conse- quences of the diversion of world trade from the Adriatic and Medi- terranean Seas to the Atlantic round the Cape of Good Hope, and to this we should add the combined hostility of the European world (including the other Italian states) against her power, culminating in the League of Cambrai in 1508. The League broke up in due course, but politically Venice never recovered from its effects. But in the world of art she has remained glorious, and the sixteenth century in particular was rich in such names as Giorgione, Titian, Sansovino, Veronese, Tintoretto and Palladio.

7. BACK TO FLORENCE (1500–1502)

It was no part of Leonardo's intentions to stay in Venice, and by April of 1500 he was back once more in his native Florence. This is clear from the fact that on 24th April of that year he withdrew his deposit of 600 florins from the Santa Maria Nuova. Thus he was back after an absence of eighteen years. During this interval the Medici had been banished and Florence was once more a republic. Leonardo's reputation for his masterly distinction as an artist had preceded him and very soon he was installed, with his favourite pupil, Salai, in the monastery of the Order of the Servites at Santissima Annunziata, taking over too readily (since, true to form, he never completed it) a commission surrendered to him by Filippino Lippi, a fellow artist,

Plate 26—Portrait of Césare Borgia (I.B.M., New York).

Plate 28—Francis I of France, Leonardo's host at Amboise (I.B.M., New York).

Plate 27—Giuliano de' Medici, Leonardo's patron in Rome (I.B.M., New York).

Plate 29 — The Royal Residence at Amboise, France (I.B.M., New York).

Plate 30—Portrait of Archimedes. From the bust in the Capitoline Museum, Rome (Mansell Collection).

Plate 31—Impression of Ptolemy taking astronomical observations, by Giotto, from the Campanile del Duomo, Florence (Mansell Collection)

for an altar-piece. The friars readily agreed to bear the expenses
of Leonardo's household, hoping that in the quiet seclusion of
the monastery the great master would proceed apace with his
commission.

He did indeed, after a long succession of complaints, get as far as
the beautiful cartoon of the "Virgin, St. Anne and the Christ Child",
now housed in the Royal Academy in London—and all Florence
flocked to see it during the Easter of 1501. But, in fact, the hours and
days during which he was expected to carry out his agreed task were
more preferably employed by him in his mathematical and mechanical
studies. The outside world was not for him. The streets of Florence
were in fact agog with the news that a new threat was closing in on
the city. A new and forbidding personality had arisen from Rome
in the person of Cesare Borgia, and the prospect was of a sinister
challenge to all its citizens. But Leonardo was living in a world of his
own. In April 1501 his admirer, Isabella d'Este of Mantua, ever
pressing for Leonardo to do a painting for her, wrote about him to
Pietro di Novellara, Vicar General of the Carmelites, and received
the following reply: ". . . In brief, his mathematical experiments
have made painting so distasteful to him that he cannot even bear
to take up a brush. However, I have done all I could, using every
art, in order to get him to accede to your Highness' wishes. . . ." There
is no doubt that this was an exaggeration. Art was in Leonardo's
blood. Rather was it a matter of moods and conflicting interests.
Leonardo was, in any case, committed at the moment to a commission
for Florimond di Robertet, a favourite of Louis XII of France and
his Secretary of State. This painting he did in fact finish, but unfortunately no trace of it has been found. However, copies of it by pupils
are known, and one of them is in the collection of the Duke of Buc-
cleuch. It was a small picture showing the Madonna trying to take a
yarn-winder of cruciform shape from the Christ Child who is play-
fully clutching it.[1]

In a sense, both Florence and Leonardo had changed during the
eighteen-year period of his life in Milan. Leonardo was now middle-
aged and somewhat tired and impatient of the life of gorgeous make-
believe that the duties of pageantry had so much demanded of him.
We should say in these days that he had been "living on his nerves"
and he was feeling the strain somewhat. Milan had demanded more
than enough of him. On the other hand, Florence was a little less
tolerant and a little more critical of its artists than had been the case
in the days of Cosimo and Lorenzo. The Medici had been expelled
and the city had been occupied by Charles and his French troops.

[1] But see Appendix D.

G

Charles was bought out for the sum of 120,000 florins by the citizens of Florence; and it was amid a confusion of consequent political thinking and internal wrangling that the great moral teacher, Savonarola, imposed the influence of his personality in the setting up of a new republic.

Florence was however to continue in a state of turmoil. It was beset with many troubles and many enemies. Internally, there were conflicting factions for power and political influence; and on the economic side there was a flagging in the prosperity of the city. Its resources had been shaken by the buying out of Charles, its credit was strained, trade was suffering, and plague was playing havoc with the health of the people. Externally there was more than enough of trouble. The surviving exiled member of the Medici family, Piero, was plotting for his return. At the same time, a hostile Pisa was in revolt, a continual thorn in the Florentine flesh; France was eternally on the look-out for an opportunity to return; and the public denunciations of papal excesses by Savonarola had incurred the hatred of Pope Alexander VI of Rome, and with it a threat of invasion.

Savonarola's sermons were meanwhile stirring up the masses against corruption and vice, and the year 1497 saw the famous bonfire of the "vanities"—indecent books, manuscripts, pictures, jewels, carnival masks and costumes and the like. Savonarola was, of course, excommunicated, and in May 1498 he was seized by an opposing faction and was executed. With this act of appeasement of the Pope, the situation became less critical for Florence. The head of its republic was its *gonfalonier*, Piero Soderini, a man of integrity but of little strength of character. He was, however, ably aided by the astute politician, Nicollo Machiavelli, and at the latter's suggestion a dependable national militia was formed to replace an unreliable army of Swiss mercenaries.

This, then, was the Florence to which Leonardo had returned. It was indeed a strange city to him. His reputation had made him welcome, but many of his old friends of former days were gone. Verrocchio was dead, and so were the brothers Pollaiuoli and Ghirlandaio. Of the humanists, Lorenzo the Magnificent had died in 1492, Marsilio Ficino seven years later in 1499, and his great and gentle lieutenant, Pico della Mirandola, much earlier, in 1494, exhausted by overwork at the early age of thirty. On the other hand, there were others of olden days who were gladdened to see Leonardo back and to renew their own enthusiasms for art in the fire and genius of the returned master —as, for example, Fra Bartolommeo and Lorenzo di Credi. But there was, too, a very young person now emerging into the Florentine scene who was destined to be great in the world of art but whose personality, even so early in his career, was so antagonistic to that of Leonardo as to create a barrier of intense dislike between them. His name was Michelangelo.

It is not altogether surprising, therefore, that Leonardo's re-attachment to Florence had little stability of foundation. The changed atmosphere made him restless and, on the whole, ill at ease. When, therefore, the powerful personality of Cesare Borgia appeared in Florence on a political mission from Rome and invited Leonardo to enter his service as his military engineer and adviser, da Vinci was prompt in accepting the invitation and he departed south with Cesare Borgia and his army to begin yet another phase of his life story.

8. INTERLUDE WITH CESARE BORGIA

Cesare Borgia (Plate 26) was the acknowledged illegitimate son of Pope Alexander VI. He was born at Rome in 1476 when his father was a cardinal. Pope Alexander indulged unashamedly in the practice of nepotism to an extent that aroused the comment of all Europe; and in due course he created Cesare Borgia Archbishop of Valencia and then made him a cardinal.

The papacy, it will be recalled, had by the settlement in Avignon largely lost its position as the protector of Italian liberties. Even in Rome itself a republic was proclaimed by Rienzi in 1347, and it lasted for seven years. Then, as the great cities of Italy came more and more under the control of the various dynastic families, the weaker became the authority of the Church. Even after the Avignon exile, ecclesiastical disputes absorbed all the time and interest of the Popes, to the exclusion of all temporal affairs. But later, as the various city-states sought each other's support in a policy of confederation, the Popes came to realise that they must fall in with the new spirit of the times and assume sovereign functions within their papal territories. They also conformed to the practice of other rulers in encouraging, within their domains, the cult of humanism and the forces of the Renaissance now dominant throughout the Italy of the fifteenth century. The master creator of this change of policy was Nicholas V. He was elected Pope in 1447 and at once set about converting Rome into a capital city worthy of its high place in Europe—fortifying, rebuilding and beautifying it, to the great pleasure of its citizens—and by the time of his death in 1455 the papacy had once more become a temporal power of wealth and strength.

In its train, however, came the inevitable complex of faction and intrigue, intensely increased by jealousies as the practice of nepotism grew in the papal family. Relatives were freely established in principalities and in other positions of power and, as a consequence, the

reigns of succeeding Popes during the second half of the fifteenth
century saw an appalling multiplicity of political crime, including
conspiracy and assassination.

This, then, was the world and the atmosphere of the Borgias; and,
as a preparation for it, Cesare Borgia early began to lead a profligate
life in which violence, lust and worse played their part. In July 1497
Cesare went, as a papal legate, first to Naples and then to France; and
later still, he accompanied Louis XII when the latter entered Milan.
Ambitious for a secular career, Borgia had by now renounced his
clerical status and had become the Duke of Valentinois.

It was during this visit to Milan that Borgia first noticed Leonardo.
He was greatly impressed both by his reputation as an artist and by
his abilities in military engineering. Louis XII had himself inspected
and greatly admired the unforgettable "Last Supper" mural and
this was recalled to Cesare Borgia's mind when, three years later in
1502, this great and unscrupulous adventurer invited Leonardo to
enter his service as architect and engineer. He was, at this time, at
the zenith of his power. The Pope had now made him Duke of
Romagna and he had raged and rampaged over much of Italy, striking
terror through his lack of scruple, his gross cruelty and his success at
arms.

In June of 1502 Cesare had come north from Rome to complete
the conquests of areas south of the River Po. He had already subdued
much of central Italy including (by an act of infamous treachery) the
Dukedom of Urbino. There was a characteristic arrogance in the
manner in which he chose to be styled: "Cesare Borgia of France, by
the grace of God Duke of the Romagna and of Valencia and Urbino,
Prince of Andria, Lord of Piombino, Gonfalioniere, and captain-
general of the Holy Roman Church."

This was the person to whom Leonardo now gave service. The
nature and terms of authority for his appointment and the scope of
his duties were clearly set forth in a decree issued from Pavia thus:

"To all those of our *locotenenti*, *castellani*, *capitani*, *condottieri*, *officiali*
and *subditi* whom it may concern, we here charge and command them,
that they everywhere and in every place give free entrance to our
highly esteemed court architect, Leonardo da Vinci, the bearer of this,
who has been commissioned by us to inspect the fortresses and strong-
holds of our states, and to make such alterations and improvements
as he may think needful. Both he and his followers are to be received
with hospitality, and every facility afforded him for personal inspection, for measurement and valuation, just as he may wish. For
that purpose a band of men is to be placed at his disposal, which is
to give him all the help he may require. With reference to the state

works already in course of completion, we desire that every engineer be prepared to further any undertaking he may find necessary."

This was indeed a thorough and a complete authority and we may take it as adequate evidence of Leonardo's competence and abilities in the fields of military and what today we would call civil engineering. He had behind him a reputation and experience extending over some twenty years; and although much of this was based upon the expression of a series of ideas and suggestions of greater ingenuity than of practicability, they made their appeal.

Leonardo's period of service with Cesare Borgia was brief—scarcely a year, since by April of 1503 he was once more back at Florence. But it was a very busy year for him—a period of hustle and travel either with or in the wake of his warring master, who was busily occupied meeting plot and counterplot against him and subduing the condottieri of the Romagna area to his rule. Leonardo's notebooks of this period are a vivid reflection of his many tasks and preoccupations. He first visited Piombino, on the coast opposite Elba. Here he studied the problem of the draining of the marshes and took the opportunity of observing the effects of wind and waves between the coast and the island. He then moved inland on his way through to Pesaro on the Adriatic; and at Siena he examined a famous bell on the tower of the *Palazzo Pubblico* to study its unusual movement. (The hours were tolled by the hammer striking a brass plate attached to a wooden statue.) He now turned south to Arezzo, where Borgia's troops were fighting, and there is an interesting note[1] to indicate that he tried to obtain here (and probably succeeded) a book by Archimedes—"Borges shall get for you the Archimedes from the Bishop of Padua, and Vitellozzo[2] the one from Borgo San Sepolcro." His travels in this region are marked by a study of the topography of the area and the maps he prepared are a model of accuracy and art. His notes indicated distances and were invaluable from a military point of view. They showed cities, rivers, water-sheds and mountains—and, needless to say, gave him an opportunity for geological speculations.

And so on to Urbino, where he made some architectural studies of the pillaged palace; and by August he reached the Adriatic at Pesaro, where he made a number of studies relating to what, in mechanics, we now speak of as the "mechanical advantage" of machines (see Chapter VII). He next went south to Rimini, and then inland again to Cesena, at which place he was engaged largely on harbour works and canal projects for some two months.

By this time the military campaigns of Cesare Borgia were beset

[1] MS. *L*, 2 r.
[2] One of Borgia's captains, shortly after to suffer the mortal consequences of disaffection.

with multiplying troubles. At Imola he found himself at odds with his own captains (who were invited to meet him for a reconciliation and, true to the Borgia form, were conveniently murdered!) and other disaffected elements from which, in due course, as usual, he extricated himself; and he then began moving south to Rome. It was at this time that Florence sent, as a friendly gesture to Borgia, its famous statesman Machiavelli with offers of help; and it was during this visit that Leonardo was able to establish friendly and personal relations with him.

But by February of 1503 the campaign was ended and Borgia had returned to Rome. Leonardo finally left his service, once more to return to Florence.

9. RETURN TO FLORENCE (1503–1506)

So by April of 1503 we find Leonardo once again installed at his native Florence, with lodgings in the vicinity of the hospital of Santa Maria Nuova, where, it will be recalled, he had deposited his savings. He very soon began to receive offers of commissions for painting. But meanwhile he had already defaulted with the altar-piece for the friars of the Santissima Annunziata, and Filippino Lippi, who, it will be remembered, had withdrawn from this project in favour of Leonardo, returned to finish it. But unfortunately he died in 1504, and the final completion of the lower panel fell to the artist Perugino.

The three years of Leonardo's stay in Florence were of tremendous importance from the point of view of his career as an artist. It was this period that saw the completion (about the year 1504) of the ever-famous portrait of "Mona Lisa", now housed in the Louvre at Paris; and the undertaking of a large-scale project of a fresco for one of the walls of the new Sala di Gran Consiglo (the new Council Chamber) in the Palazzo Vecchio. The invitation for this fresco was made on the initiative of the gonfalionier, Piero Soderini, who wanted as great a mural for Florence as Leonardo had done for Milan in his "Last Supper". A parallel commission for one of the other walls was given at the same time to the younger Michelangelo, who, it will be recalled, had developed a profound hostility towards Leonardo. This was a most unfortunate and quite irreconcilable attitude which gave rise to one or two notably unfortunate public scenes.

The topic chosen by Michelangelo for his mural was a scene from the Florentine war with the Pisans, which he called "Soldiers Bathing". Leonardo's theme was the famous Florentine victory of June 1440 over the Milanese, which was called the "Battle of Anghiari". It was, in fact, a magnificent theme, for which Leonardo carried out a series of masterly studies in cartoon and sketch-book. To these studies

Leonardo gave all he knew in his ability as an artist and as a master of perspective. During the years 1504 and 1505 he was hard at work on the cartoons, and by 1506 was actually started on the massive mural itself, for which he designed a special movable scheme of scaffolding. Michelangelo, too, was hard at work, in keen competition to finish his mural ahead of Leonardo. Unfortunately, something went wrong with the heat-drying of Leonardo's colouring. The colours in the upper parts either ran or scaled from the wall. The result was failure, and the mural was never completed. Soderini was naturally very angry. Leonardo had received an advance payment for the work from the state treasury. His offer to repay this was refused, and Leonardo decided to leave Florence and return once again to Milan.

On the purely personal side of his life, it is of interest to note that Leonardo's father, Ser Piero da Vinci, had died in 1504. He was then nearly eighty years of age and had left ten sons and two daughters by a succession of marriages. During this period, too, Leonardo's mother, Caterina, died in a hospital where, however, he was able to visit her during her last illness.

Finally, before we pass to the next phase of his life at Milan, we should note that the Florentine years 1503 to 1506 saw Leonardo engaged upon a number of scientific studies in addition to his artistic work. Some anatomical work, for example, quite quickly engaged his attention. He had become extremely competent in the dissection of corpses, and possessed an exceptionally fine saw for the purpose. He found this work intensely engrossing. Thus he writes[1] in April 1503, of an old patient in the hospital of Santa Maria Nuova: "This old man, a few hours before his death, told me that he had lived a hundred years . . . and thus, while sitting on a bed . . . he passed this life. And I examined the anatomy to ascertain the cause of so sweet a death and found that it was caused by a weakness through failure of blood and of the artery that feeds the heart and the lower members which I found to be very parched and shrunk and withered; and the result of this examination I wrote down very carefully. . . . The other autopsy was on a child of two years old, and here I found everything the contrary to what was the case in the old man. . . ."

In July 1503 the Florentine authorities invited Leonardo as a military engineer to visit their forces who were besieging Pisa. Leonardo was impressed by his observations on river erosion which prompted him to note:[2] "They do not know why the Arno never keeps its channel. It is because the rivers which flow into it deposit soil where they enter and wear it away from the other side, bending the river there." After investigation, Leonardo devised and recommended a

---

[1] Windsor MS., 19,027 v.   [2] Windsor MS., 12,279.

plan to alter the course of the River Arno in such a way as both to deprive Pisa of its water and to give Florence a direct access to the sea. Machiavelli, having regard to the years of discord and strife with Pisa, recommended the acceptance of the plan, and the work was actually put in hand in August of 1504; but, not surprisingly, it was abandoned two months later. Nevertheless, the problem remained in Leonardo's thoughts and from time to time he returned to it in his notes.

It was during this Florentine period of his life that Leonardo wrote his little notebook *On the Flight of Birds*, now housed in the Royal Library at Turin (see Chapter VIII).

10. LEONARDO'S SECOND STAY IN MILAN (1506–1513)

Leonardo returned to Milan in the spring of 1506 at the pressing invitation of Charles d'Amboise, Maréchal de Chaumont and commander of the forces of Louis XII of France in Lombardy. He was obviously influenced to accept the invitation after his disappointment at the failure of his work in the Council Chamber of Florence. Soderini grudgingly gave him leave of absence, but subsequently, at the personal request of Louis, this was formally converted into Leonardo's appointment as "painter and engineer-in-ordinary to the French Government". This was in May 1507, and Leonardo now resumed much the same round of life in Milan and its court as he had done formerly. Indeed, at the festivities which were arranged to greet Louis' triumphant entry into Milan in 1509, following a great victory in the field, Leonardo had his usual duties of organising the entertainment as pageant master, to the great pleasure of everybody.

Leonardo had to return to Florence once or twice in order to deal with matters involving him in protracted and vexatious litigation with his half-brothers in connection with his late father's estates; and it was not until 1511 that his law-suits were finally ended. During these visits to Florence he stayed at the house of Piero di Braccio Martelli, himself a scholar and art patron, to whom he referred in the introductory note to his projected book on physics.

Meanwhile he continued in the service of Louis, receiving a royal stipend. He worked on a number of plans relating to prospective but unfulfilled commissions, one of which was for a sculptured tomb for Gian Costello Trivulzio, general of the forces.

But on the whole there are few works of art attributable to Leonardo during the seven years of this period of his stay in Milan. His personal interest in all matters relating to mathematics and the sciences continued unabated, and it was at this time that he collaborated so closely in anatomical studies with the distinguished Marcantonio della Torre at Pavia (p. 30). Another friendship he made at this time was with a young and devoted admirer of his work, Francesco Melzi. Melzi became his pupil and was to remain his friend and companion to the end of his life. The Melzi family were of the Milanese nobility, and Leonardo was a frequent visitor at their family villa at Vaprio. But apart from his art and his own scientific studies, he continued to be officially occupied on those practical duties and projects in relation to the irrigation works in Lombardy which he had initiated during his earlier stay.

Leonardo was now approaching his sixtieth year, and, judging by his very fine self-portrait drawing in sepia, now housed in Turin and completed about this time, he looked somewhat older. It depicts a magnificent head and so obviously reflects in the clear, deeply-lined features and fine, penetrating eyes set below bushy eyebrows, his firm mouth and majestic hair and beard, a most outstanding personality (Plate 38).

But developments in the political scene now call for our attention. His protector and patron, Louis XII, was beginning to find his hold on Lombardy threatened just at a time when Leonardo was hoping for peaceful leisure and opportunity to set his vast collection of notes and observations in some sort of order. It will be recalled that Ludovico Sforza had been exiled and imprisoned in France, where he died in 1508. Now the shadow of his son, Maximiliano, was to rise and develop substance. Hostile political powers were gathering together, and in June 1512 Spain and Venice, aided by the Swiss, joined with the forces of Pope Julius II with the object of re-establishing the Sforza dynasty in Milan. The French were taken completely by surprise at this turn of events. Neither their diplomatic nor their military abilities were equal to the occasion. At first, at the great Battle of Ravenna, the young Gaston le Fira, Louis' nephew and viceroy of Milan, more than held his own against superior forces under the Spanish general Pedro Navarro; but he himself was killed in the fight, and with his death the heart had gone from the French army; and when later 20,000 Swiss troops marched into Milan with Maximiliano Sforza, the French moved out. Maximiliano was, nevertheless, destined only to govern there for a space of three years.

For Leonardo the position had become more or less untenable. The new ruler had known da Vinci as a servant of his father and was well aware of his great distinction. But he also knew of him as a servant of the French King Louis and so gave him no employment. Leonardo decided to move on. The question—not only for him but for other artists similarly placed—was where? The answer came with the death

of Pope Julius and the accession in 1513 of Pope Leo X. Leo was a
Medici and, like his predecessor, who had done much to make Rome
a centre of Italian art, was a patron of culture. Leo's youngest brother,
Giuliano de' Medici, was a special friend and admirer of Leonardo.
In September of 1512, through the promptings of Pope Julius, Giuliano
had become the head of the State of Florence in a bloodless revolution.
Its former head, Soderini, gentle, patriotic but ineffective, quietly disappeared from the scene and died in exile. There was, therefore, both
in Florence and in Rome, a resurgence of the house of Medici. And,
encouraged by the advice of Giuliano, Leonardo left Milan for Rome
on 24th September 1513, accompanied by a band of brother artists
and pupils—Giovanni, Francesco Melzi, Salai, Lorenzo il Fanfoia,
Boltraffio and others.

11. ROME AND AMBOISE—THE LAST PHASE

Rome, as a city, was at this time something of a jumble. Its approach
from the north lay through the People's Gate—the Porta del Popolo;
and within its walls was a strange mixture of the ruins of ancient Rome
and the purely medieval Rome of thickly populated irregular lanes
dense with little houses whose upper floors projected beyond the
latticed window-fronts of the floors below—and, on all sides, were
square medieval towers of churches and *palazzi*. But now to these
had come the newer Rome, with the *Via Giulia*, one of its main thor-
oughfares cutting through it all and bringing with other similar newer
streets and their gleaming newer palaces and stately houses a life of
affluence and courtliness, of gaily-dressed, jaunty young men and
women, escorted by servants whose main task seemed to be that of
jostling aside the curious crowds of the poorer lookers-on. It was a
vivid contrast of wealth and poverty—a holy city of cruel carnival,
of bull-fights, races and Jew-baiting, and of masques and ballets and
organised hunts.

The main waterway of Rome was the River Tiber. It divided the
city of narrow lanes from the city of the Vatican, where even now the
first signs of the new St. Peter were beginning to show—intended to
be the largest and most magnificent of all churches in Christendom.
On his arrival Leonardo first stayed with his pupils and servant
in one of the various inns of the city, while rooms were being prepared
for him in the luxurious Belvedere Palace at the top of the Vatican
Hill. The Belvedere commanded a magnificent view of the surrounding country. It also contained a beautiful and restful garden—
the *Giardino della Pigna*—one of Rome's wonders and a source of delight
to Leonardo for its beautiful flowers and vegetation, its statuary, its
marble fountains, and its birds—to say nothing of a fine menagerie

which Leo X had assembled in an adjoining plantation on the slope of the hill.

But things were not to turn out so happily in Rome for Leonardo as he had hoped. He was soon to learn that here, with one or two exceptions, it was the day of youth both in art and at the papal court. Renaissance life in Rome belonged to a coterie of young cardinals; and Leonardo's generation was over-shadowed by such young artists as Michelangelo and Raphael, both of whom had been drawn to Rome by the lure of its development as the new centre of Renaissance culture. There was little sympathy between these and Leonardo. Raphael was, in fact, a protégé of another former friend of Leonardo's Milanese years—the distinguished architect and artist Donato Bramante. Bramante was one of the dominant figures and personalities of Roman culture, but he appears to have ignored Leonardo's presence completely. This we must infer from the fact that, whilst his earlier notes make frequent and friendly references to Bramante, his name is completely absent from the notebooks of the Roman period.

Leonardo's patron, Giuliano de' Medici (Plate 27), the Pope's younger brother, had assured him an ample allowance of 33 ducats a month in Rome, and there was therefore no financial worry ahead —on the whole a novel experience for Leonardo. But other worries there were, of a different kind. The younger artists, fresh from their own great achievements, spread the influence of their hostility to da Vinci and the commissions for which he hoped proved scanty. Unfortunately, too, when the Pope, who had commissioned him to paint a picture, was told (probably by some busybody) that Leonardo was to be seen busily preparing a solution of distilled oils and herbs to provide a varnish for a work for which he had as yet made no design, he was reported to have remarked: "This man, alas, will assuredly never get anything done, since his thoughts are of the end before he has even made a beginning." Unfortunately, too, Leonardo found himself more or less shut out of the Pope's court entourage because of his lifelong difficulties with Latin. This was the current language of the court, and, although Leonardo was continually trying to master it, he never succeeded.

Once intrigue led to another and the overall consequence was that Leonardo, for all his great reputation, continued to be left with relatively little to do in the field of art. He felt this keenly and it began to affect his health and his nerves. But there were compensations— for he could and did take refuge in his everlasting interest in mechanics, optics and anatomy. Giuliano de' Medici had set up a workshop for im in the Belvedere and here he could retire contentedly to his experiments and investigations—whilst in the lovely gardens he was able to find intense interest and diversion in plant and botanical studies with which to enrich both his notebooks and his sketches. Here he could relate his art to his science. Problems of light, shade and colour; the phenomenon of capillary attraction in relation to the rising of the sap; the larger aspects of landscape problems and the effects of solar movement on colour and shadow—all these interested and absorbed him and gave him peace of mind from the human pin-pricks that were worrying him.

For his worries were to continue. He had serious trouble with a German mechanic who was employed to assist him in his workshop—a man who in addition to persistent insolence of demeanour, apparently connived with a fellow-German outside to use Leonardo's plans and designs for the making of mirrors and lenses for their own ends. All this continued to tell heavily on Leonardo's health. Now over sixty years of age, he began to feel, perhaps for the first time in his life, a weakening in his physical strength. In the winter he actually had to call in a physician to deal with what were probably the first symptoms of the nervous sickness that was later to affect his hand.

As his health recovered, Leonardo turned all the more to his scientific work—various problems of mechanics, the flight of birds, studies on the effects of air currents, and some anatomical and physiological studies in relation to the human speech. On this latter subject he prepared a series of notes which he called a *Trattato della Voce* (Treatise on Speech) and these he sent to the Privy Chamberlain to the Pope, hoping they would be passed on. But instead they simply disappeared.

He also at this time found useful diversions in excursions into the surrounding country, and a project for draining the Pontine Marshes probably dates from this period. A careful map he drew of the district is now housed in Windsor Castle. The project was put into effect successfully a few years later.

Pope Leo X, lazy-minded and weak, was now being drawn quite against his will into the whirl of political events, whilst Leonardo's patron, Giuliano, was too frail to be of much consequence. Leo's was a vacillating and inconsistent policy. The balance of power was his basic formula, and in February of 1515 he signed a coalition treaty with Spain, Milan, Genoa and the Swiss. Yet in the next month he was also offering a secret treaty with their enemy, the young Francis I of France (Plate 28), successor to Louis XII who had died in the last days of 1514—an offer which Francis curtly refused. Instead, Francis surprised Europe by making a sudden advance with his army across the Alps. His objective was Milan. Vacillating and

hesitant as ever, Leo finally ordered his ailing brother Giuliano de'
Medici, in his capacity as *gonfaloniere* of the Church, to lead the papal
forces northwards; but Giuliano was too ill and suffered a physical
collapse instead. So Leo had to lead his troops himself.

Rome was no longer tenable to Leonardo. But when Pope Leo X,
fearful of a threat to the fortified port of Civitavecchia, went north
with his forces, knowing of Leonardo's abilities and reputation as a
military engineer he invited his help. Leonardo was glad to go, and
at the port he was able to study and report on the antique methods of
harbour construction that he found. But meanwhile, the French were
once more in Milan in great strength, and a battle was fought at
Marignano. Here Francis and his generals were victorious. So
Maximiliano Sforza's brief reign in Milan was over and Francis pushed
on southwards towards Rome. Leo, now decided on a policy of
appeasement, made overtures of peace with France, and arranged
to meet Francis secretly at Bologna.

It was probably here that Francis was able to meet the ageing
Leonardo when he was secretly meeting and rejecting Leo's offer of
alliance. Francis knew of Leonardo's reputation and the great affec-
tion that his predecessor, Louis XII, had for him. All Leonardo's
old charm and courtliness must have been summoned to the occasion.
It was to bear the fruit of comfort and French asylum for his last years.
For when, towards the end of the year 1516, Francis turned north to
Milan on his way back to France, he invited Leonardo to accompany
him and to accept an invitation to join his French court as painter
to the king.

So we come to the last phase in the life of Leonardo da Vinci. His
remaining two and a half years were spent peacefully at the small
castle of St. Cloux, near the royal residence at Amboise. An ample
pension was allotted to him and at long last all went well (Plate 29).
The king was a sincere lover of culture and never hesitated to express
his great admiration for Leonardo as one whose knowledge and ability
both in art and philosophy was superior to that of all other mortal men.
Francis never tired of visiting Leonardo at Blois whenever the court
came to Amboise.

His days were leisurely but full—concerned either with his art, his
notes, or his scientific experiments. A visitor, Cardinal Louis of
Aragon, mentions his suffering from a slight paralysis which affected
the power of his hand, but Leonardo was, nevertheless, able to show
the cardinal some fine examples of his art at Blois. But his strength
was now failing and on Easter Eve of 1519 he made his will. Although
throughout his life he had been neither friend nor enemy of the Church,
since he was temperamentally opposed to the dictates of authority as

against the evidences of experiment—nevertheless his notes frequently recorded evidences of profound spiritual insight; and in his will he made provision for masses to be said and candles to be offered at three different churches, and asked to be buried at the Church of St. Florenten. He received the sacraments of the Church and died on 2nd May 1519.

IV

LEONARDO'S SCIENTIFIC SETTING

1. THE PYTHAGOREAN DOCTRINE OF THE STRUCTURE OF MATTER

Our next task is to portray the background against which Leonardo da Vinci developed his many scientific interests and studies. What was the state of science in the days of the Renaissance and to what extent was Leonardo familiar with the writings of those who contributed to this knowledge?

In considering this we are immediately confronted with the fact that, just as culture in its widest sense was initially a legacy of Greece and Rome, with an interlude of transition to Islam during the Dark Ages of western Europe, so similarly were these the sources from which were derived the scientific thinking of the Middle Ages.

We may summarise the relevant factors as follows:

1. The Pythagorean doctrine of the structure of matter.
2. The Platonic philosophy of the relationship between man and the universe in terms of his doctrine of macrocosm and microcosm.
3. The physical world of Aristotle.
4. The founding of the science of mechanics by Archimedes.
5. The Ptolemaic theory of a geocentric universe.
6. The steps leading to the breakdown of the Ptolemaic theory in favour of the heliocentric cosmology of Copernicus, a contemporary of Leonardo da Vinci.

We have already stressed the fact that the Greeks were the first people who sought knowledge for its own sake. The earliest of their philosophers was probably Thales of Miletus, who founded the Ionian school in the sixth century B.C. He was the first to pose the question: "Of *what* is the world made?" This, after all, was a fundamental question, and the fact that it was posed at all was a significant tribute to Thales and the Ionians. His answer was "*Water*". In other words, he regarded water as the first principle out of which all the "stuff" of the universe is formed and into which all things are finally resolved, and he pictured the earth as a flat disc floating on water like a log.

A sequence of Ionian teachers followed with variants to this theory until we come to the name and time of Pythagoras (580–497 B.C.).

He was born in the Ionian Island of Samos and founded a school of philosophy in Croton, a Dorian colony in southern Italy. His followers are referred to as the Pythagoreans. They were a mystical brotherhood and their studies of mathematics and science were apparently incidental to their moral and religious doctrines.

There is some doubt as to what teachings may legitimately be attributed to Pythagoras himself and how much to his disciples, because it was the practice of his school to pass on all its learning verbally. Like their predecessors, they sought for first principles, but they found them in the less material directions of order, harmony and proportion. Through these agencies they gave a great stimulus to the study of number, in which they found the essence of all things. Thus, ten was a perfect number because it was the sum of $1+2+3+4$. Three was also sacred to the Pythagoreans—it was the "number of the universe" because everything had its beginning, its middle and its end.

We must not omit to mention also the inauguration by Pythagoras of the scientific study of sound. The story goes that while passing a blacksmith's shop he was attracted by the musical notes emitted by the anvil when struck with the hammer; and subsequent experiments on stretched strings of various lengths on what today we speak of as the monochord established the relations to one another of what are now known as the musical intervals. Pythagoras found by experiment that the necessary length ratio to produce an octave was $2:1$; to produce the interval known as a fifth was $3:2$; and to produce a fourth was $4:3$. So he got back to his magical series of 1, 2, 3, 4, and to his doctrine of harmony and proportion. This he applied to his famous conception of the "harmony of the spheres"—the picturesque scheme of a central solar fire at the centre of the universe, with the planets revolving round them with varying speeds that created celestial notes in harmonic ratios excelling in sweetness all earthly music—so sweet, indeed, as to be inaudible to mankind.

We find a reference to this by Pope in his *Essay on Man*:

> If nature thundered in his opening ears
> And stunned him with the music of the spheres,
> How would he wish that heaven had left him still
> The whispering zephyr and the parting rill!

But probably the most important teaching we get from the Pythagoreans was their view that matter is composed of four elements—earth, air, fire and water; that the *earth is spherical in shape*; and that it is at rest, poised in the centre of a huge spherical universe which rotates around it.

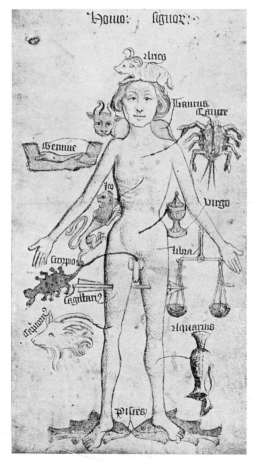

Plate 34—Roger Bacon with a pupil. From a fifteenth-century MS. of his *De Retardatione Senectutis* in the Bodleian Library (Hart, *Makers of Science*—O.U.P.).

Plate 35—Nicolas Copernicus, 1473–1543 (from a photograph supplied by the Radio Times Hulton Picture Library).

They taught, further, that the four primary elements are imperishable and unchangeable in quality and that they are brought into various combinations by the agency of two divine forces: one of attraction—concord or love; and the other of repulsion—discord or hate (Fig. 3). Thus, water is opposed to fire but is allied to earth. Further, with these four elements are associated the four primary *qualities* of heat, cold, wetness and dryness—producing affinity and opposition in the same way as do the elements. In this way they supposed the elements to combine in various proportions, thus producing all the natural phenomena around us.

Later this doctrine of the four primary elements, including the Pythagorean concept of all things being in a state of love or hate, was accepted by Aristotle and was incorporated in his writings. With

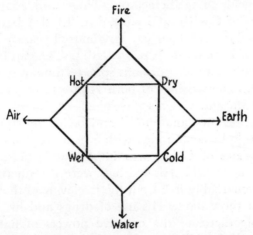

Fig. 3. Pythagorean Doctrine of the Primary
Elements and Qualities.

the stamp of his authority, it was accepted by both Christian and Islamic theology and thus received almost unquestioned support well beyond the days of Leonardo da Vinci.

A contemporary of the Pythagoreans was the philosopher Democritus of Abdera. He is of importance because of his association with the early history of alchemy—a study which played so great a part in the pseudo-sciences of the Middle Ages. Alchemy developed as a compound of alleged theory and mysticism, but its practical aim throughout was the preparation of gold and silver by artificial means. All through the Middle Ages this was the lure—to get rich quickly. No wonder it survived for century after century.

Democritus was also important for his elaboration of an atomic theory of matter. He taught that the universe was a vast void in which matter moved and that this matter was composed of an infinite

H

number of extremely small, finite and indivisible bodies called atoms, the combination and separation of which produced the great variety of physical phenomena on the earth.

Democritus found a powerful disciple later in Epicurus, and his atomic doctrine was also later incorporated in the *De Rerum Natura* by the Roman Lucretius. Unfortunately, a completely contrary view was taken by the giants of the Greek era—Socrates, Plato and Aristotle— who preferred the concept of the *continuity* of matter to that of the *discontinuity* with which an atomic theory must necessarily be associated. Against such formidable opposition it can well be understood that the atomic theory was quietly forgotten until it was revived in the nineteenth century by Dalton.

In passing, we should mention the work of two creative Greek teachers in the fields of medicine, physiology and anatomy. These were Hippocrates of Cos (b. 460 B.C.), who lived a bare generation before Plato, and the much later (by six hundred years!) Alexandrian physician Galen of Pergamum (A.D. 131–201). The gap between these two men is indicative of the enormous span of time over which Greek culture extended. The writings of both Hippocrates and Galen were known to Leonardo and Galen's physiological system was of special interest to him in his own anatomical and biological studies. Hippocrates of Cos (not to be confounded with a near-contemporary mathematician Hippocrates of Chios) was important because of the sane objectivity of his approach. His writings were genuinely scientific in spirit and were remarkably free from the irrelevances that might have been expected in those days. His use of drugs and his emphasis on cleanliness, simple diet and the curative powers of nature strike a modern note—and the Hippocratic oath has become a symbol of medical ethics throughout civilisation.

In the related field of physiology Galen provided the main sources and inspiration for centuries, right through the Middle Ages and up to the sixteenth century. His works had survived where so many others had been lost or destroyed, and were freely translated with extensive commentaries (and variations) by successive writers in Latin, Hebrew and Arabic. He had revived a practice of dissection which had earlier fallen into some disrepute, and as a consequence he was led to a physiological theory of the human body which he based upon the conception of three "vital spirits", or pneuma, as he called them, the details of which are outside our scope.

2. THE COSMOLOGY OF PLATO

We have already referred in Chapter II to Socrates and his pupil, Plato, and what was known as the Socratic method of investigation, whereby beliefs and opinions are analysed and discussed by question and answer in order to bring out any fallacies underlying them. Plato was the creator of a "doctrine of ideas", which in effect denied reality to individual objects as perceived by the senses. He regarded these as unreal because they are either continually changing or are subject to change. For him permanent and unchangeable reality lay in the abstract "types" of which the visible objects were the mere shadows. He called these abstract realities "ideas", but he did not mean them to be regarded as "thoughts" or images of things in the mind. They were substantive existences that were in being before matter, or man, or the objects of sense came into being. These "ideas" constituted the pattern or archetype to which all sensible things more or less conform.

Plato's "doctrine of ideas" became, in one sense, a deterrent to scientific thought because it tended to divert interest from earthly objects and phenomena to more abstract problems. But in his *Timaeus* he presented one aspect of his philosophy which made a profound appeal throughout the Middle Ages. The *Timaeus* was a work which ranged over a wide field of physics, mathematics and philosophy. Moreover, this work was one of the few that survived the vicissitudes and destruction of Greek literature through the Dark Ages; and therefore, for better or worse, what it contained was bound to be the subject of periodic commentaries and variations. Unfortunately, it was not one of his better books, and much of its contents bore the stamp of the mysticism of the Pythagoreans. Its principal translator and commentator was the fourth-century monastic Latin writer, Chalchidius, whose work was, in fact, the main source of Western knowledge of Plato, at least up to the twelfth century.

Rather vaguely, Plato developed, through the mouthpiece of Timaeus, a doctrine of relationship between man and the universe about him which has come to be known as the "doctrine of macrocosm and microcosm".

He supposed that the Creator of the universe, desiring that all things should be good, set in order a world which He found in turmoil and disorder. In it He planted an intelligent soul, and thus the universe became a living thing like an animal. Between fire and earth, the necessary elements of a visible and tangible creation, God placed air and water as their bond of union in continuous proportion; that is, as fire is to air, so is air to water, and as air is to water, so is water to earth. He desired that this created living thing (i.e. the universe) should be perfect and everlasting, and therefore He gave it the form of a sphere. Since this was the most perfect of all figures, everywhere similar to itself, and in every direction equidistant from the centre, there was no need either for limbs or organs. Nothing could exist outside the universe, and to it was assigned the motion appropriate to its shape, namely, a constant revolution upon its axis.

Timaeus next goes on to say that before making the body of the universe God made its soul from a compound of three ingredients—an unchangeable essence, a corporeal essence, and what he described as an intermediate essence. The creation of the sun, moon and five planets had for its object the distinction of days and nights, and months and years. To the moon was assigned an orbit nearest the earth. Next beyond that was the orbit of the sun, in which God had lighted a fire to illuminate the whole. Somewhat vaguely, he mentions the Morning Star, and "the star sacred to Hermes", but the movements of the other wandering stars are referred to as numerous and intricate. Next, the Creator formed within the universe four races: the gods, the birds, the aquatic animals, and the land animals. Of these, the first, the divine race, were made out of fire and, after the likeness of the universe, were distributed in a circular form over the heavens. The Creator then delegated to these gods the task of forming mortals. But He Himself provided for these a divine and immortal part, for when the universe was formed He assigned to each star a soul, which was to be received into a mortal body; and He indicated that the soul which had lived righteously during its appointed time would return to the habitation of his star.

So was born the medieval doctrine of macrocosm and microcosm, to be accepted into the corpus of Middle Ages beliefs, according to which the macrocosm, the whole universe, is a vast living organism, every part of which is intimately related to every other and, similarly, the microcosm is man, every part of whose living organism is also related to every other. And further, these two organisms, man and the universe, are interdependent so that man, the microcosm, merely reflects the great world, the macrocosm, about and above him.

An obvious consequence of this doctrine was to give an official stamp of authority to the pseudo-science of astrology, just as Democritus had done for the pseudo-science of alchemy. There was, of course, an astronomical foundation for this, since astronomy and mathematics were the only forms of science which emerged unscathed from Plato's "doctrine of ideas" previously referred to. But the natural proclivity for the supernatural and the superstitious in mankind, both in classical and medieval days, provided a harvest for a large body of fortune-tellers, sooth-sayers and the like. One consulted the astrologer as a matter of course. It was necessary for him to know under which star the "client" was born. It was a bad business to be born under Saturn (hence a "saturnine" personality!)—but being born under Mars would endow one with martial instincts—and so on. On the whole, astrology was a serious matter. One should make due allowances for the conditions and way of life in medieval times before embarking on hasty judgments about it. The beliefs and superstitions as developed from Plato's doctrine of macrocosm and microcosm did, in fact, provide a natural compensation for the ignorance with which the people of those days were surrounded.

The views of Leonardo da Vinci on these matters are quite unmistakeably modernistic. Alchemists, astrologers, necromancers and the like are summarily dismissed in a number of notes of which the following is representative[1]: "For nature, as it would seem, takes vengeance on such as would work miracles and they come to have less than other men who are more quiet. And those who wish to grow rich in a day shall live a long time in great poverty, as happens and will to all eternity happen to the alchemists, the would-be creators of gold and silver, and to the engineers who think to make dead water stir itself into life with perpetual motion, and to those supreme fools, the necromancer and the enchanter."

On the other hand, Leonardo was more definitely tolerant of a doctrine of macrocosm and microcosm, as witness the following[2]: "Man has been called by the ancients a lesser world, and indeed the term is well applied, seeing that if a man is composed of earth, water, air and fire, this body of earth is similar. While man has within himself bones as a stay and framework for the flesh, the world has stones which are the support of earth. While man has within him a pool of blood wherein the lungs as he breathes expand and contract, so the body of the earth has its ocean, which also rises and falls every six hours with the breathing of the world; as from the said pool of blood proceed the veins which spread their branches through the human body, so the ocean fills the body of the earth with an infinite number of veins of water."

3. THE PHYSICAL WORLD OF ARISTOTLE

The giant influence of the classical period upon the science of the later Middle Ages was undoubtedly that of Aristotle, the most famous of Plato's pupils. His writings were wide enough in range to merit their description as an encyclopaedia of the learning of his day. He was modern in the sense of stressing the importance of direct observation and systematic classification. But we must remember that the full tide of his influence did not come till after the Dark Ages. Just as the *Timaeus* was the only Dark Ages survival of the writings of Plato, so, in the case of Aristotle, the only writings available were his lyrical

[1] Windsor MS. *I*, 13 v.
[2] MS. *A*, 54 v.

works—the *Categories* and the *De Interpretatione*, both of which were the subject of study and Latin translation by Boethius in the sixth century. The many other writings of Aristotle came to light much later, during the Age of Arabic Infiltration and the subsequent scholastic period in western Europe.

From the philosophical standpoint it has been said that everyone is either a Platonist or an Aristotelean—Plato standing for the mystical and idealistic; and Aristotle for the more cautious insistence on the rules of logic and the evidence of observation. In Raphael's great fresco painting in the Vatican, entitled "The School of Athens", Plato is shown raising his hand towards heaven as the region of his *Ideas*, whilst Aristotle is shown pointing downwards to the earth. Aristotle's philosophy involved the idea of a *dual* reality, according to which a certain measure of reality belonged to individual objects (and in this he differed from Plato), though the thoughts and ideas which the human mind perceived *from* these objects were also equally real. It was a logical inference, therefore, that man need not be deterred from the more earthly "studies" from which Plato's "doctrine of ideas" had tended to divert them. And, indeed, Aristotle's own force of example in this was immense. It was opposed later, as we have seen, by St. Augustine's Christianised version of Plato's philosophy, but it subsequently prevailed nevertheless.

In the more purely modern sense, Aristotle's greatest work was in the biological field. His observations on living things were exemplary and his *History of Animals* gives a schematic "Ladder of Nature" which indicates an upwards gradation of species, emerging from "inanimate matter" at the base, through to lower plants, higher plants, zoophytes, molluscs, insects, shell fish, octopuses, reptiles and fish, and so on to whales, mammals and Man. His relationship of whales to mammals was a masterly achievement of observation in his day.

Next to his work in the biological field, we should record his notable contributions in the field of deductive geometry. Here he was led to found the system of deductive logic, in which one argued from general principles to particular cases. As it turned out, Aristotle applied this scheme of argument at times with a rigidity that led him to a number of fallacies (the "deduction" that a heavy weight will fall more quickly than a light weight is an example), which, through the influence of his great authority, gained acceptance for centuries.

We have already mentioned that Aristotle, in his picture of the universe, both accepted and elaborated upon the Pythagorean doctrine that the earth was composed basically of the four primary elements of earth, water, air and fire, and the four associated primary qualities of heat, cold, moisture and dryness. But for celestial matter he introduced the idea of a *fifth* element—the *quinta essentia*, the ether more subtle and divine than the other elements. So we get the modern term "quintessence".

For Aristotle one important distinction arose from this *quinta essentia* —that, whereas terrestrial matter implied a great variety of possible combinations and disintegrations within the limits of the four primary elements, there could be no such changes in celestial matter. The skies were perfect, and therefore immutable, and there could be no breakdown in their uniformity.

The foundation stone, so to speak, of Aristotle's cosmos was that the earth was fixed, immovable, and at the centre of the universe. He regarded the shape of the universe as spherical because, just as the circle was the most perfect figure in a plane, so the sphere was the seat of unchangeable order in space, revolving towards the right—that is to say, from east to west (because this was the more "honourable" direction). He also considered that to this outermost sphere of the universe were attached the stars, which also went round with it.

Next he taught that inside this outermost sphere were a number of other spheres, one inside the other, each carrying a planet and all having a common centre at the earth. Actually this scheme of homo-centric spheres was not original to Aristotle. We speak of the "spheres of Eudoxus", because it was this earlier astronomer and mathema-tician who first propounded the idea as a possible hypothesis. But Aristotle converted it from a hypothesis to an allegation of physical fact.

Let us next consider his views on the subject of motion. Aristotle distinguished between natural and unnatural motions. Natural motion was *circular* for celestial bodies and *rectilinear* for terrestrial bodies. For the former there could be no such thing as an "unnatural" motion —celestial bodies must persist in their uniform circular paths for ever because they are "perfect". But for terrestrial bodies motion could be either "natural" or "unnatural" or "forced".

Aristotle's analysis of the terrestrial motion of bodies is as follows: He begins by stating that as lines are measurable in one direction only, and planes in two, so bodies are measurable in three directions. Body is therefore made complete by three magnitudes, and three is therefore the number of perfection.

As matter, then, is made complete by three, the same must also be true for motion. There are, therefore, three simple motions: (*a*) motion towards the centre; (*b*) motion from the centre; and (*c*) motion round the centre. The first two are rectilinear motions and are natural to earthly substances, whilst the circular motion appertains to the heavenly bodies.

As far as motion towards and from the centre is concerned, we have here a sort of theory of gravity. Plato had already attempted such a theory, arguing that a downward motion was really a motion towards the centre of the earth and that there existed a tendency for all bodies to be attracted towards larger masses of the same material. According to Plato, for example, a lump of rock or stone is attracted down to the earth, whilst a "vapour" rises by attraction to the larger masses of vapour above.

Aristotle took a different view. He argued that there were two classes of bodies—heavy bodies, which have a natural tendency to move down towards the centre of the earth, and light bodies, whose natural tendency is to move up from the centre of the earth. Further, he held that there were degrees of heaviness, the heavier bodies tending to move farther down than the less heavy bodies, so that, e.g., earth, being heavier than water (both in the "heavy" class of matter), we expect to find the water above the earth, as indeed we do. On the other hand, both "fire" and "air" belong to the "light" group, and, since fire is lighter than air, both have a tendency to go up, but the fire more so than the air, and so the air is above the water and the fire nearest the celestial regions.

One of his deductions as to falling bodies was that a heavier body would fall faster than a lighter one. This was destined to prove a serious obstacle to progress in mechanics for very many centuries and it is somewhat astonishing that, with his vigorous mind, it should not have occurred to him to put such a simple problem to the test of experiment.

These are, of course, but a very small fraction of Aristotle's teachings. They are given as being most relevant to the special angle of Leonardo da Vinci's work (i.e. in the field of mechanics) with which this book is mainly concerned. It is an astonishing thought that, although Aristotle lived and worked eighteen hundred years before Leonardo's time, his influence was nevertheless paramount in the field of science during the Renaissance years of the fifteenth century.

4. THE MECHANICS OF ARCHIMEDES

For the next great factor to influence the mechanical science of the Renaissance we turn to the earlier Alexandrian School, founded by the Ptolemys who ruled Egypt after the death of Alexander the Great. Euclid the Geometer, Aristarchus the Astronomer and Eratosthenes the Geographer are but a few of the great men of this period. But in relation to Leonardo's scientific backgrounds our interest must be focused on *Archimedes* of Syracuse, the founder of the science of mechanics in its modern sense. He differed from both Plato and Aristotle in avoiding the complication of mixing scientific thinking with philosophic conceptions. In that sense he was a true scientist. His procedure was simple and direct. He investigated his problems step by step, and never passing on until he had established the validity of the particular point he had reached.

Archimedes (287–212 B.C.) (Plate 30) was born in Syracuse, in Sicily, a city which was founded as far back as 734 B.C. by colonisers from Corinth, itself at the time a Greek city of eminence in both trade and the arts. The standards attained in Syracuse were accordingly high.

Archimedes was brought up in an atmosphere of science. His father, an astronomer, sent him as a young man to the School of Alexandria. Here he came under the influence perhaps of Euclid himself, but certainly of pupils and successors to Euclid. He then returned to Syracuse to spend the remainder of his life in meditation and study.

Although he is more generally known for his work in mechanics, he was himself very proud of his mathematical discoveries. One of these was his elucidation of the relation between the areas and volumes of a sphere and its circumscribing cylinder, and he was so proud of this that he expressed a desire for these figures to be recorded on his tomb.

In mechanics, his study of the doctrine of equilibrium was masterly. His starting point was the principle of the lever, the demonstration of which was made to rest ultimately on the truth that equal bodies at the ends of the equal arms of a rod, supported at its mid-point, will balance each other. Proceeding from this, he pursues his proof to the conclusion that bodies will be in equilibrium when their distances from the fulcrum (i.e. the point of support) are inversely as their weight. Hence, given a sufficiently long lever, any weight, however big, may be suitably moved. "Give me," said Archimedes to his king, "where to stand, and I will move the earth."

From this he passed naturally to a discussion on centres of gravity, establishing several propositions relating to them, and working out the positions of the centre of gravity for variously shaped bodies.

Archimedes, too, was virtually the founder of the branch of physics known as hydrostatics, i.e. the study of the laws of fluids at rest. The story of his discovery of the famous Principle of Archimedes—namely, that a solid body, when immersed in a liquid, appears to lose a portion of its weight equal to the weight of liquid it displaces—has indeed, in one form or another, become a classic. It appears that the principle occurred to him, as a result of his observations of the water rising in his bath following his immersion therein and that he was so excited at the discovery that he ran out without stopping to clothe himself, exclaiming, "Eureka!" (I have discovered it). The story usually linked up with this relates how a golden crown, ordered by King Hiero of Syracuse, was suspected of adulteration in its manufacture; and Archimedes was invited to find a means of proving or disproving this. After the reputed incident of the bath, he was able to base his solution of the difficulty on the fact that when two masses of equal weight, but of different density or specific gravity, are successively immersed in water, the less dense, being the larger, will displace a larger body of water. Hence, if the adulterated crown contained some metal lighter than gold, it would displace a greater quantity of water than a crown of pure gold of the same weight.

Archimedes excelled in the design of mechanical contrivances both for peace and war. His famous "screw", virtually a pump and used for raising water from a lower level to a higher one, is applied in practice to this very day. In effect, it is a pipe twisted in the form of a corkscrew, and is held in an inclined position with one end immersed in the water source below. It is rotated on its axis by means of a handle at the top and the water is thus brought up with the successive turns of the screw and ultimately runs out at the top.

Archimedes died in 212 B.C. under tragic circumstances at the taking of Syracuse by Marcellus, during the second Punic War. Marcellus, with commendable reverence for learning, had ordered that the philosopher should be spared. Unfortunately, he was discovered by a soldier who did not recognise him, and, according to one account, Archimedes was so engrossed in a mathematical problem, the diagram for which he had figured in the sands, that he did not hear the angry calls of the soldier, who thereupon slew him.

5. THE COSMOLOGY AND OPTICS OF PTOLEMY

In the setting of the medieval scene in science, the final element of importance contributed during the Greek era was the formulation of the geocentric picture of the cosmos by Claude Ptolemy. This he did in his famous Greek work, the *Megalis Syntaxis* (the great composition) which, it will be recalled, was translated into Arabic under the title of the *Almagest*.

Ptolemy (Plate 31) belonged to the second School of Alexandria—a period of cultural revival that followed the decline of the first school. Neither the place (? Pelusium) nor the date of his birth are known, but he was a native of Egypt and lived during the reigns of Antoninus Pius and Adrian. He taught at Alexandria from about A.D. 127 to 151 and died about A.D. 168.

We have already given some account of his work as a geographer. It is curious that Ptolemy's *Geography* was not translated into Latin until the fifteenth century, whereas the *Almagest* was translated in the twelfth century. His astronomical system was, therefore, a greater factor of influence in the Middle Ages than was his geography.

To appreciate his work properly, it is necessary to refer to two earlier astronomers of the first Alexandrian era. These were Aristarchus of Samos and Hipparchus of Nicaea. To Aristarchus of Samos (*c.* 310–230 B.C.) belongs the distinction of affirming, seventeen hundred years before Copernicus, that the sun and *not* the earth is at the centre of the universe. He was led to this decision following an attempt (the first of its kind) to measure the distances of the sun and moon from the earth, and he described this in a work, still extant, *On the Sizes and Distances of the Sun and Moon*. As one would expect, his result was badly out, but, for a two-thousand-years-old investigation it had merit. He at least established that the sun was a much larger body than the earth and this led him to question the current Pythagorean doctrine that the earth was fixed, immovable and the centre of the universe, and that this very big sun was going round the earth. It seemed contrary to common sense. Philolaus, a late Pythagorean, had previously suggested that *all* the planets, including the earth and the sun, revolved round a "central fire"; and yet another philosopher, Heraclides, had taught that the two inner planets, Mercury and Venus (seen, in association with the sun, as morning and evening stars), revolved round the sun. In the light of his own experiment, Aristarchus decided that these theories were pointers to the view that *all* planets, including the earth, move round the central sun. Thus was born the heliocentric theory of the Greek era. It had a following for a short time, but a growing chorus of disapproval culminated in a tract by Cleanthes the Stoic, calling Aristarchus a blasphemer and demanding his silence and punishment.

But observational astronomy was now becoming a reality, calling for and attaining a relatively high standard of accuracy. One of its most diligent exponents was *Hipparchus of Nicaea* (Plate 32), who set up an observatory at Rhodes and continued the task of his predecessors in recording the positions of the brighter stars relative to standard points in the sky. Hipparchus charted the motions in particular of the sun, moon and planets, and determined, with reasonable accuracy, the duration of the lunar month and the solar year.

All this data was, in due course, available to Ptolemy, and one result of his study of these records was to establish that they simply failed to fit in with the current view that the planets were moving round the earth in accurate circles. Observation showed that, although planets seem to move across the skies steadily for long periods, there are other periods when their motion is most irregular and anything but uniform. Here was an impasse with a vengeance! Faith and tradition demanded uniform circular motion. The facts of observation called for something else. Somehow the two had to be reconciled.

As it happened, Ptolemy recalled a simple mathematical device of epicycles, suggested earlier by Appolonius of Perga, a mathematician of note. This was the ingenious idea that the planet P (Fig. 4) is moving uniformly in a circle round a centre C which, in *its* turn, is also moving uniformly in a larger circle whose centre is the Earth E. The circle of P was called the *afferent* and the circle of C the *deferent*. By a careful choice of dimensions, based on his observations for each planet separately, this scheme did seem to fit in with actual observations of the variable motions of the five then-known planets sufficiently

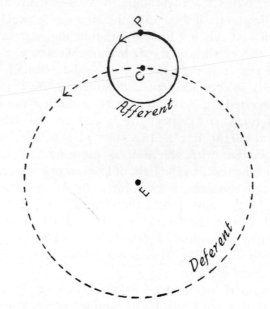

Fig. 4.   Ptolemy's Device of Epicycles (originated by
Appolonius of Perga).

approximately and thus satisfy the people of those times that the be-loved principle of uniform circular motion was preserved.

So we get the famous Ptolemaic system or scheme of the universe. At the centre was the earth. Round it was a system of circles, each of which was the orbit, not of a planet, but of the centre of the deferent circle round which the particular planet was moving. For each separate planet it was a question of choosing the right dimensions for the radius of each epicycle in relation to the radius of the deferent to fit in with the facts of observation of the irregularities of motion in each case (Fig. 5).

It has been alleged, and it may indeed have been true initially, that Ptolemy evolved this scheme of epicycles more or less as a mathematical exercise. The original scheme of one simple circular orbit round the earth for each planet was in danger because the improvements in the instruments of accurate observation (the gnomon, the quadrant, the astrolabe, and the armillary sphere were the chief ones) were against it. As an exercise in geometry, therefore, the problem was to choose an *additional* scheme of circles that *would* produce orbits to fit in with observations, "and thus" (to use the current phrase of the times) "to save the phenomenon"—the phenomenon being the requisite "perfect" motion of the planets according to a formula of circles. Having found the geometrical solution, we may take it that Ptolemy and his followers accepted it. Yet it will not surprise the reader to be told that as time went on and instruments became yet more accurate

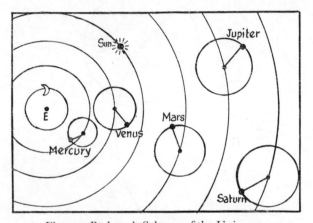

Fig. 5.   Ptolemy's Scheme of the Universe.

it was found that even with these epicycles chosen by Ptolemy the charted orbits showed yet further irregularities. But the device of epicycles had pointed the way and all that was now necessary was to add yet another epicycle to each epicycle. Thus (Fig. 6) a planet *P* would now be moving round a circle (1) whose centre was moving round a circle (2) whose centre was moving round a circle (3) whose centre was the earth, *still* fixed, immovable and at the centre of the universe. And this was the sort of pattern that held for 1,400 years!

6. THE COSMOLOGY OF THE MIDDLE AGES

But, as we have seen, there lay a large gap in time between the scientific activities of the Greeks and the renewal of culture in the Middle Ages—the gap of the Dark Ages. What was happening to science in general, and to speculations regarding the cosmological

structure of the universe in particular, during this long and dark interval of cultural decline?

The depths to which the decline could reach may be illustrated
by two examples. With the advent of Christ there had emerged a
Christian philosophy which basically taught that the answer to everything about God and the universe lay in the Bible. Fundamentalists
have for centuries claimed that the Bible would provide all the astronomy
and physics, mechanics and geology that man needed to know without
requiring him to use his own powers of observation and deduction.

One of the patristic writers of the late third and early fourth century
was Lactantius Firmianus (c. 260–340). He believed in the inseparable
union of true wisdom with true religion and joined in a current battle

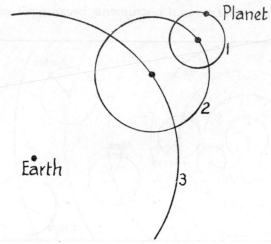

Fig. 6.   Saving the Phenomenon—extension of the
Scheme of Epicycles.

of his day against the heresy of the Greek teaching that the earth was
spherical in shape. He made great play with the idea of an "antipodes"
as follows: "Is there anyone so senseless as to believe that there are
men whose footsteps are higher than their heads? . . . That the crops
and trees grow downwards? And does anyone wonder that the hanging
gardens (of Babylon) are among the seven wonders of the world when
philosophers make hanging fields and seas and cities and mountains?"
And so he goes on, pouring ridicule upon ridicule upon all "who
imagine they know natural things which cannot be known by men!"

Three centuries later, about the year 548, a monk known as Cosmos
Indicopleustas of Alexandria wrote (in a cloister in Sinai) a work called
Topographia Christiana, one purpose of which, like that of Lactantius,
was to denounce as a false heathenism the doctrine of the rotundity

of the earth. His reading of the Scriptures led him to a picture of the earth as a rectangular plane, covered by the vaulted roof of the firmament, above which was heaven itself. In the centre of the rectangular plane is the inhabited portion of the earth, surrounded by ocean, beyond which lies the Paradise of Adam. To the north is a conical mountain, and the sun revolves round the summit of this in summer and round the base of it in winter, thus giving the different periods of the length of the day.

Clearly, the exponents of Christianity must take much of the responsibility for the ignorance of the Dark Ages.

During the many centuries between the days of Ptolemy and Galen, between A.D. 200 and the advent of Roger Bacon (b. 1214), practically no serious work of scientific importance and originality was carried out in Christian Europe. An exception must be made, however, to work of the type of Boethius, who, it will be recalled, studied and translated into Latin Aristotle's *Categories* and the *De interpretatione* (i.e. the logical and not the scientific books) and who wrote his own mathematical textbooks; and always there was Pliny, with his vast compendium of sense and nonsense. We have already referred, too, to the succession of encyclopaedists who varyingly displayed and kept in survival some record, if a low one, of ancient science—Cassiodorus (490–585), Isidore of Seville (560–636), whose late sixth-century *Origines* was widely read and used, the Venerable Bede (673–735), Alcuin (735–804), Raban (786–856) and perhaps finally Byrhtferth (c. 1000). Their writings, all derived from Pliny, constituted the main sequence of Dark Ages literature in science.

The new millennium after A.D. 1000, however, began to usher in the first consequences of the infiltration to western Europe of Arabian science. Moreover, a reaction had set in against the rigidity of outlook of works of the type of Lactantius regarding the Greek speculations on cosmology. This reaction was based largely on the appeal which the mysticism of astrology made to the medieval mind. To the people of the early Middle Ages the Aristotelean picture of a universe of concentric spheres seemed very real. For them the harmony of the spheres was a fact, not a theory. The perfection of the outermost heavenly sphere in which God dwells, and of the benign influence penetrating inwards from an unchanging, immortal and harmonious sphere to an imperfect, changing and mortal earth (compounded of its four basic elements and qualities)—these were actualities. They made sense, and, in the light of Plato's doctrine of macrocosm and microcosm, provided a satisfying conviction. Ultimately these ideas seemed, after all, to fit in with the needs of Christian theology, and we have seen how, in the later centuries of the Middle Ages St. Thomas Aquinas provided the final compromise between these doctrines and brought Christianity to terms with Greek science.

Thus it was that Byrhtferth, a monk of Ramsey in Huntingdonshire, wrote an Anglo-Saxon "compotus" or "handbook" of astronomical and astrological lore—much of it derived from Bede—which indicated

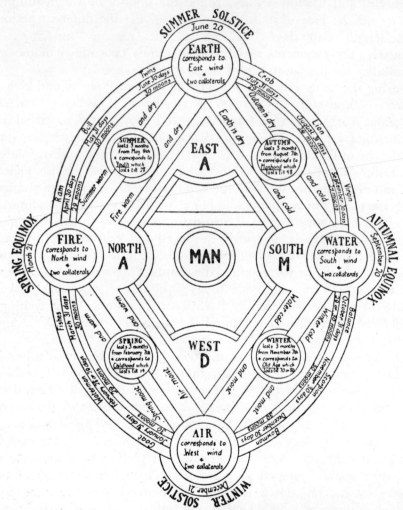

Fig. 7.　English version of Byrhtferth of Ramsey's diagram of Macrocosm and Microcosm.

clearly in a diagram (Fig. 7) the extent to which the doctrine of macrocosm and microcosm had become incorporated in the minds of the times. The diagram repays scrutiny. The relationship of man the microcosm to the macrocosmic outer world is shown by the ring of Zodiacal signs; and it is interesting to note that a subsequent frequent

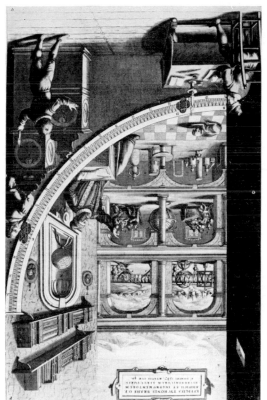

Plate 37—Tycho Brahé in 1587, with his astronomical instruments, including a large quadrant. From *Cosmographia Blaviana, Amsterdam, 1662* (from a copy in the Library of Worcester College, Oxford).

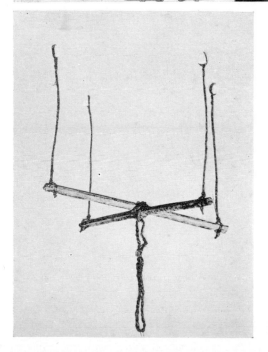

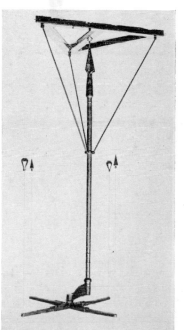

Plate 36—The Groma. *Left*, reconstruction from a Pompeii instrument. *Right*, a Groma found in the Fayyûm (from R. W. Sloley, "Ancient Egypt", Sept. 1926).

Plate 38—Self-portrait of Leonardo da Vinci (*c.* 1512) in his sixtieth year, from a crayon portrait in the Royal Library, Turin.

Plate 39—A facsimile page from Leonardo's Book on the Flight of Birds (Hart, *Mechanical Investigations of Leonardo da Vinci*).

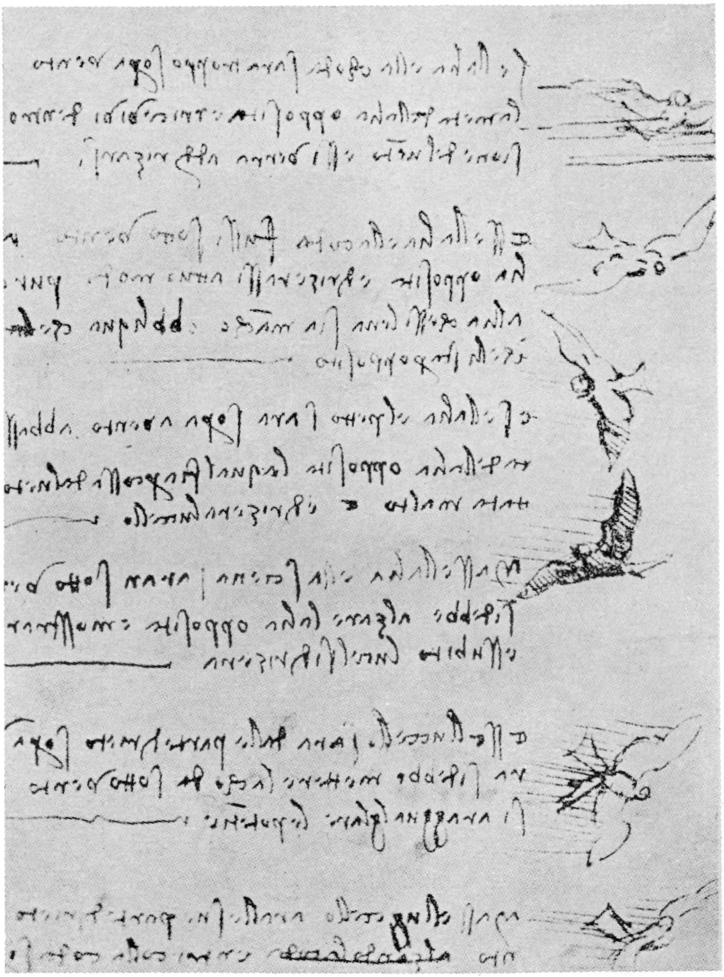

feature of the scientific literature of the times was concerned with the astrological consequences of this scheme, particularly after the infiltration of Arabian influence. The standard of illustration, copied with many variants from writer to writer, showed what was called "Zodiacal Man". Plate 33 is a typical example and indicates the particular parts of the human body (replacing in the diagram the central earth as his abode in the universe) and the particular planets and other signs of the Zodiac which influence those parts.

Perhaps the most picturesque and best-known example of the accepted cosmology of the Middle Ages is that given by Dante Alighieri (1265–1321) in his memorable *Divine Comedy*. Dante, it will be recalled, was contemporary with Petrarch and Boccaccio in the task of establishing new literary standards in the vernacular of Italy in the thirteenth and early fourteenth centuries. But in general these latter were realistic writers in the "troubadour" pattern as against the mysticism of Dante. The *Commedia*—built up of one hundred cantos (he is influenced here by the Pythagorean perfection of the number ten)—portrays a vision of the state after death, as conceived by the poet on the Good Friday of the year 1300—but it is also an allegory of man's state on earth. Similarly, his visions of Hell, Purgatory and Paradise portray the common views and doctrines of his times. Fused with the whole were the experience of his great love for Beatrice, with whom he is first reunited in vision; and subsequently for the divine Lady Philosophy, who becomes man's guide when human reason fails.

The universe of the *Divine Comedy* (Fig. 8) shows the earth in the centre, with Jerusalem in the middle, and a hemisphere of water from which Purgatory emerges, and above it the Earthly Paradise. Beneath the earth's surface is Hell. Above and surrounding the sphere of the earth are the successive realms of air and fire, after which come the separate and successive spheres of the "planets"—Moon, Mercury, Venus, Sun, Mars, Jupiter and Saturn. Above these are the spheres of the zodiac and the fixed-stars. Then, finally, the outermost crystalline sphere of the *primum mobile* and so to the dwelling-place of God, the Empyrean Paradise. The pattern follows Aristotle closely and extends to the picture of divine control at all levels. With God at the top and minor deities and angels in control of the successively lower spheres, the Seraphim guided the Primum Mobile, the Cherubim the sphere of the fixed stars, Saturn was controlled by the Thrones, and so on down to the Angels in control of the Moon.

With such a picture predominant as a conception of the universe, we can readily see why the astrological factor as an application and a consequence of the doctrine of macrocosm and microcosm was inevitable. The celestial powers that ruled the spheres similarly ruled every

I

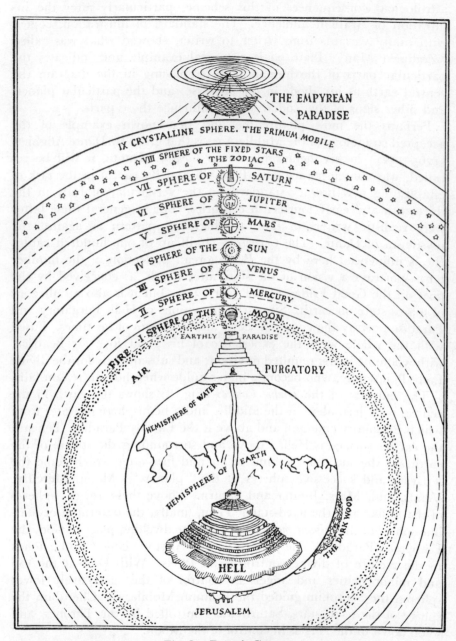

THE EMPYREAN
PARADISE

IX CRYSTALLINE SPHERE. THE PRIMUM MOBILE

VIII SPHERE OF THE FIXED STARS
THE ZODIAC

VII SPHERE OF SATURN

VI SPHERE OF JUPITER

V SPHERE OF MARS

IV SPHERE OF THE SUN

III SPHERE OF VENUS

II SPHERE OF MERCURY

I SPHERE OF THE MOON

FIRE

EARTHLY PARADISE

AIR PURGATORY

HEMISPHERE OF WATER

HEMISPHERE OF EARTH

THE DARK WOOD

HELL

JERUSALEM

Fig. 8. Dante's Cosmos.

part of the human body. Such a scheme seemed right and eminently acceptable to the medieval mind. The stamp of Aristotelean authority and the subsequent cautious acquiescence of the Church gained for it a day-to-day background to the lives of the "common people".

7. ISLAMIC SCIENCE—THE OPTICS OF ALHAZEN

We have already surveyed the broad aspects of Islamic culture and the processes of its gradual transmission to and influence upon western Europe. We have seen that with the rediscovery of Greek learning the initial task was that of rendering these writings into Islamic languages. Next came the commentaries upon them, by which time the philosophers of Islam were able to make their own original contributions to knowledge, notably in the fields of mathematics, astronomy, chemistry and optics. In chemistry the Arabian alchemists (of whom Gebir was the outstanding example) made very real progress under the materialistic spur to produce gold from the "drosser" substances, and a magical "elixir of life" which would give perpetual youth to their "clients". On the other hand, in medicine their knowledge of the human body and of the functions of the human organs was far in excess of their Greek predecessors. In astronomy the Arabians charted the heavens diligently and accurately, mainly for the successful navigation of both land and sea. In mathematics their outstanding contribution was to the new field of algebra, originally derived from India; whilst in physics the most notable Arabian advance was in optics.

But, in the main, the dominant influence upon Arabic philosophy and science was Aristotelean. Their thinking was in terms of deductive logic—that is to say, by arguing from the general to the particular as against the converse methods of inductive logic. A notable exception to this was the philosopher Ghazali (1058–1111), whose penetrating attacks on the current trends of Islamic philosophy and the whole Aristotelean tradition upon which this was based were very effective in his day. Generally speaking, however, it may be said that the cosmological outlook of Arabic philosophers differed from that of the Greeks in being more dynamic. Where the Greeks regarded the universe as a complete and unchanging entity, Islam was more for the conception of continual change and development.

We have referred to optics as the special branch of physics with which Arabic science was most concerned, and, since this was necessarily a field of considerable importance to the artists of the Renaissance, it is desirable to survey this in further detail. Its greatest exponent was Alhazen (965–1038), a native of the city of Basra, in Mesopotamia.

In earlier times Euclid had stated that light travels in straight lines and had discussed, somewhat crudely, the phenomenon of refraction. Later this was also considered by Ptolemy. Its importance to him was naturally as an astronomer, since by refraction through the atmosphere, as the light passes through to an observer, the stars are seen deviated from their true positions in the skies. Ptolemy examined with great care and accuracy the angles of refraction corresponding to all angles of incidence from 0° to 80° in the case of a ray of light passing from air to a glass or water medium. He also distinguished what we now speak of as the virtual focus of a convex lens—i.e. the point at which the diverging reflected rays would meet if produced backwards behind the lens.

So we come to the time of Alhazen, whose famous book, *Thesaurus Opticæ*, displayed an originality and skill generally superior to Ptolemy. Especially refined were his applications of geometrical methods to the elucidation of optical effects in curved mirrors. For example, he solved the problem of finding the point in a convex mirror at which a ray coming from one point would be reflected to another given point. He offered the suggestion that the sun and moon on the horizon appear larger than in the zenith owing to the influence upon our judgment by comparison with terrestrial objects. In his treatment of refraction he gave an explanation of the cause of twilight, and he considerably improved upon Ptolemy's apparatus for measuring the angles of refraction in different media.

Contrary to the views current until his day, Alhazen held that vision resulted from rays coming from the object to the eye and were not a result of emanations from the eye to the object. Alhazen, too, was considerably in advance of previous writers on the subject of the structure of the eye, placing the lens (the *humor crystallinus*) in the centre of the optic globe, and regarding it as the centre of conversion of the external light-rays into the sensation of sight.

Alhazen's works were later translated into Latin by an unknown writer, and this Latin translation was made the basis of a detailed study about 1260 by Witelo, a Polish writer, whose book greatly influenced the famous Roger Bacon shortly after. Witelo's work was, in fact, little more than an unacknowledged revised edition of Alhazen, and his tables of refraction were little more than a repetition of those of Ptolemy.

There is reasonable evidence that Leonardo da Vinci was familiar directly with the works of several of the more important Arabic writers and, at least indirectly, with the optical work of Alhazen. He refers, in a note in the *Codex Atlanticus*,[1] to having borrowed from Fazio Cardan a copy of a book by Alkindi, *Le Proportioni d'Alchindi*, whilst

[1] *Codex Atlanticus*, 225 r.b.

Avicenna's writings are frequently referred to; and although Alhazen himself is not mentioned, Leonardo specifically refers to Witelo[1] and therefore, inferentially, must have been aware of Alhazen's work.

8. ROGER BACON AND THE EARLY RENAISSANCE OF THE THIRTEENTH CENTURY

Meanwhile, in western Europe, a minor renaissance in science was developing during the thirteenth century. We have noted the development of education on the pattern of the seven liberal arts, with mathematics and astronomy as factual subjects, and grammar and dialectic as the basis for expression and discussion; and, inasmuch as the universities were increasingly the focus of scholars from all parts of Europe, we can well appreciate the importance of these institutions in the development of science.

The influence of the unusual personality of Frederick II (A.D. 1194–1250) is particularly worthy of notice. As Emperor of the Holy Roman Empire he was at loggerheads with the Pope, who had excommunicated him twice over differences in connection with the Crusades. But his interests were wide and varied. He was a scholar as well as a statesman. He aided the founding of universities at Naples and Padua, and he encouraged all who were engaged in the translation of Arabic works into Latin.

Among his protégées was the famous Leonardo Fabonacci of Pisa, whose *Liber Abaci* was one of the best-known mathematical textbooks of those times. This book was well-known both to Leonardo da Vinci and to his friend Fra Luca Pacioli. In fact, Pacioli's own book, printed at Venice in 1494 (the *Summa de Arithmetica, Geometrica, Proportione et Proportionalita*), was based upon the writings of Leonardo of Pisa.

Another thirteenth-century writer of importance from the point of view of Leonardo da Vinci was Jordanus Nemorarius, the author of a work on mechanics called *De Ponderibus*. This book was well known to Leonardo and clearly influenced him in a number of his notes. Jordanus was born at Borgentreich, near Warburg, and he entered the Dominican Order in Paris in 1220. He was essentially a follower of the Greek tradition of Aristotle, Archimedes and Euclid in mechanics and mathematics, and he had a considerable following.

We have mentioned Frederick II as a patron of science in the thirteenth century, but there was another monarch of this period whose patronage of science was a factor of major importance. This was Alphonso X of Castile. Ruling in a country bordering on that of the Arabs (who were at the time in occupation of the south of Spain), he gathered about him at Toledo a number of astronomers drawn

[1] MS. S.K. Mus., 53 r.

from the Moorish universities of the south. These he employed to elaborate a series of accurate astronomical tables founded upon the earlier observations of Ptolemy. Known as the Alphonsine Tables, they became the basis of all subsequent astronomical practice for many years throughout Europe.

We should now remind the reader that, in addition to the influence of the universities, the thirteenth century saw the foundation of the two great monastic orders—the Franciscans or Gray Friars (founded in 1209), and the Dominicans or Black Friars (founded in 1215). Although brought into being for purely religious purposes, both profoundly influenced the course and progress of science and philosophy during this century. More particularly, we may say that, on balance, the Dominicans provided the philosophers and the Franciscans the scientists. St. Dominic was himself a great theologian who set up standards of asceticism and austerity which the Order tried to carry over into the universities. They founded and held Chairs in most of them and pursued their faith to a degree of fanaticism and intolerance of which the famous Inquisition under Torquemada was a noted example. But they also gave to the world of Christian philosophy such giants as Albertus Magnus and St. Thomas Aquinas.

The less austere Franciscans, on the other hand, developed a tradition for producing men holding high office in the Church, who were also eminent in mathematics and science. Such were Robert Grosseteste (c. 1175–1253), who was both Bishop of Lincoln and Chancellor of the University of Oxford; Alexander of Hales in Gloucestershire (d. 1215), the first of the great scholastics to study the works of Aristotle as a whole; John of Peckham (c. 1220–1292), to whose optical writings, known to Fazio Cardan and thence to Leonardo da Vinci, we have previously referred; and, greatest of all, Roger Bacon.

Viewed collectively, these were primarily concerned with a revival of the study of Greek and the consequent first-hand study of Aristotle; but individually they each developed their separate specialities. In this sense, however, Roger Bacon stands apart both for the ubiquity of his interests and for the vivid originality of his outlook. Where the scholars of the thirteenth century were still looking backwards to the classical past, he alone looked forwards and demanded of a problem not the reply given under the authority of a great name such as Aristotle, but that provided by independent investigation and direct observation and experiment.

Roger Bacon (Plate 34) was born at Ilchester in Somerset in 1214. He first studied at home in 1227 and later at Oxford. Here he came under the influence of Edmund Rich, then lecturing on Aristotle, and of Robert Grosseteste. Under their influence Roger Bacon studied

Greek and afterwards entered the Franciscan Order. From Oxford he went to the University of Paris, where his experimental methods brought him under the suspicions of the General of his Order, who banished him to the confinement of a house in Paris. Here he stayed from 1257 to 1267. Towards the end of this term he wrote his three large treatises, the *Opus Maius*, the *Opus Minus* and the *Opus Tertium*. It was possibly owing to the papal influence of Pope Clement IV that he was allowed to return to Oxford. Here in 1271 he produced the first part of his *Compendium Studii Philosophia*. Once again, however, he incurred the displeasure of his Order and for fourteen years, from 1278 to 1292, he was again confined in Paris. He spent the last two years of his life in Oxford, and died in 1294 at the age of eighty. He was buried in the Church of the Franciscans.

Bacon's scientific activities covered a very wide range and included mathematics, astronomy, geography, alchemy, astrology and physics. His influence upon Leonardo da Vinci is clear. Bacon is specifically referred to in a notebook in the possession of the British Museum.[1]

Bacon developed some remarkable views on the subject of the propagation of force. They link up with his work on optics because, for Bacon, the radiation of light was just one type of all radiant forces. He conceives an emanation of force to be continually proceeding from every bodily object in all directions. The first result of this emanation he calls the "species", or image, or impression. This is a doctrine previously met with in varying forms among the writings of Lucretius and other ancients, and it was later to find some support by Leonardo da Vinci in his optical notes. Bacon, however, was less crude and far more specific. For example, he rejects the notion that the "species" is something emitted from the acting body, since, if it were so, it would be weakened and ultimately destroyed, which does not, in fact, happen. As developed by Bacon, this conception had much in common with the later undulatory theory, in that for him the "species" is a motion or change in successive portions of the medium, propagated in straight lines and deflected in direction when the medium changes.

This subject absorbed Bacon's attention for some ten years of his life and fills a fifth part of his *Opus Maius*. Greatly indebted to Alhazen, he nevertheless showed great superiority over his Arabian precursor and shows proof of a steady appreciation of the practical possibilities involved in the phenomena of reflection and refraction. He was certainly quite clear about the simple microscope. Thus he writes:

"If the letters of a book, or any minute objects, be viewed through a lesser segment of a sphere of glass, or crystal, whose plane base is laid upon them, they will appear far better and larger. Because by

―――――――

[1] MS. Brit. Mus., 71 b.

the fifth canon about a spherical medium, if its convexity is towards the eye, and the object is placed below it, and between the convexity and its centre, all things concur to magnify it. For the angle under which it is seen is greater and its image is also greater and nearer the eye than the object itself, because the object is between the centre and the eye; and therefore this instrument is useful to old men and to those that have weak eyes; for they may see the smallest letters sufficiently magnified."

Bacon's ideas on refraction are well seen in his explanation of the action of the burning glass (Fig. 9).

But although, too, he was aware of the possibilities of lens combinations, it cannot be said that he invented the telescope. He certainly introduced the possibility of distant vision by instrumental means, but it had to be left to a later generation to find a solution.

Bacon was one of the first to realise that the great obstacles to learning in his day were: (1) regard for authority; (2) force of habit; (3) theological prejudice; and (4) a false concept of knowledge. The

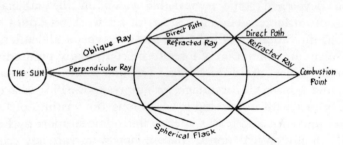

Fig. 9.   Bacon's Theory of the Burning Glass.

record of his life and his writings show a consistent attack upon these obstacles that did much to induce the gradual decline of scholasticism in Europe and to produce the full Renaissance of learning of the fifteenth century.

In an era devoid both of scientific personalities and scientific appreciation, Roger Bacon stands out as a vivid figure. Ahead of his contemporaries in outlook, it was inevitable that his great example should find little response. But it remains to his glory that, in an age of intellectual slavery to tradition, he upheld the claim to responsible criticism, the insistence upon which has ever been, and must continue to be, a necessary preliminary to human advancement.

9. HERALDS OF THE RENAISSANCE IN SCIENCE

In our review of the scientific backgrounds of Leonardo da Vinci we are now approaching the crescendo of events and tendencies leading to the full tide of the Renaissance of the fifteenth and sixteenth centuries. Let us summarise the main factors in the transition from medieval to modern science. It will have been noted from the foregoing that, broadly speaking, the philosophers of the Middle Ages created nothing for themselves. Their science was not of their own production. It was almost entirely that of the ancients in the somewhat distorted and garbled form in which it had been passed on to Medieval Europe through the vicissitudes of the intervening ages.

Why should there have been this total lack of originality on the part of the philosophers of the Middle Ages? Does it not seem a little remarkable that, throughout Europe and stretching over a period of hundreds of years, there should have been hardly anybody with something new to offer to the world? We have seen an answer to this question in the circumstances under which ancient science gave way to the ignorance of the Dark Ages—the decline and fall of the Roman Empire, the devastating penetrations of the barbarian and Saracen soldiery, and the narrowing restrictions of both the outlook and the discipline of the Church. A world cannot emerge to the fullness of wisdom from such intellectual darkness in a hurry. In these days, with our organised schemes of historical studies, the past is an open book, and each fresh scientific discovery becomes merely the jumping-off point for the next. But the position then was very different. The first problem for the Middle Ages was the recovery of the ancient knowledge. In this task there was neither room nor intellectual fuel for originality. An appreciation of the wisdom of the ancients as it emerged from the efforts of reconstruction was the full extent to which the scholars of those days could go. And, in a sense, it was far enough. We can understand how a student, whose backgrounds of culture were stimulated by the handling of a recovered manuscript, must have felt instinctively but deeply that he was in the presence of great wisdom. The idea of criticising what these ancients taught never so much as entered his head. And so there came, quietly but effectively, the tradition of the infallibility of the old philosophers, and even the Church was won over to their teachings.

Next came the day of the scholastics, to be followed by the rise of humanism.

So we approach the Renaissance proper, with the passing of the Eastern Empire, the revival of the Greek language, the temporary diminution of the power of the papacy, the invention of printing, and the historic voyages of Columbus. Beginning in Italy early in the fifteenth century, it swept over the whole of Europe, shaping, however, a different course in each country and finding its final expression, so far as science is concerned, in the Baconian[1] philosophy of the experi-

[1] This, of course, refers to Francis Bacon (1561–1626)—not Roger Bacon.

mental method. The early phase of reliance upon the schoolmen, with their endless discussions directed exclusively to the doctrines of the past, gave way to the final overthrow of dogma and the direct appeal to experiment. We have seen how, in Italy, the birthplace of the Renaissance, the new spirit of humanism, inaugurated by Petrarch (1304–1374), found its fuller development in the efforts of Marsilio Ficino (1433–1499).

The humanistic outlook was intensive but was at first limited to an intellectual few. It took a little time to become a very general feature of the Renaissance in Italy.

The chief mission of the humanists was the reconciliation of knowledge with Christianity. Yet in all this, science was initially but little touched. It was at first the day of letters. But we have seen that literature was for long extensively influenced by the recovered past. It needed a Boccaccio and a Dante to break into purely contemporary ground. Luckily, when art, following letters, next came under the influence of the revival, there was little of classical tradition to draw upon. As a consequence, there was a much more vigorous display of originality, producing the typical cinquecento humanism in painting of Raphael, da Vinci, Titian and Corregio; in the sculpture of Michelangelo, Bologna and Sansovino; in the architecture of Bramante, Omodeo and the Venetian Lombardi. So we come to science, which, touched last of all by the Renaissance, curiously enough received its first impetus in a warfare against the logicians and materialists through the medium of men of art—Alberti, da Vinci, Toscanelli, della Porta and others. These addressed themselves to attempts at a modernistic approach to such studies in the field of science as could aid their art. The fifteenth century was thus a meeting-ground between art and science.

We have already discussed the terms of the general legacy of science to which the dawn of the fifteenth century found itself the heir. There was the medieval acceptance of the doctrine of macrocosm and microcosm, the astrological implications of which, in spite of a temporary setback during the fourteenth century, gained added strength from the neo-Platonic vogue of the time; the so-called Aristotelian four-element scheme of earth, water, air and fire and the four primary qualities of hot, cold, moist and dry—a macrocosmic conception which was brought into its proper microcosmic relationship by linking up with elemental earth the imaginary "humour" of black bile; with water, phlegm; with air, red bile; and with fire, the imaginary "humour" of blood. Among themselves, however, the alchemists were also by now developing their theories of the basic importance of a salt-mercury-sulphur scheme, but without in any sense displacing the original scheme in the affections of the masses. In cosmography, the principle of geocentric spheres was still the prevailing influence, and Dante's conception of the universe was almost completely representative of current conviction.

Gradually, however, circumstances were shaping themselves towards a growing discontent with the Ptolemaic scheme. The world-wide epidemics of the Black Death in the latter part of the fourteenth century found their reflection in a vague dissatisfaction with accepted dogmas, and by the fifteenth century we find evidences of the discontent extending to the entire medieval scientific scheme. For one thing, there was emerging out of the "mental-equipment chest" of the fifteenth-century philosopher an increasing knowledge of mathematical processes, the effect of which was to make for a greater clarity of thought. On the one hand we have the revival of trigonometry, due to the work of Regiomontanus (the Latin pseudonym of Johannes Müller (1436–1476) of Königsberg) in his *De triangulis*, and, on the other, a development of algebra due to the labours of Fra Luca Pacioli, friend and intimate of Leonardo da Vinci—with his *Summa de Arithmetica, Geometrica, Proportione et Proportionalita*, modelled after the writings of Leonardo of Pisa.

One of the obvious consequences of the clearer thinking induced by this mathematical advance was a demand for the correction of the many inaccuracies in the existing copies of Ptolemy's *Almagest*; and this work of correction, in the able hands of Georg Peurbach (1423–1461) and Regiomontanus, undoubtedly led ultimately to the intellectual revolution in cosmography which produced the Copernican system of a heliocentric universe.

But this was not all. In many another direction a different atmosphere was creeping over mankind. The spirit of adventure was abroad and we have already discussed how the great geographical discoveries of Columbus and his contemporaries fired the imaginations of all thinking men. Leisure for thought was increasing with commercial prosperity, and the printed book was now available to all. In Germany the Hanseatic League was monopolising the trade of the north, and it was here, too, that Church authority was first successfully fought. The issue of the conflict against the dogmas of Rome carried with it the issue for science.

In this fight Italy, too, played its part. Thus, the Neapolitan philosopher Bernardino Telesio (1509–1588) began an attack on Aristotle's conception of matter and form as two separables. In his *De Rerum Natura*, published about 1563, he argued that these were strictly in and of each other. He developed a conception of a fundamental "force principle" of heat or life in interaction with its opposite, cold or death. It was neither a consistent nor a sound system, but Telesio did to a considerable extent lead a South Italian movement against accepted authority and sowed the seeds from which sprang the beginnings of a modernistic outlook on science. Needless to say, the teachings of Telesio angered the Church, who placed his writings on the Index.

Another great exponent of a new outlook on the relations between science and theology was Pietro Pomponazzi (1462–1525). In his great work *De Immortalitate Animi* he boldly attacked the Aristoteleanism of St. Thomas Aquinas upon which the whole theological standpoint of Rome was founded. Pomponazzi claimed the right of independent study and interpretation of Aristotle (a heresy in itself!), and in the exercise of that right he followed the Averroists in the contention that immortality does not imply the eternal separate existence of an individual soul. He went further. Following the second-century contentions of Alexander of Aprodisias, he taught that, as soul is the form of the body, it must perish with the body. Here, then, was a philosophical materialism new to the fifteenth-century world of theology. "Virtue for its own sake" by contrast with "virtue for the sake of the after-life" was a wholly new doctrine. It carried with it implications of importance in scientific method. Developing his views further (we must remember that Pomponazzi throughout claimed his adherence to the Catholic Faith) in his *De Incantatione* he definitely insists on the orderly sequence of cause and effect in nature and was the forerunner of the teachings of Francis Bacon a century later.

Such, then, were the general conditions of science in the fifteenth century and the general forces at work to promote the larger developments yet to come. The changing conditions were not sudden in their advent. The progress was slow and gradual—halting, even. Yet they were definite enough and, indeed, began to manifest themselves early in the century through the teachings of the illustrious German philosopher and divine, Nicholas of Cusa, who, fittingly enough, was born in the first year of the new era, i.e. in 1401. In 1417 Nicholas went to Padua, where he developed a friendship with Toscanelli, the famous cosmographer. As we know, Toscanelli spent much of his life at Florence, and here Leonardo must have known both him and his work. Moreover, Toscanelli was himself in correspondence with Cusa and was indeed called to the latter's deathbed in 1464. Hence it is not unreasonable to suppose that da Vinci must to some extent have been aware of the work and the views of Nicholas of Cusa.

Having graduated at Padua as a Doctor of Canon Law, Nicholas entered the Church in 1425. For the next three years he studied divinity at the University of Cologne and shortly after he began a career of ecclesiastical diplomacy and affairs which kept him wandering over one part and another of Europe until his death. In 1460 his activities brought him into conflict with Sigismund, Duke of Austria, who, in defiance of the Pope (now Pius II), imprisoned and ill-treated Cusa. From this ill-treatment Nicholas never recovered. He escaped to Rome and afterwards resumed his wanderings on Church business. He died at Todi in Italy in 1464 in the presence of his old friend Toscanelli.

Cusa wrote extensively. He was profoundly interested in all matters of observation and experiment, but this interest was at all times subservient to a larger metaphysical purpose. Standing in the forefront was his discussion on the movement of bodies, outlined in his *De Docta Ignorantia*, written between 1439 and 1440. In this work Cusa's main thesis is that "all human knowledge is mere conjecture and man's wisdom is to recognise his ignorance". The discussion centres round his definition of the finite and the infinite and pleads for a system of philosophy tending to the unity of all experience. He embraces in this the principle of a union of contraries in the divine unity of God. Applying these conceptions to the problem of motion, he attacked the medieval standpoint of a fixed earth (which, nevertheless, persisted throughout the next two centuries).

Let us briefly trace his argument. Soul, the spirit, is the universal motor—moved by God. Movement is therefore a fundamental attribute of existence and matter, united with and impregnated with the world soul. All things move and motion is ceaseless. There can therefore be no such thing as a centre of the universe and neither is it at rest. "I have long considered that this earth cannot be fixed but moves as do the other stars," he writes, and in a further note, undiscovered until after his death, he says: "To my mind the earth revolves upon its axis once in a day and night." Cusa never got as far as a heliocentric theory; nor did he abandon the conception of homocentric spheres. Nevertheless, in so far as he did attack the Aristotelean doctrine of a fixed earth (a courageous standpoint for a Churchman to take up), he was a true inaugurator of a scientific revolution.

But there was another aspect of this inauguration—the institution of a definite experimental bias in philosophical enquiry. Not only do we find traces of this in his *De Docta Ignorantia*, but we find it in full swing in the *De Staticis Experimentis*, the fourth book of a series of papers entitled *Idiotae Libri Quatuor*. In this work, purporting to be a discussion between two characters, the "Idiot" and the "Orator", the first two books are on "Wisdom", the third on "Mind" and the fourth on "Statical Experiments". In this last work Cusa gives his fundamental ideas on the use of the balance in medicine and in science generally. He quotes Vitruvius, recently rediscovered by Poggio, and gets ideas therefrom for a number of his problems, such as the estimation of the speed of ships—a problem, incidentally, which later fascinated both Leon Battista Alberti and Leonardo da Vinci. Throughout, Cusa's contention is that by accurate comparisons by weight various physical facts and properties are capable of investigation. So he suggests the comparison of waters from different springs, or water from the same spring at different times, of the blood and urine from old and young men, or of the same man in health and in sickness, and so on; suggestions which led directly to work on metabolic studies by Sanctorius and to Van Helmont's gravimetric analysis of urine. Another suggestion, virtually on plant respiration, produced in effect the first biological experiment of modern times and offered the first formal proof that the air has weight.

So we find in Nicholas of Cusa, in spite of the burden of medieval theology which he carried throughout his career, the first fifteenth-century philosopher with a truly modern outlook. He was the starting-point of the Renaissance in science in many a direction. In the world of philosophy he was the forerunner of an illustrious line of thinkers, from Pomponazzi and Ramus to Francis Bacon and Descartes; in his conceptions of the nature of matter he foreshadowed the work of Paracelsus and so led to the dawn of modern chemistry; and in astronomy he was the first of a line which led through Peurbach and Regiomontanus and Paul of Middleburg to Copernicus and Kepler and ultimately to Sir Isaac Newton.

Our last study in this chapter on Leonardo's scientific setting must be that of Nicolas Copernicus (Plate 35). He was a late contemporary of da Vinci and was born at Thorn on the Vistula in 1473, when Leonardo was twenty-one years of age. He died in 1543. His epoch-making book, *De Revolutionibus Orbium Caelestium* (On the Revolutions of the Celestial Orbs), was published in the year of his death, in 1543, though he really carried out the work to which it relates at least twenty-five years earlier. Copernicus earns his place in the history of science as having accomplished a revolution in astronomy by the overthrow of the Ptolemaic doctrine of a geocentric universe. It was as a Canon of the Cathedral at Frauenberg that he began his systematic study of the movements of the planets. He was a patient and painstaking observer, using the simple instruments available to him at the time. He prepared planetary tables from his observations and inevitably checked the results against the Ptolemaic pattern of "deferent and epicyclic" circles around a central earth. In particular, he was engaged in observations of the planet Mars and he found, quite specifically, that its variations in brightness, magnitude and position were out of proportion to what was necessary in terms of the Ptolemaic pattern. This led him to test the other planets, with similar results.

Now Copernicus recalled that the literature of the ancients had included the theory by the Pythagorean philosopher Aristarchus of Samos that it was the sun and not the earth that was the centre of the universe and that around it all the planets, including the earth, revolved in circular orbits. These teachings of Pythagoras and Aristarchus had been, as we know, submerged and forgotten under the flood of Aristotelean and Ptolemaic doctrines which formed the staple material for the science of succeeding ages. But now, two thousand years later, Copernicus revived this theory simply because it fitted the

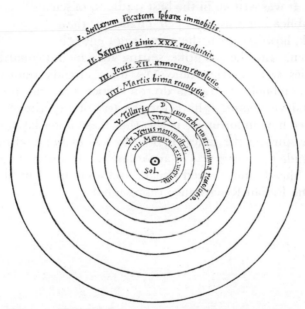

Fig. 10.   The Solar System as depicted by Copernicus.

facts of his own observations. The Ptolemaic pattern of deferents and epicycles *might* conceivably give the bigger variations in movement that he had observed, provided that more and more deferents and epicycles could be brought into the picture. But this would, of course, produce a more and more clumsy, complex and "synthetic" picture of the universe. On the other hand, all these complicated schemes of deferents and epicycles would be rendered unnecessary by simply transferring the centre of the universe from the earth to the sun (Fig. 10).

Yet, psychologically, what a tremendous step and decision this involved, in a world in which both Church and tradition were completely wrapped up in the acceptance of a central earth! Nevertheless, Copernicus made this decision. As a Churchman himself he did not put his heliocentric argument forward as a *fact*. What he most carefully did was to submit that the heliocentric picture provided a geometrically simpler scheme that fitted in with the facts of observation. He dedicated his book to Pope Paul III, and with its publication a new era had begun for science.

Interestingly enough, in that very same year of 1543 another epoch-making book was also published by Andreas Vesalius (1514–1564), *On the Fabric of the Human Body*. Vesalius was the true father of work on anatomy and his book was the first great work of modern science dedicated to an insistence upon the independent and objective study of natural phenomena by observation, experiment and deductive argument. It was written in the best tradition of scientific investigation and its publication was an open challenge that the authority of a man's work, however great the man, is not enough.

This, then, was the scientific setting in which Leonardo's many-sided studies were carried out. We have already quoted passages from the notebooks of Leonardo da Vinci stressing precisely this fundamental viewpoint, calling for the test of experiment, and once again we see how unfortunate it was that these notes lay unpublished. In the new spirit of the times, Leonardo was in the forefront of those whose attitude to science was in accordance with the spirit of Vesalius. He looked ahead, and worked ahead, and epitomised in his being the best that the Italian Renaissance represented.

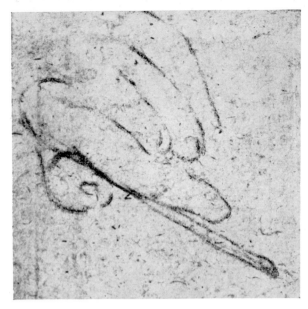

Plate 40—To illustrate Leonardo's left-handedness—his sketch of a left-hand holding a pencil (*Codex Atlanticus*, 283 v.b.).

Plate 41—Facsimile letter to a London newspaper by a bi-dextrous writer.

July 28 [illegible]

Dear Sir:
Please read to the end and I feel sure you will be more than interested. Millions write with both hands but I write:—
It is a gift for me to write backhand and I write it at dictation speed. (HOLD TO LIGHT OR MIRROR)
Hundreds of thousands write back. hand but:— BOTH TOGETHER.

I am now writing both hands together at the same time. (TO LIGHT OR MIRROR)	I am now writing both hands together at the same time.
To do this it is the Eye CONCENTRATION that is the hardest. I really need FOUR EYES.	To do this it is the Eye CONCENTRATION that is the hardest. I really need FOUR EYES.

← Both hands together from left to right. →

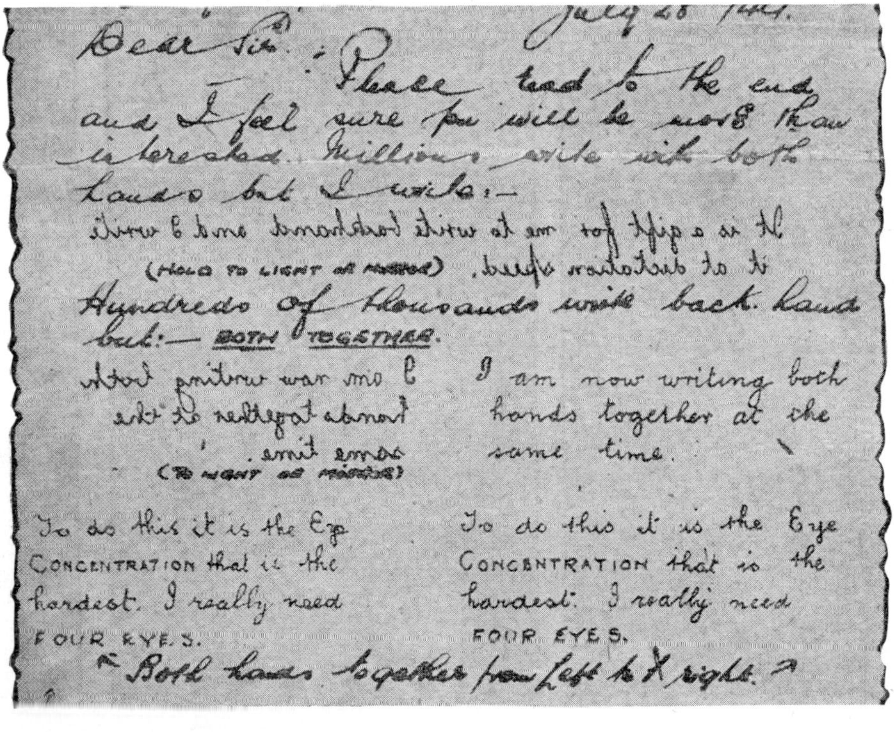

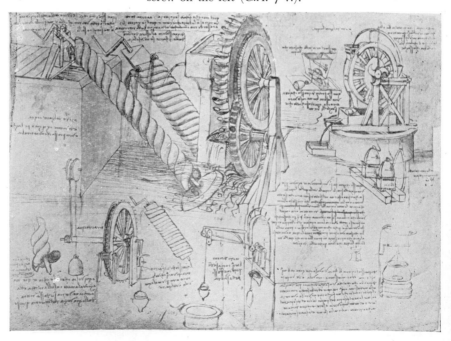

Plate 43—A common example of Roman Steelyard (from *A Short History of Weighing*).

Plate 44—A page of hydraulic studies, showing an example of the Archimedean screw on the left (C.A. 7 v.).

V

LEONARDO'S TECHNOLOGICAL BACKGROUND

1. THE DEVELOPMENT OF CRAFTS

Since so much of Leonardo da Vinci's career was concerned with mechanical science and engineering, we cannot regard the setting of the fifteenth-century scene as complete without a survey of the technology and applied sciences of his day. We have indicated the sequence of Renaissance culture as having developed, first in literature, then in art, and then in science. Now, following in the wake of science, but much later and more haltingly, came technology.

The dictionary defines this term as "the science or systematic knowledge of the industrial arts". If technology is to be regarded as an industrial extension of what is called "applied science"—that is to say, the application of the facts and discoveries of science to industrial processes—there could have been very little of it in the fifteenth century, since the mechanical sciences were not sufficiently advanced by that time. But if we use the term more loosely to embrace craft procedures and all those other activities and skills involving hands, tools and machines such as are normally associated with a communal life, then it must be said that a technology of sorts had certainly developed. From the earliest times man had realised that co-operation with his fellows assured the best means of securing the primary necessities of safety and food, and so through the ages there runs a thread of improving skills and techniques in the handling and processing of the materials provided by nature to ensure easier and better standards of comfort, of warmth and of safety.

For long centuries these developments were obviously empirical in character. They were improvements suggested by instinct, by experience, by common sense and by "hunches". Naturally "hunches" came more readily to those of greater mental development. Thus Thales of Miletus, to whom we have referred as one of the first abstract thinkers of the Greek period, was able to suggest to Croesus, when his army, advancing against the Persians, had been held up by the River Halzo, that he could get his troops across if he were to construct a canal to divert the waters of the river at the point of obstruction. Thales was *not* an engineer—he simply had a "brain-wave".

The difficulty in those early days was that, although a philosopher might also be an engineer, he did not seem to bring his philosophy and his engineering into adequate relationship to each other. But gradually those concerned with mathematics, astronomy and mechanics were able to attain a better understanding of the principles of exact measurement, of the simple laws of the balance and the lever, of elementary conceptions of force, and of the formal relationship between cause and effect. As a consequence, ultimately the writings of such men as Ctesibius, the water-engineer; Archimedes, the father of mechanics; and the civil engineer and architect, Vitruvius, were able to reflect a new spirit whereby science became more mechanical and mechanics more scientific.

We have indicated that the fundamental adjunct to the technologies that lay ahead were materials, tools and weapons concerned with the day-to-day tasks of life. The flints of the Stone Age were the earliest of these materials, and the skills which developed from their use, together with the discovery and use of fire, provided the earliest steps in a long and progressive evolution towards the technologies of the Middle Ages. As far back as the days of "reindeer man", over 20,000 years ago, flints could be made either razor-sharp, or serrated, or made into drills which could pierce holes into needles of bone or horn or ivory.

As man emerged gregariously from the nomadic family and tribal units to form larger and more settled communities, fresh technical advances in human development came from a variety of common needs—the provision of water on a "pooled" basis, the domestication and harnessing of animals for use as beasts of burden, the conversion of tracks into roads, the means to ford streams, the development of an early agriculture, the organised hunt for animal food, and the invention of various devices for the defence of the community against other and hostile communities. But all these continued to be based largely upon experience. Until such a time as scientific principles could be applied to them, the dictates of necessity were to persist as the mother of improvisation, and the only school of training was the school of experience.

Perhaps by about 4000 B.C. it could be said that town life had begun to reach a relatively mature stage; and the discovery of metals was now to produce a new phase in technical progress. Copper mines were known in Cyprus by 3000 B.C. and were soon followed by tin—later to be known as "British Metal" from the tin-mines of Cornwall. Mirrors were made of tin, and copper vessels were coated over with it. Nor was it long before the superior qualities of a copper-tin alloy were realised and used in the making of tools and weapons. So came the Bronze Age of about 2000 B.C., and with it an expansion in the methods of mining and ore treatment, hammering, founding and casting. By this time copper was being used mainly in alloy form. For example, *aurichalcum*, or golden copper was a brass made from the ores of copper and zinc. Lead and tin were looked upon as varieties of the same metal—the one was called *plumbum nigrum* and the other *plumbum candidum*.

Iron came much later. In central Europe we learn of Austria as the earliest centre of its metallurgy from about 800 B.C. and thence its workings moved westwards, until by 400 B.C. it had reached Spain. Yet, curiously enough, iron had found little favour in a bronze-using world. When, for example, the highly civilized Aztecs and Mayas of South America built their wonderful temples and pyramids of stone, artistically ornamented with intricate carvings, they did so with tools of copper, bronze and stone. The technical skill of these peoples was relatively great. They knew how to move into place massive stones weighing as much as fifteen tons. They were good miners and the silver and gold workings penetrated deeply below ground. Yet they ignored the rich deposits of iron ore in the extensive mountains about them. It remained for Cortez and his invading Spanish armies to initiate the home population into the value of iron and into the then known technology of its workings.

Most of the legends concerned with the early discovery of iron tell of great fires that devastated the forests on the mountainside, creating such intense heat as to cause the molten ore in the earth to run out in streams. Possibly this practice was employed in the region of the Caucasus Mountains and along the shores of the Black Sea. Here a famous iron known as "*barzel*" was used to make the weapons for Alexander the Great when he marched against Persia.

The Romans were superstitious about iron. For them it had protective powers against witches. A nail taken from a grave and driven into a door-sill was a recognised protection against nightmare. For the same reason wedding-rings were made of iron—and, after all, even today we regard the iron horse-shoe as an omen of good luck!

Diodorus describes the making of iron thus: "In the Island of Aethalie there is an ore that contains iron which is melted in batches to make metal. The workers first cut up a great quantity of it and put it into the furnace in a peculiar manner [referring to alternate layers or ore and charcoal]. When the heat has melted the ore, what is left is broken up into blocks and sold to the merchants, who . . . sell it again to the blacksmiths . . . who make it into all sorts of figures, birds, beasts and the like, and into tools."

The most famous of the ancient iron works were the Catalan furnaces of Spain (Fig. 11). The base of these was usually a large flat stone, slightly cupped, and set in a pit dug into a hillside so that the hill itself formed the back wall of the furnace. The front was built up of stones. The inside was lined with clay, leaving an opening near the base to allow for the use of bellows, the nozzle of which was called a tuyère. The purpose of the bellows was to promote a draught. Later the Catalans obtained an improved draught by making a flue. This ran off near the top of the furnace a little way up the hill. To charge the furnace a capstone at the top was removed and alternate layers of ore and charcoal were introduced. This standard form of Catalan furnace remained in use, crude as it was, for many centuries.

Iron usually exists in nature in chemical combination with oxygen or carbon, together with varying amounts of sulphur, arsenic and other impurities. The heat of the burning charcoal in the air draught liber-

Fig. 11.   Catalan furnace.

ated much of these impurities from the ore and the metal would then partially melt into a stringy, spongy mass called a bloom. This was taken from the furnace and broken into pieces small enough to handle. The bloom was now passed on to the blacksmith for reheating and was worked on the anvil under a hammer. The effect of these further operations was to drive out most of the residual carbon, thus producing a compact and malleable wrought-iron—tough, elastic and strong, but, unlike cast-iron, not very hard.

Actually, it was early realised that the wrought-iron could be rendered into steel, hard enough to be used for sword blades or tool points, by the process of tempering. Homer relates how, when Odysseus fire-hardened a piece of olive-wood and drove it into the eye of the sleeping Cyclops, it hissed, "just as does an axe when the smith plunges it into cold water that it may be tempered, for thence comes the strength of iron".

And so, slowly but surely, iron came to replace bronze in the use of tools and weapons—a substitution that would have been impossible without a comprehension of the process of tempering. The conversion was slow, largely because the process of accurate tempering was difficult to master. It took time. Pliny thought it was mainly a matter of choosing the right sort of water—but he was wrong. The difficulty lay in ensuring that the metal was not hardened completely before the final shape or form required was fashioned—since, once tempered, it is very difficult to change the form or pattern. With its mastery, however, a metallurgical industry of fundamental importance to community life may be said to have been achieved. To gauge its full extent it should be realised that by now at least six metals were well known to antiquity—gold, silver, tin, iron, copper and lead. Mercury (from Spain) was also known to a lesser extent, as was also zinc. It is common knowledge that the ancients were highly skilled in metal-work, both utilitarian and decorative. The precious metals were in particular favour since they occur naturally in a bright, pure state and were obviously suitable for ornamentation. The cupellation process for the purification of gold and silver was known long before the Christian era where these were found and mined separately, but the means of separation of gold from silver where, as frequently happened, the alloy of the two was found, was not known. The alloy was not then recognised as such. It was called *electrum* and was later prepared artificially in the proportion of three parts of gold to one of silver.

2. BASIC FACTORS IN THE CRAFTS OF ANTIQUITY

It cannot be too clearly stressed that the variety of activities in the arts and crafts of daily life in classical antiquity were not merely the forerunners of the later and more scientifically-based technologies of the post-Renaissance period but they also produced, in their aggregate, a considerable measure of comfort. We are too apt to regard life as it was lived two thousand years ago as primitive and relatively un-civilised. Standards are naturally relative—but a measure of content, even happiness, and certainly a freedom from want, could be experienced without the push-button amenities of our modern age. In ancient days a city was as much a community of streets and homes and shops and workshops, as well as churches and civic buildings, and even of theatres, as it is today. People were clothed in textile products; they were shod with leather footwear; homes were furnished, and individuals, according to their "station in life", were adorned with domestic and personal ornamentation. Even though the general level of individual knowledge, as we understand the term, was low, it remains, after all, relatively low in many parts of the world today. Nevertheless, as we have seen in our survey of the history of culture, both wisdom and scholarship were to be found in many gifted individuals whose activities, pronouncements and writings in a variety of fields—soldiers, statesmen, poets, essayists, historians, story-writers and philosophers—measure up to the highest standards of modern civilisation.

A survey of the broader developments of technology from classical times to the days of Leonardo da Vinci must therefore accept the early establishment of a wide range of crafts and the artisan skills that went with them, including of course an understanding of the materials, tools and equipment required for these crafts. Three aspects cover the main range of these crafts—the metallurgical, the chemical and the mechanical. We have already outlined the first of these in our discussion of the evolution of man from the Stone and Bronze Ages to the Age of Iron; and we have referred to the mining and working of the main metals of classical antiquity. A few remarks must now be offered upon the other two factors—the chemical and the mechanical.

In the chemical field, the naturally-occurring minerals and salts that were then known were employed for a variety of purposes. Thus the two oxides of copper were used in glass-making. Red lead was used for paint work, whilst white lead was used by the ladies of Athens as a base for their cosmetics. They also used a native antimony sulphide called *stibium* to paint the eye-lashes (still in use in the East under the name of *kohl*). For pigments, the sulphides of arsenic known as *realgar* and *orpiment* were well-known—and, indeed, these continued to be used by artists throughout the Middle Ages. There were, of course, a number of other mineral colours used by artists for brush paints. These included preparations made from white lead, cinabar, litharge (the red lead already mentioned above), smalt, verdigris, ochre, lampblack and stibnite. All are referred to by Pliny and some were used for dyeing. Soda and potash (from wood ash) were both used in the washing and whitening of clothes. Soap was made by mixing the wood ashes with animal fats (usually goat-fat) and was used as a kind of pomade or unguent for rubbing on the body.

Many substances were known and used for their medicinal properties. Thus Homer referred to sulphur as a disinfectant and a protection from evil spirits. Other medicaments included *realgar*, the scarlet sulphide of arsenic (referred to by Aristotle as *sandarach*); and lead plasters, made from litharge (known to the Latins as *molybdena*) and oil—almost identically with modern practice. Dyeing, tanning and calico printing were well-understood processes. The famous purple dye of the Tyrians dates as far back as 1500 B.C.; and the dyeing of Egyptian cotton was referred to by Pliny thus: "The white cloth is stained in various places, not with dye-stuff but with substances that have the property of absorbing colours; these applications are not visible upon the cloth, but when they are dipped into a hot cauldron of the dye they are drawn out, an instant after, dyed. The remarkable circumstance is that though there be only one dye in the vat, yet different colours appear on the cloth; nor can the colour be afterwards removed."

The tanning of leather was done with bark, much as it is done basically today, the bark being first removed by the use of lime. And, finally, the craft of glass-making and blowing was also known from early times. The Egyptians used the metallic oxides for their colouring.

On the whole, from these fleeting examples, it will be appreciated that the earlier civilisations possessed a very real range of crafts, involving the operations of a crude form of technical chemistry. But the craftsmen worked in relatively "water-tight" compartments, limiting the handing on of their knowledge to successive members of their guilds. In consequence, this naturally limited the scope for enlargement which a more enlightened sense of co-operation with allied crafts and industries outside their own field would have provided. But we must remember that these earlier civilisations were based upon an "aristocrat-slavery" relationship in which the ruling classes had little sympathy with the work and operations of the artisans apart from the utilitarian advantage of their labours.

3. THE MECHANICAL FACTOR—WATER SUPPLY PROBLEMS IN ANCIENT TIMES

In reviewing the main aspects of the development in engineering through the early and Middle Ages we must at once refer to the fundamental significance of the invention of the wheel. This greatly influenced, first, the problems of transport, and later the use of mechanisms in the development of machinery. It was founded upon the instinctive knowledge that rolling friction (using the terms of modern science) was much easier to overcome than sliding friction. This has been true at all times but much more so in the days when smooth surfaces were a relative rarity. But quickly the use of rolling surfaces and mechanisms became a commonplace in all phases of activity and completely transformed the whole problem of power transmission in an innumerable range of day-to-day activities. The practical limit was reached in cases where the objects to be moved were so large that the then available wheeled mechanisms were unable to cope with them. But in such cases a limitless supply of slave labour and an indifference to a sense of time and speed could always provide the answer.

The next point of importance is the fact that much of the engineering of the early civilisations was necessarily concerned with the problems of water supply. Besides having to drink water, man needs it for the irrigation of his land as well as for the needs of his animals. Communities were therefore to be found established in terms of the easy availability of water. So we find the early tendency for peoples to settle in the valleys of the world's great rivers—the Indus and Ganges of India, the Tigris and Euphrates of Mesopotamia, the Nile of Egypt, and so on. And beyond the cities which had emerged from the early and more primitive villages were the individual tillers of the soil, working to provide the needs of the cities. But the soil needed water and thus the problem of irrigation became of supreme importance.

In both Egypt and Mesopotamia the country is flat and the seasonal rise of their rivers, if not otherwise controlled, produces indiscriminate and wide flooding. The problem of control was solved differently in the two areas. In Egypt, the scheme of irrigation was determined by the seasonal rise and overflow of the Nile during the autumn period from August to October. Under central administration, dykes were cut at right-angles to the river-flow at appropriate intervals and the diverted water, after depositing its rich fertilising salts, was then channelled back to the river by further cuts downstream. In effect, this formed a series of richly irrigated basins. In Mesopotamia (now Iraq), "the land of the two rivers", the Tigris and the Euphrates, the problem was not so straightforward. The rise is somewhat irregular in its advent during the wet season between April and June and is not well related to the timing needs of the spring and winter crops. This determined the policy of the ancient water-engineers, who built a system of canals to lead the richly silted waters into a series of basins. The stored water could then be used as required. A striking example was the system of five canals radiating from the water of the Diahlah, a tributary of the Tigris north of Baghdad, built by Nebuchadnezzar, King of Babylon, early in the sixth century B.C., in the region of Samarrah. The remains of these even today are a striking testimony to the efficiency of their construction.

Where the contour was not so simple, however, other devices had to be employed. The geological formation lent itself in some cases to the digging of artesian wells, in connection with which water-towers were successfully used. An example of this is seen in the Phoenician erection of the wells of Ras-el-Ain, near Tyre. Four wells were sunk, and over each was a strong octagonal tower, whence the accumulated waters were led by conduits to reservoirs near the shore. Later the Romans conveyed the water (previously carried in vessels or skins) across to the island by means of an aqueduct.

Aqueducts were either tunnelled through hills or carried over bridgework, according to the nature of the ground. The tunnelling operations naturally called for skill and accuracy in maintaining direction, and the earlier methods, and therefore the results, were sometimes not too happy. An interesting example of this is the tunnel which was constructed about 700 B.C. by Hezekiah, one of the kings of Judah, for supplying the city of Jerusalem with water in the event of a siege. The two boring parties, working from either end, were so uncertain of their direction that at intervals they pierced air-shafts above them as a check on their alignment, in spite of which they nearly passed one another. The zigzag result will be evident from the fact that what should have been a straight line of some 1,100 feet became an aqueduct of over 1,700 feet. It is interesting to note the evidence upon which it is believed that borings were carried out from both ends. The tool-marks are seen to run in opposite directions from the ends to the middle. Even with the help of instruments, however, the alignment was not always successful. Thus the Roman engineer Nonius Datus sent in the following very human report regarding the blunder made during the excavation of a tunnel at Saldae, in Algeria, in the year A.D. 152:

"I found everybody sad and despondent. They had given up all hopes that the opposite sections of the tunnel would meet, because each section had already been excavated beyond the middle of the mountain. As always happens in these cases, the fault was attributed to me, the engineer, as though I had not taken all precautions to ensure the success of the work. What could I have done better? For I began by surveying and taking the levels of the mountain, I drew plans and sections of the whole work, which plans I handed over to Petronius Celer, the Governor of Mauretania; and to take extra precaution, I summoned the contractor and his workmen and began the excavation in their presence with the help of two gangs of experienced veterans, namely, a detachment of marine infantry and a detachment of Alpine troops. What more could I have done? After four years' absence, expecting every day to hear the good tidings of the water at Saldae, I arrive; the contractor and his assistants had made blunder upon blunder. In each section of the tunnel they had diverged from the straight line, each towards the right, and had I waited a little longer before coming, Saldae would have possessed two tunnels instead of one!"

In the early days of the Greek era, when the communities were small, the water supply was usually adequately secured from natural springs and cisterns hewn in the rock. As the communities grew, however, such sources of supply became inadequate, and the age of the tyrants saw a great advance in the methods employed. One of the most successful of the engineers of those days was Eupalinus of Megara, who was in the service of the tyrant Polycrates. Polycrates was a lover of learning, who attracted to his court and to the library which he had accumulated a large school of philosophers, and it was in this atmosphere that Eupalinus laboured. His most famous achievement was the construction of a tunnel through Mount Castro for the passage of a conduit from the water source to the town of Samos. The tunnel was 4,200 feet long, 8 feet high and 8 feet broad, and along it the conduit was dug to a depth of 3 feet, the water being always in contact with fresh air. It was given a natural declivity and was led by suitable masonry to the town, where it supplied fountains, baths, pipes, and latrines, and was carried out ultimately into the harbour. The tunnel with its conduit was discovered by Greek archaeologists in the year 1882 in an excellent state of preservation, and was seen to be perfectly straight. It led to a fountain under the present village of Tigani. At intervals along the tunnel were found the niches in which the workmen placed their lamps and tools during the processes of construction.

4. ROMAN ENGINEERING

One of the greatest feats of successful tunnelling for the purposes of water supply was carried out in the time of Julius Caesar under the direction of the blind engineer, Appius Claudius. It was over three miles long, one mile of it under a mountain of hard cornelian, and involved sheer chiselling inch by inch. It was designed to carry water from Lake Fucinus.

An important authority on water-engineering in Roman times was the military writer Sextus Julius Frontinus (c. A.D. 40–103). He held the post of "Surveyor of Aqueducts" during the reign of Nerva (A.D. 97), and he described the great system of Roman aqueducts in his *De Aquis Urbis Romae*. There were, within and around the city of Rome, some 250 miles of such aqueducts, of which a combined length of some fifty miles was supported on stone arches. In the aggregate they provided a daily water supply of some 300 million gallons.

But perhaps the best-known engineer and architect of Roman antiquity was Pollio Vitruvius. He lived in the days of Julius Caesar and Augustus. The Roman architect of those days was in fact an official, but actually how far Vitruvius was typical of his time is doubtful, since his was the only book on architecture to survive. His style of writing was somewhat heavy and his introductions rather fulsome; but in his introduction to the first of his "Ten Books" he gives us the following idea of what a good architect should be: "Let him be educated, skilful with the pencil, instructed in geometry, know much history, have followed the philosophers with attention, understand music, have some knowledge of medicine, know the opinions of jurists, and be acquainted with astronomy and the theory of the heavens."

One wonders how many architects, either of antiquity or in subsequent eras, have measured up to these ambitious standards. There is little evidence that Vitruvius himself did. We have in his famous *De Architectura Libri X* the most complete summary of the position of applied science, engineering, architecture and technology in the Roman era. It was the standard textbook of the engineer and the architect for many centuries but was completely lost sight of from about the tenth century A.D. On its rediscovery, however, in the fifteenth century, in the library of the Monastery of St. Gall by Poggio, it at once found fresh favour; all the great architects and engineers of the later Italian Renaissance used it, and its influence spread far and wide.

It does not need the mere testimony of such a work as that of Vitruvius to show us the high standard of engineering in Roman times. Their great structures remain with us today, some in decay, some in a fine state of preservation, but all of them eloquent, if silent, tributes to the great era of construction to which they belong. It is an interesting fact that, although engineering practice and scientific knowledge are so linked together, much can be accomplished with the mere aid of past experience together with that indefinable "horse sense" without which the engineer is helpless. These, in fact, constituted the chief equipment of the engineers and technologists of the Roman era.

It was on this account that the organisation of large-scale hygiene and sanitation in Rome was both efficient and highly developed. The position and orientation of buildings received careful attention, and considerations of sanitation were at all times prominent. Burials were forbidden within the city walls, the water supply was assured, whilst the drainage of buildings, the provision of latrines (some of them flushed with water from a constant fountain), and the evacuation of sewerage were all carried out with efficiency. The main drain of Rome in the Tarquin era (sixth century B.C.) was a noteworthy achievement. Known as the Cloaca Maxima, it was constructed to drain and carry to the Tiber the waters of the valley where the Forum Romanum was built. Later, in the time of Augustus, it was modified and largely reconstructed on a higher level, serving as the main sewage-channel of the city.

Turning in greater detail to the general features of Roman engineering and architecture, it may be noted with regard to the erection of buildings that the two chief characteristics were solidity of construction and magnificence of conception. Although stone masonry was not new to the world, Roman stone-work was far superior to any that had preceded it, and indeed to much that followed it. Thus the Venerable Bede, the Anglo-Saxon encyclopaedist, proudly refers to the stone churches which were then beginning to appear as having been fashioned "after the manner of the Romans". In addition to stone, the chief materials employed in building were brick and concrete. Relatively light and plastic, these made the vaulting of great spans a simple matter. The durability of the concrete employed is amply evidenced by the way in which structures of that material have stood the test of time, long after the weathering and disappearance of the outer decorative coverings of brick or marble which originally concealed them. In these days the use of concrete is once again to the fore; it is reinforced with steel perhaps, but it is a return to ancient ideas, nevertheless.

With regard to the other great characteristic of Roman architecture above mentioned, it has been well said that "Egyptian architecture could be sublime; the greatest Greek temples were both sublime and beautiful, but the . . . Roman imperial buildings were magnificent". Indeed, we can well picture how the semi-civilised barbarian hordes of Goths and Huns, mostly accustomed to live in huts or wooden houses, were stirred with feelings of awe and wonder when, in the days of its decline, they advanced towards the heart of the Roman Empire and were "confronted by cities built of stone, bricks and marble, boasting decorous public offices, temples, statues, mosaics and paintings, linked to one another by paved roads, mostly watered by still efficient aqueducts". Here was something greater than the might of the sword. Here was indeed the might of civilisation.

One of the most important features in constructional conception for which we are indebted to the Romans is the development of the arch. It created a virtual revolution in the methods of bridge-building. Prior to the Roman arched bridge, there was nothing better in the shape of development from the crude bridge-of-boats scheme of Xerxes, than the running of platforms across sets of stone piers. At Babylon the platform over the piers across the Euphrates was of wood. At Assos, in Asia Minor, a similar Greek bridge had a stone platform. But the arched bridge comes from Rome by whom it has been handed down as a perpetual legacy to mankind.

Let us turn next to the typical features of Roman road construction, the planning of which was done chiefly for military purposes. The roads were narrow (about ten feet wide) and were made in long straight lines. Usually, on either side of the main road were two other tracks prepared for pedestrian use and laid down without artificial foundation. The question of upkeep, a sore point in these days, was taken into account in a manner that might well be resorted to once again, namely, by the strength, firmness and efficiency of the initial construction. Usually paved, they had at least four layers: the *statumen* and the *rudus* composed of small stones with a little cement, the *nucleus* of real concrete, and the upper paving (the *summum dorsum*) formed of big blocks of basalt, shaped polygonally, and some twenty inches high. The Appian Way is one of the most famous examples of this type. It was begun in 312 B.C. by the Censor Appius Claudius Caecus, and extended originally from the Capena Gate at Rome to Capua, a distance of about 132 miles. Later it was extended and has very truly been called the Queen of Highways. The Via Flaminia, begun in 220 B.C., was another long and important road.

Finally, we turn to what were perhaps, from the engineering point of view, the most wonderful works of Roman times—the fine system of aqueducts erected for the purpose of carrying water to the cities in large quantities for drinking and for irrigation. Some reference to this has already been made. Frontinus refers to them as being magnificent beyond all comparison. The waters from the springs and rivers of the surrounding country were collected and conveyed along them, sometimes underground along tunnels and sometimes across great arched walls, according to the contour of the ground, until they reached the reservoirs from which the distribution to the city began. Generally speaking, the down-flow of water was regulated by an open channel, so that the question of gradient was of importance. On the whole, aqueducts built across valleys were preferred to pipes carried underground. Economy was frequently the deciding factor. Underground pipes would either have to be of lead, which was weak, or of expensive bronze, or, alternatively, of wood or terra-cotta. The casting of large pipes for withstanding great pressure was beyond Roman skill at that time. The water, too, was hard and the inside walls of the channels were liable to damage. They therefore required constant overhauling and repair. In all, there were no less than fourteen magnificent examples of aqueducts in Rome, and many others elsewhere.

In distributing from the reservoirs to the houses and buildings, the pressure system was employed and, judging by the specimens of plumbing which have come down to us, many efficient devices were in operation. One such was a bronze double-acting pump. It was found in Bolsena, in Etruria, and is now housed in the British Museum. The principle employed was the invention of Ctesibius of Alexandria (*c.* 250 B.C.) and is not dissimilar in its action from the double-acting pumps of today.

5. EARLY INSTRUMENTS OF SURVEYING AND ENGINEERING

The instruments of surveying and engineering used by the Greeks and Romans in the setting out of roads, canals, tunnels, aqueducts, etc., were three—the *groma*, the *dioptra*, and the *chorobates*. The *groma* or *ferramentum* was used for setting out right angles. An actual specimen was recently found, together with other mathematical instruments, at Pompeii, whilst still more recently an Egyptian specimen has been brought to light by Sloley, and is of Graeco-Egyptian times (Plate 36). The groma consisted of two horizontal cross-pieces pivoted about a vertical axis (Fig. 12). From the extremities of each end of the cross-pieces were suspended a plumb-line and bob. Frontinus describes the use of the instrument as follows:

"To use the instrument we must steady all the plumb-lines and look at the cords or string stretched by the weights, setting them in a line until the eye can see the nearest only. Then put in the stakes and, having carried the apparatus to the last stake, set up as before and look at the stakes in the opposite direction by way of a check. Then, to continue the staked-out line when interrupted by obstacles, carefully

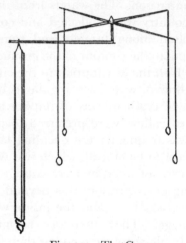

Fig. 12. The Groma.

set out the right angles given by the plumb-lines by perpendicular lines at every point of interception."

Hiero of Alexandria objected to this instrument because of the difficulty of preventing the plumb-lines from swinging. Nevertheless, as both agriculture and town planning were mainly carried out on rectangular lines, there is no doubt that the groma was widely used.

We turn next to the *dioptra*, an instrument about which Hiero of Alexandria wrote somewhat extravagantly as follows:

"It is advantageously employed for the setting out of water channels, ramparts, harbours and buildings of every kind. It is used for many astronomical purposes in connection with the observation of the sky, such as the measurement of the distances which separate stars, their size, and the determination of the distances and the eclipses of the sun and moon. Again, it is used for geographical or surveying purposes, and for the determination of the relative positions of islands and seas and generally for the estimation of distances between inaccessible points."

The instrument as used for the setting out of lines at right angles to each other is illustrated in Fig. 13 (A). The upper plate *P* is graduated in degrees, and swivelling round it is a bar carrying cross-wire sights *SS*, at right angles to which are two pointers *pp*. Adjustment of the horizontal is assured by the control of the toothed vertical half-wheel *A* operated by *B* on the rack-and-pinion principle, whilst a similar horizontal device *C* gives control of orientation in a horizontal plane. Used in conjunction with this was a levelling staff (Fig. 13 (B)).

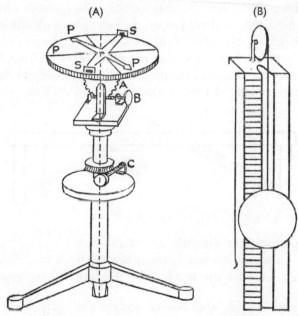

(A)   (B)

Fig. 13.   The Dioptra and Levelling Staff.

This was practically a long graduated rod carrying a plumb-line to indicate when it was in a vertical position. A pulley wheel was mounted at the top and from it there could be raised or lowered a disc marked with a horizontal index. This was moved up or down until the man operating at the sights signalled that he had obtained alignment with his cross-wires; the readings and bearings were then taken, and the subsequent procedure was similar to that employed with the groma. For the purposes of water-levelling the plate *P* was replaced by a simple water-level of two vertical glass tubes joined by a horizontal tube.

We may claim for the dioptra, invented as it was nearly two thousand years ago, that in theory it has persisted ever since as one of the chief instruments of field measurement. Virtually, it is the theodolite of today. The modern theodolite was the invention of Thomas Digges, who described it in his Pantometria in 1571 (he was the first to apply to it the term *theodolitus*), and the only new essential features it possessed over that of its forerunner, the dioptra, were (1) the attachment of a magnetic compass for control in orientation, and (2) a definite mechanism (of which the wheel *A* and control *B* in Fig. 13(A) constituted its possible predecessor) for elevation control and measurement.

We turn finally to the third instrument of field engineering of antiquity, the *chorobates*, which Vitruvius, in his *De Architectura*, lib. 7, tells us he prefers to either the groma or dioptra. It was a large instrument, some thirty feet (twenty cubits) long, whose chief features (Fig. 14) were a long rod supported on two legs, with diagonal pieces joining each leg to the rod. On each of these diagonal pieces was scratched a vertical line such that the cross-piece *BC* would be horizontal when each of two plumb-lines at the ends were in direct alignment with the scratch. In the event of wind disturbances making the

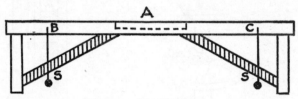

Fig. 14.   The Chorobates.

use of the plumb-lines difficult, a central water channel *A* was employed, the horizontal being here indicated by filling it with water and observing whether the levels were the same at the channel ends.

6. MECHANICAL DEVICES AND POWER SOURCES IN ANTIQUITY

We may now consider the general extent of the knowledge of mechanisms in the days of antiquity. Of these there were a large variety, some distinctly utilitarian and essential to the easing of labour conditions and others more purely ornamental in character. Initially, of course, the strictly utilitarian aspect prevailed, and presumably the first germs of the evolution of devices for the production of what in mechanics is spoken of as a mechanical advantage resulted from the need, in the erection of buildings and monuments of various kinds, for the quick transport of materials either from one place to another, or from the ground to a place of higher elevation.

Some of the earliest evidences of the applications of mechanical principles to the service of civilisation are seen in the methods employed for the hauling of water. They are all naturally related to what, in

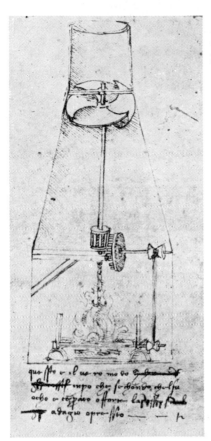

Plate 45—Plan for a roasting spit based on the convection principle.

Plate 46—Leonardo's sketch to illustrate the compass property of a magnet.

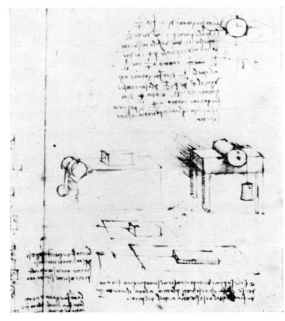

Plate 47—Experiments on friction between various surfaces.

Plate 48—Aids to muscular effort—the use of hand-tools and other devices out-of-doors (Windsor Royal Library).

modern applied mechanics, is referred to as the transmission of power. Such was the "endless chain of pots", generally regarded as having originated in the East. The "chain of pots" (Fig. 15) was the fore-runner of the modern bucket elevator and consisted, in effect, of an endless rope *B* carrying at regular intervals a series of earthenware pots. The rope passed over a wheel *A* and the lower end was sub-merged below the level of the water in the well *C*. The pots discharged their contents in turn into a trough *D*. Each pot was pierced at the base by a small hole to allow the air to escape, thus making possible the filling of the pot in an inverted position in the well. The method employed for the transmission of the power from the man or beast

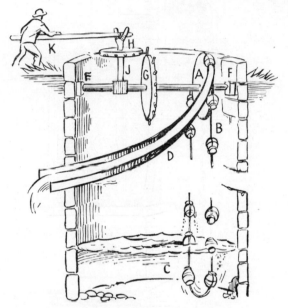

Fig. 15. The chain of pots.

working the mechanism to the wheel *A* is interesting. The axle *EF* of this wheel was fixed to the two sides of the well-wall and carried a second wheel *G* from which projected a number of crude teeth or spokes. These geared with a similar wheel *H* mounted horizontally on a vertical axis *J*, to the top of which was firmly attached a long wooden arm *K*. The man or beast worked the mechanism from the end of this arm. It is believed that the water used for the famous Hanging Gardens of Semiramus was brought up to a height of 300 feet by this means, a remarkable achievement, having regard to the fact that modern elevators rarely work to a height greater than 150 feet.

The use of toothed gearing is an important feature in the mechanisms of antiquity. The theory of such power transmission carries us right back to Aristotle, who, in his *Mechanica*, describes the possibilities of three wheels in rough contact, the first of which is made to rotate.

The development of this form of power transmission was very rapid. Thus Philo of Byzantium (*c.* 230 B.C.) not only describes an endless chain of pots but also mentions a pump, the principle of whose working is based on the idea of the rack and pinion.

Still later, in the time of Vitruvius, the improvement in the work-

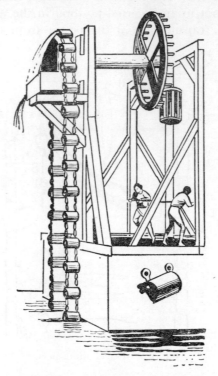

Fig. 16.   Improved Roman type of chain of pots.

manship of toothed wheels is more marked. The chain of pots, for example, has now developed into a workmanlike elevator (Fig. 16). Finally, with regard to the more general aspect of weight-lifting mechanisms in Roman times, we find depicted on one of the monuments the mechanism of a giant crane worked by a treadmill. Although it is a little difficult to follow the details, its existence as a typical weight-lifting device is ample evidence of the advanced state of efficiency of this class of activity in the days of Vitruvius.

It is appropriate at this stage to refer to the development of mechanical devices during antiquity for the harnessing of water-power to the needs of civilisation. The force developed by moving water was utilised from very early times. In Book 10 of his *De Architectura, On Machinery*, Vitruvius describes a vertical undershot water-wheel mounted on a horizontal axis; and the overshot water-wheel, in which the water is delivered to the top of the wheel for utilisation as a power source, followed as an early development from the undershot type. A fourth-century example has been found near Arles, in southern France, used evidently to work millstones for corn-grinding during the Roman occupation; and a later mid-fifth-century example, used for the same purpose, has been discovered on the site of the market-place at Athens. In this latter case the wheel was about 11 feet 6 inches in diameter and was mounted on a long wooden axle.

Another interesting device, originating from the necessities of war, was an undershot water-wheel used to operate a floating mill. An early example dated from A.D. 537 on the River Tiber, at a time when Rome was besieged by the invading Goths. The Goths had breached the aqueducts whose waters had provided the normal power for the corn-grinding mills. The Roman engineers accordingly set up a series of undershot water-wheels, each between two supporting boats in the river; and so were able to grind sufficient corn for the needs of the besieged people of the city. Examples of the floating mill have been recorded from time to time throughout and beyond the Middle Ages—on the Tigris in the tenth century; on the Seine in the twelfth century; on the Rivers Garonne and Loire in the early fourteenth century; on the Thames in the sixteenth and eighteenth centuries. In Italy some examples even survived until the close of the nineteenth century. Certainly it may be said that during the lifetime of Leonardo da Vinci the water-wheel had become the main power-source for all industrial and agricultural purposes in Europe.

The windmill was another and obvious power device, though of lesser efficiency and extent than the water-wheel. It was little developed before the tenth century (though Hiero of Alexandria had suggested a scheme for operating bellows mechanically by means of a small windmill device) except in Persia and Afghanistan. Subsequently it was taken up seriously, first by the Arabs and, consequent upon the accounts of their use by returning crusaders, by the various countries of western Europe. This was more particularly the case in flat regions fronting the sea coast, like the Low Countries, where the winds were found uninterrupted and therefore most effective.

7. MEDIEVAL TECHNOLOGY

With the foregoing in mind we may now enquire into the state of mechanical technology in the fifteenth century. The natural basis of such technology is the science of mechanics; and we shall see later that Leonardo da Vinci covered a very wide ground of original speculation into the problems and principles of this basic science. But his notes were unknown to others and he had no serious forerunners. So far as mechanics were concerned, the study of dynamics was practically non-existent, and in statics very little advance had been made from the days of Aristotle and Archimedes. Consequently, the effective era of experimental mechanics came after the fifteenth century and so, on the whole, progress in the various branches of technology could come only from the practical needs of the times.

Organised communal life has always required the services of the tinker, the tailor and the candlestick-maker, the wood-worker, the mason, the miner and the carpenter, and a host of other craftsmen. If these people lacked a scientific background, they had at least developed their techniques and their traditions. In this day-to-day round, therefore, the stimulus of necessity evolved a considerable range of skills.

But for the beginnings of an evolution towards a true technology, however, a larger stimulus than this was needed; and regrettable as it may seem, this arose largely from the needs of war, with the needs of the Church as a close second. The war factor was responsible for such activities as the mining and smelting of ores, the manufacture of charcoal and the casting and working of metals, all applied to the making of munitions and weapons. The needs of the Church involved such manifold activities as wood-carving, the arts of the mason and the carpenter, the making of lead-glass windows, the working of precious metals, organ-building, bell-casting, chalice-making, and so on.

The directing minds for these various activities were the medieval equivalents of the architects and the engineers of today. The term "engineer" did not then exist, and the architect was frequently a shadowy figure more usually represented by the "master mason". Much of the evolution of building technology during the eleventh and twelfth centuries is due to the stimulus of the Benedictine and other monastic orders. We recall to the reader the rule of St. Benedict not merely to encourage manual work but to enjoin it as a duty. In Italy the monks were aided by guilds of artisans, but there were not yet such guilds in France or England. So the inmates of the monasteries had to be their own builders, masons, carpenters and glaziers. Much more than mere craftsmanship was required in these tasks. The Churches and other monastic buildings were very large. Problems relating to the strength of pillars and columns, and the best methods for their support, and of vaulting and the like, all had to be tackled; and so, slowly, empirical experience brought a growing understanding of how to lighten structures and of how to concentrate the weight of fireproof stone-vaulted roofs at fixed points. The directing mind may have been an architect or he may have been the lesser-sounding master-mason, or both—but he was all-important. The Frenchman, William of Sens, for example, was responsible for the rebuilding of Canterbury Cathedral in 1174. His work included the designing of the cranes for transferring the fine Caen stone from ship to shore at Richborough. He also designed the stone mouldings and directed all the work of the masons (Fig. 17).

In general, there is no doubt that the master-mason was a person of undoubted and recognised importance to the community. But

Fig. 17. Impression of a thirteenth-century architect.

whether he was a professional person at architect's level, or a crafts-man cast in a lesser mould, was not always so evident. When the great Brunelleschi of the Italian Renaissance, for example (who, like so many other artists, began life as a goldsmith and then became an architect), entered a competition for the vaulting of the cathedral at Florence, he found as a fellow-competitor the carpenter whom he employed to make his models for the competition. Nor was this so strange as it sounds, since in fact the dividing line between carpenter, mason and architect was frequently very thin. It was quite normal for the master-mason to be the chief person concerned in the construction of a building, drawing the plans, supervising the work of construction, and even providing the tools, plant and materials of stone and timber from his own yard.

Turning from building and architecture to the technology of the arts of war, we find a close parallel to the medieval master-mason of the one in the gun-master of the other. The gun-master was one of the keymen in those days and well he knew it! Gun-masters were men of importance. They cloaked their affairs with an air of some mystery; and largely because so much was expected of them, they were relatively few in number and were organised in a sort of secret "brotherhood". Their profession, if so we may call it, was usually carried on as a family tradition. It called for a widely varied range of qualities and technical ability. It embraced such arts as the casting of great and small guns, the making of gun-powder, preparing lifting tackle, making protective armour for both guns and war carriages, and erecting bridges for their overland transport; and in times of peace the erection of houses, the making and laying of earthen and wooden pipes, setting up water-, wind- and horse-mills, and a host of other activities. In other words, they had to be expert in practically the whole range of the engineering and structural technology of those times.

One of the best known of the gun-masters of the late fourteenth and early fifteenth centuries was Konrad Kyeser von Eichstadt (1366–1405), whose *Bellifortis*, a finely illustrated textbook of the military engineering of his day, was first published in 1405. The original is in the University Library at Göttingen and comprises 190 parchment pages filled with technical descriptions and sketches. It stood as a model of its kind for one hundred and fifty years, until it was superseded in the sixteenth century by the textbooks of technology by various writers. These included Jacques Besson, whose book, entitled *Theatre of Instruments*, was published in 1578; Agostino Ramelli (1531–1590), who wrote on *The Various and Ingenious Machines*; Jacopo da Strada, author of *Survey of All Kinds of Water, Wind, Animal-driven and Hand-driven Mills and Beautiful and Useful Pumps* (1617); Agricola and others.

The technical development characteristic of the later medieval period—that is to say, the period leading to the Renaissance—fell broadly into two categories. On the one hand there was a steady progress in the metallurgical processes, mainly, but not wholly, in the development of the smelting furnace, and in the production of cast iron; and, on the other hand, there was a persistent urge towards the improvement of mechanisms to provide greater mechanical advantage and easier power transmission. Indeed, the two factors were not unrelated. By A.D. 1300, for instance, water-wheels, now in considerable use, were improved to operate larger bellows in order to produce higher furnace temperatures with a resulting absorption of a larger percentage of carbon. This made possible the use of a better grade of cast iron for cannon, though smaller arms and tools continued to be worked in wrought iron. Meanwhile gunpowder had come into military use, and, as we know, Leonardo da Vinci himself had developed no small interest in the design of weapons of war. In 1495 he designed a gun to be fired by compressed steam (Plate 100)—an idea somewhat hazardous in execution—to say nothing of more orthodox and probably more efficient designs, including a modern-looking breech-loading mechanism and some delightful and vicious contraptions of the "quick-firing" variety.

There was, of course, very little background of theoretical mechanics to the medieval development of mechanisms. The liberal availability of slave-labour characteristic of ancient times had disappeared with the advent of Christianity in Europe, and developments were more and more based on what we might refer to as Archimedean mechanics. So, progressively, the introduction of horse-, wind- and water-power was having its effect, mainly in association with the design of such mechanisms for power transmission as the crank, toothed gearing, pulley-wheels and the like.

In addition to Konrad Kyeser, whom we have already mentioned, the technical writers of the fifteenth century included Johannes Fontana, Jacopo Mariano, Hans Hartlieb, Francesco di Georgio Martini and Roberto Valturio. Fontana was the author of a work the original of which, catalogued as Codexicon No. 242, is housed in the State Library of Munich. It was written in cypher about the year 1420 and contains descriptions and illustrations of automata, mechanically-propelled boats, dredges, organs and even a magic lantern. Jacopo Mariano was a celebrated engineer of Siena between the years 1438 and 1450. Copies of his *De Machine, Libri X* are to be found in Venice, in the State Library at Munich, and in Paris, at the Bibliothèque Nationale. Valturio, however, is of particular interest to us because he was a contemporary of Leonardo da Vinci. He was the author of an important work on military engineering, the *De re militari*, first published in Latin at Verona in 1472, and in an Italian translation in 1483. A copy of this work was in the possession of Leonardo. Consequently, when we consider his own contributions in parallel fields of investigation it is important to recognise that many of his notes and sketches are frequently indications, in terms of his own brilliant sense of intuition and his inimitable draughtsmanship, of much that already existed.

8. INSTRUMENTS OF MEASUREMENT IN THE FIFTEENTH CENTURY

(i) *The State of Mathematics during the Renaissance*

No consideration of the scientific and technological backgrounds to Leonardo da Vinci and his times would be adequate without some notes on the standards and use of instruments of measurement and precision during the fifteenth century. It is a commonplace in scientific investigation that no understanding of any of the facts or phenomena of science is possible unless and until they can be measured accurately. Progress in experimental science is inevitably bound up with the development of accuracy in measurement. It is this relationship which has given rise to the term "exact sciences", now in common use.

The basic requirements in this relationship are naturally twofold: an adequate knowledge of mathematical principles; also the design and use of the necessary instruments of precision which embody those principles. Mathematics had, of course, been an element of study in all medieval schemes of education, and from time to time various men of learning had contributed fresh advances of knowledge in the fields of geometry, algebra, and their hybrid relative, trigonometry. We have seen, too, that the main trend of their application was in the field of astronomy (with all too frequently more than one eye to the astrological tricks of drawing up horoscopes for credulous clients). A main task, as we have seen, too, was the compiling of astronomical tables designed to make possible the accurate observation of the positions and movement of the heavenly bodies.

It will be recalled that the normal medieval courses of study, both at schools and universities, comprised the seven "liberal arts". But most students failed as a rule to get beyond the *trivium* phase of what was regarded as the primary group—the humanities—namely grammar, rhetoric and dialectics. Those who could proceed to the *quadrivium*, which formed the second order of study comprising astronomy, arithmetic, geometry and music, were the relatively select few. Nevertheless, in some schools in the twelfth century, particularly those in England and Italy, more time was deliberately given to mathematical sciences. We have already referred to Leonardo Fibonacci of Pisa, the learned mathematician who brought back from his journey to the East the algebraic notation which Gerbert, two centuries earlier, had there found to be in general use. And it will be recalled that in England both Robert Grosseteste and Roger Bacon had become distinguished mathematicians and physicists. Another pupil of the Oxford School was John of Holywood, usually referred to as *Sacrobosco*. He left Oxford for Paris with a great reputation as an astronomer and cosmographist, and he taught mathematics there with great success. His treatise on the Celestial Globe *De Sphæra Mundi*, virtually an abridgement of Ptolemy's *Almagest*, was a standard work in all schools of Europe for more than three centuries. In addition, he wrote a work on time measurement, *De Anni Ratione*, and a treatise on the astrolabe, an instrument to which we refer later.

The savants of Italy seemed particularly to be attracted to mathematical studies from the thirteenth century onwards. They had their difficulties because the study of the exact sciences was too often open to a suspicion of heresy on the part of the theologians. Campano, a translator of Euclid, for example, was always under suspicion, while Pietro d'Abano, professor of astronomy at Padua, paid for his leanings to astrology by being condemned to the stake. The Florentine School, particularly noted for its mathematicians, included Dugomari (better known as Paul the Geometer) and, of course, Abbaco, who taught Leonardo da Vinci the rudiments of the subject. On the whole, mathematics was very much alive during the Italian Renaissance and was actively taught (with a wholesome freedom, in the main, from the dangerous illusions of astrology) at various centres—Rome, Naples, Padua, Bologna, Pisa and, more especially, at Florence. Even the Church took it up, since, fortunately, a very distinguished mathematician, Æneas Sylvius Piccolomini, was elected Pope in 1458 with the title of Pius II. It will be recalled that Nicholas of Cusa was his contemporary; and it is fortunate that both Paul II and Sixtus IV, successors to Pius II, carried on the tradition of patronage towards those who studied mathematics and the exact sciences. It was Sixtus IV who, in 1463, summoned to Rome the celebrated German astronomer and mathematician, Johann Müller (better known as *Regiomontanus*). Regiomontanus was a pupil of the famous Georg Peurbach. His lectures on Ptolemy attracted enormous audiences. He died prematurely in 1476 at the age of thirty-nine years, but his work upon the calendar and on problems of triangulation, with his commentaries on Ptolemy's System, had left an indelible impression.

But the supreme centre for the study of mathematics and the exact sciences in Italy continued to be at Florence. The Florentine Academy had a considerable following, and its influence extended to the applications of mathematics to the arts and to industry. We have referred to Toscanelli and to Pacioli, both distinguished members of this school and both in active contact with Leonardo da Vinci. Here indeed art and technology found common ground. Battista Alberti, Michelangelo and others were active devotees of mathematical studies and their applicability to art, and Leonardo himself repeatedly extolled the importance of mathematics in his notes. "There is no certainty," he writes,[1] "in sciences to which one of the mathematical sciences cannot be applied, or which are not in relationship with these mathematics." And again[2]: "Mechanics is the paradise of the mathematical sciences because here we come to the fruits of mathematics."

[1] MS. *G*, 95 b.   [2] MS. *E*, 8 v.

(ii) *Units of Measurement during the Renaissance*

Before we consider some of the chief instruments of observation and measurement in general use in the fifteenth century it is desirable to comment briefly on the basic units and standards of length, weight and capacity current at the time. Such standards were, of course, used for the rulers, measures, balances and weights generally available from place to place, but unfortunately there was little uniformity of practice in these respects not only as between one country and another but even as between one district or area and another in the same country. In primitive times the units of length, for example, were expressed in terms of the human body. The width of the fore-finger was the digit, the "foot" explains itself, the yard was a normal pace, the fathom the distance between extended arms, and so on. But it needed legal enactments to overcome the facts of variation in human sizes, and even these did not always succeed. Bishop Fleetwood discussed the matter in his *Chronicon Preciosum* in 1745 thus: "What can be more vexatious and unprofitable . . . than to find that when they go out of one country into another, they must learn a new language or cannot buy or sell anything. An acre is not an acre; nor a bushel a bushel if you travel but ten miles. A pound is not a pound if you go from a goldsmith to a grocer, nor a gallon a gallon if you go from a tavern to an alehouse. What purpose does this variety serve, or what necessity is there, which the difference of price would not better answer and supply?"

Generally, the standards of the Middle Ages were derived from the Roman *pes* (foot), the *palmus* (width of the hand) and the *digitus* (the width of the finger). In Italy the units had become the *passo* (one pace), the *piede* (foot), the *brasso* (length of the arm) and the *pouce* (the width of the thumb). But quickly local changes produced not only different values in different cities but also in different trades in the same city. In Italy the "foot", the piede, had a value of 17·134 inches in Milan, 14·07 inches in Padua, but 11·73 inches in Rome. Actually the Roman piede was widely used by engineers and architects. A length often quoted in Leonardo's notes was the *braccio*, derived from the length of the arm. This was a common unit in Italy, yet its value (in inches) differed from city to city and from trade to trade. In Florence it was 23·0 inches for the builder and engineer, and 21·7 inches in land measurement. In Milan the corresponding value was 23·4 inches. And the same types of variations were to be found in units of weight (the English *pound*, the French *livre*, and the Italian *libbra*). Expressed in terms of the English pound weight, the libbra was 1·073 in Padua, 1·052 in Venice, but 0·798 in Bologna, 0·748 in Florence, 0·720 in

Milan and 0·748 in Rome, and similar and confusing variations were to be found in money values.

(iii) *Instruments of Draughtsmanship*

It may reasonably be said that the standards of efficiency in works and problems of construction, as well as of observation, are directly related to the standards of draughtsmanship. Pictorial preparation was as much an early requirement for the technologies of tool-making, machine construction and building as it was for practical science. The preparation of working drawings for these purposes was in evidence as early as the fourteenth century, but the straight-edge, square and compasses used by masons, carpenters and others for setting out, aligning and trucing up were of much earlier origin.[1] Specimens in bronze, going back to the early Christian era, are to be seen in the British Museum in London and in the Museo Nazionale at Naples, and sketches of them figure on the tombs of various Roman architects. Theophilus the Monk (*c.* A.D. 1100) refers to the preparation of a design on a wooden board by means of a ruler and compasses. It was about this time that paper-making was introduced into Europe and with it came refinements in the development of the compasses and a corresponding improvement in the standards of draughtsmanship. These refinements were applied to the growing volume of building activities associated with the very elaborate and often ornate churches, cathedrals and other ecclesiastical structures of the day. One of the architects whose sketch-books have survived was Villard de Honnecourt (*c.* 1434). His drawings, lined in with quill pen and ink, show clearly that he must have used a stylus and a pair of compasses.

By the end of the fifteenth century and early in the sixteenth, it is clear from the way in which the growing volume of printed books was being illustrated that the technical level of draughtsmanship had developed considerably, though Dickinson suggests that, in England at any rate, the earliest drawings that could reasonably be described as *engineering drawings*, albeit in free-hand, were of John Payne's *Human Power Engine*. In this respect, however, it must at once be said that even the most cursory scanning of some of Leonardo da Vinci's notebooks show examples of engineering draughtsmanship that are unequalled in modern days even with the use of the most elaborate drawing instruments. For example in the *Codex Atlanticus*[2] there is shown Leonardo's conception of a device for shaping and tapering iron rods for the purpose of making cannon. This drawing, which dates probably

[1] The information given in this section is based upon a paper "A Brief History of Draughtsmen's Instruments" by the late H. W. Dickinson in the *Transactions of the Newcomen Society*, vol. 27, 1949–1951.
[2] *Codex Atlanticus*, 2 v.a.

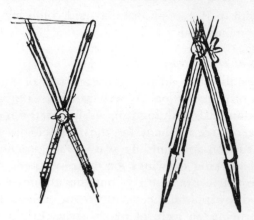

Fig. 18.   Leonardo's compasses—methods of compass-
leg adjustments.

about the year 1500, is justly described by Popham[1] as "a model of
elegance and precision". But then, not all architects and engineers
could be expected to be embryo Leonardos, let alone draughtsmen.

By Leonardo's day the making of scientific instruments had become
a separate trade in its own right, appropriate guilds for which were
established in various cities in Europe. These were not necessarily
guilds purely for the making of instruments but were of the crafts considered to be the closest allied to them—the Guild of Armourers in
Milan, the Cutlers and the Metal Founders in Paris (later formally
applied to the Founders with the addition to their title of "Maîtres
Faiseurs des Instruments de Mathématiques, Globes et Sphères"),
and so on.

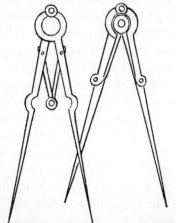

Fig. 19.   Leonardo's design for compasses.

[1] A. E. Popham, *The Drawings of Leonardo da Vinci*, p. 106 (London, 1946).

The use and design of compasses in Leonardo's day may be seen from his own notebooks. Fixed proportional compasses, known actually in classical times, were still in use, but in the *Codex Atlanticus*[1] Leonardo has drawn examples of the adjustable kind. In one sketch his method of adjustment is by lengthening one pair of the legs and in another (Fig. 18) he shows the more modern device of slotting the legs and holding them down at the required point by means of a screw and nut. Two excellent sketches of compass and calipers are shown in Manuscript H (Fig. 19).[2] Lock nuts in each case ensure the setting of the legs as required. Again, the type known as the beam compass, used for drawing circles of particularly large radius, was first shown by Leonardo in 1493 in MS. *B*.[3] The centre point is shown wedged on the beam and the tracing point, fitted with a fixed adjustment screw, is able to slide along as required.

Finally, it is of interest to note that tracing-paper, the inevitable adjunct to the draughtsman's equipment, was very well known from early times. The Italian artist Cennini (*c.* 1370–1437) refers to it in his *Treatise on Painting* thus: "The paper must be thin, even and very white; oil it with linseed oil as before directed. It will be transparent and very good."

(iv) *Astronomical Instruments of the Renaissance*

After the Dark Ages observatories were set up by Arabian Caliphs at Damascus, at Baghdad (A.D. 829), on the heights of Mokattam, near Cairo (about A.D. 1000), and by the Mongol Khans at Maragha, in north-west Persia (*c.* 1240), and elsewhere. It was not, however, till the fifteenth century that observational astronomy became a progressive study. During this century Ulugh Beg founded an observatory of importance at Samarkand (*c.* 1420), whilst in Europe the first observatory was erected in 1472 at Nuremberg by Bernhard Walther (1430–1504), a German scientist of independent means, who collaborated with the famous Regiomontanus, and who was the first to employ astronomical clocks driven by weights. Further developments, notably by Tycho Brahe, carry us beyond the limits of our period.

Allied from the point of view of mechanical science to the problems of astronomical measurement, we have the subject of practical navigation. Here, however, we come upon very barren soil, for navigation as a practical science was in a very crude and primitive form in the fifteenth century. So far as the ancients were concerned, although they possibly realised that the practical problems of fixing positions afloat were similar to those ashore, the probability is that the unsteadiness of their boats prevented them from developing this subject. Apart

[1] *Codex Atlanticus*, 248 r.a.; and 27 v.a.   [2] MS. *H*, 108 v.   [3] MS. *B*, 50 v.

from the introduction of the mariner's compass during the fourteenth century (the magnet had, of course, been known long before this, though not used in ships), the true pioneers of scientific navigation were the Portuguese. In the fifteenth century Prince Henry of Portugal systematised the study of nautical science, and his successor, John II,

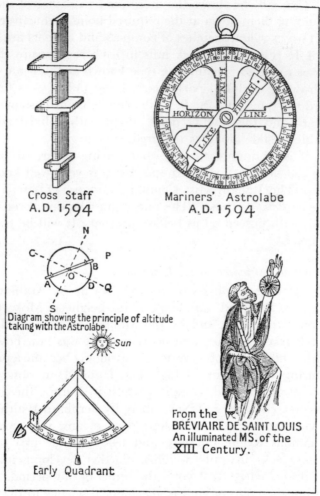

Cross Staff
A.D. 1594

Mariners' Astrolabe
A.D. 1594

Diagram showing the principle of altitude taking with the Astrolabe.

Sun

From the
BRÉVIAIRE DE SAINT LOUIS
An illuminated MS. of the
XIII Century.

Early Quadrant

Fig. 20.   An assembly of medieval instruments of navigation.
(From Sir W. Bragg's "Old Trades & New Knowledge"—with acknowledgements to Messrs. Bell & Son, Ltd.)

followed this up in 1482 by setting up a committee on navigation. This resulted in the drawing up of solar declination tables, in the improvement of the instruments of the day, and in the organisation of proper instructional courses for pilots—courses which included a study of *Sacrobosco's*[1] recently printed *De Sphæra Mundi* and Ptolemy's

---

[1] Sacrobosco (John Holywood, d. *c.* 1250). The *Tractatus de Sphæra* was first printed at Ferrara in 1472 and achieved a phenomenal circulation. It was the second astronomical

Almagest. The determination of longitude was both unknown and unhoped for, and the entire equipment of the fifteenth-century navigator comprised either a cross-staff or an astrolabe, a magnetic compass, tables of declination of the sun and of pole-star altitude corrections, possibly a very crude chart, and what was known as a traverse-board.

Additional instruments used, chiefly in astronomy, navigation and surveying, were the Astrolabe, the Armillery Sphere, the Mural Quadrant, the Cross-staff, the Clock, and the Dioptra. (Fig. 20.) We propose offering a few brief remarks on these.

The Astrolabe[1], literally meaning "to take a star", was used for measuring angular distances between any two objects. In principle, a graduated circular plate (made of copper or tin) has a datum line, *AB*, and a rotating alidade or index *OC* pivoted at *O*, and carrying

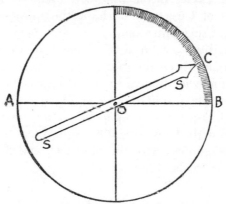

Fig. 21. The principle of the astrolabe.

two sight holes *SS* (Fig. 21). The instrument is held in the plane of the two objects (e.g. stars), so that *AB* points towards one of them. The alidade *OC* is now rotated to point to the other object and the angle is read on the instrument. This instrument was used in one form or another from the time of Eratosthenes onwards. When the Arabs introduced it into Spain it was a very costly device. Roger Bacon probably used one in Toledo, but by the fourteenth century it was simplified in design and more widely used. It was first described in English by Chaucer for his son, that he might learn "to knowe every tyme of the day by light of the sonne, and every tyme of the night by the fixed starres". Although originally intended for astronomical purposes, its use was gradually extended until by the fifteenth century

work to be printed. By A.D. 1500 twenty editions had been printed and forty more were issued by 1647, when the last edition was issued from Leyden.

[1] See J. Frank, *Zur Geschichte des Astrolabs* (Erlangen, 1920).

it was made in all sizes for a variety of purposes, including surveying and navigation and land travel. Christopher Columbus used a simple modification known as the *mariner's astrolabe*, the design of Martin Behaim (*c.* 1480). Three observers were necessary—one to hold the instrument, another to sight it, and a third to read the result; and what with the unsteadiness of the ship and the personal equation thrice involved, the results were not very reliable.

The Armillary Sphere was of common origin with the astrolabe, beginning with the armilla, a ring fixed in the plane of the equator and developing, by the addition of other rings, into a sort of graduated model of the celestial sphere, one circle representing the horizon, another (graduated) the meridian, a third the equator, a fourth the ecliptic, and so on. Armillary spheres were of little use for quantitative work during the fifteenth century, little advance having been made in their design until Tycho Brahe modified them during the sixteenth century. Nicholas of Cusa was perhaps the most efficient fifteenth-century designer of such intruments.

The Mural Quadrant was an astronomical forerunner of the transit circle and has already been mentioned in connection with the observations by Copernicus leading to his heliocentric theory (p. 142). Its principle is shown diagrammatically in Fig. 22. The quadrant was mounted with reference to an aperture *A* in the observatory wall, *C* being on a level with *A*. A travelling sight *S* was swung round until *S* and *A* were in alignment with the object *O*, and the altitude was at once read off on the scale (Plate 37).

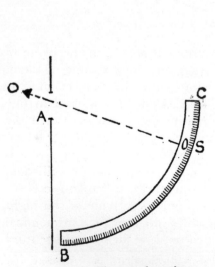

Fig. 22.   The mural quadrant.

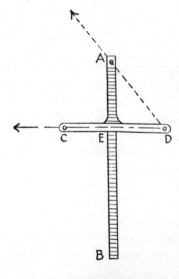

Fig. 23.   The principle of the cross-staff.

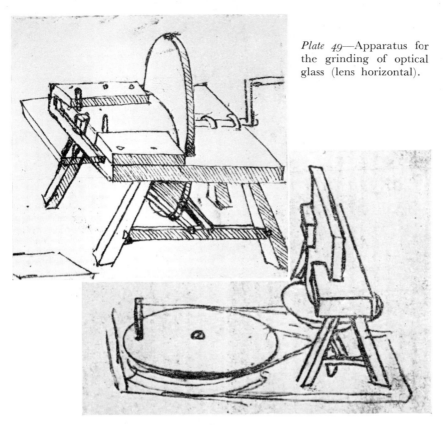

Plate 49—Apparatus for the grinding of optical glass (lens horizontal).

Plate 50—Apparatus for the grinding of optical glass (lens vertical).

Plate 51—Scheme of discs for grinding and polishing plant.

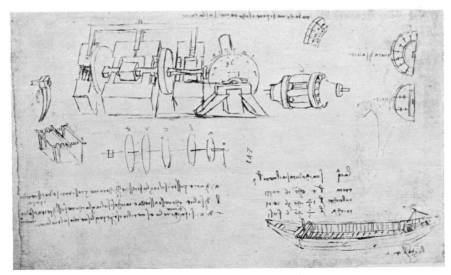

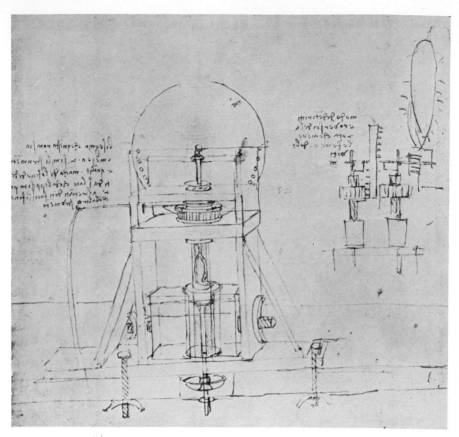

Plate 52—Mechanism for grinding and polishing hollow cylinders.

Plate 53—Framework of rings of fixed and movable pulleys to give a large mechanical advantage.

The Cross-staff, again, was an instrument of general use in astronomy, navigation and topography for the purpose of measuring angles subtended by objects. The theory is extremely simple. A graduated rod *AB* (Fig. 23) could slide into various positions at right angles to a shorter rod *CD*. There were sight holes at *A*, *C* and *D*. Sights *D* and *C* were first brought into alignment with one object and kept there, and the position of *AB* was then adjusted until the sight holes *D* and *A* came into alignment with the other object. The reading of *AB* at *E* was then taken; and *DE* being of constant length, a reference to a table of angles gave the corresponding angle.

Up to the fifteenth century little improvement had been effected in the measurement of time—the clepsydræ (water clocks), sand-glasses and sundials[1] remaining in general use throughout this period. Clocks based on mechanical power are recorded here and there as far back as the thirteenth and the fourteenth centuries.[2] The earliest had no dials, and hours were recorded by automatic figures striking bells. These were succeeded by dial clocks having an hour hand only. The first reliably known was set up in Milan in 1335, and in England about 1370. Nevertheless, the fifteenth century saw the inauguration of one innovation of importance in mechanical time measurement, for Bernhard Walther, to whom we have already referred as the pupil and collaborator of Regiomontanus, tells us that on 16th January 1484, on the instant of the rising of the planet Mercury, he set in motion for the first time a clock driven by a hanging weight. The hour wheel was fitted with fifty-six teeth, each therefore representing a fraction more than a minute. At sunrise one hour and thirty-five teeth had passed, from which he concluded that Mercury rose one hour and thirty-seven minutes before sunrise. In spite of Walther's lead, the measurement of time intervals for experimental purposes remained crude. A typical example of the experimental conditions which obtained in the days of Leonardo da Vinci was the method used for ascertaining the speed of a ship. A piece of wood was flung into the sea from the bows of the ship. Two observers stood on deck at a known distance apart, and the time taken by the wood in moving through this distance was estimated.

So far as general surveying is concerned, it must be confessed that the position in the fifteenth century was little advanced in the matter of instruments beyond that which obtained in the days of Hiero of Alexandria. The dioptra, which was the main instrument of the ancient engineers and surveyors, probably persisted throughout the

---

[1] Nocturnals or night-dials (for telling the time by the aid of the fixed stars at night) were first made in 1520 and their development therefore falls outside our period.

[2] F. J. Britten, *Old Clocks and Watches and their Makers* (London, 1911). See also L. Bolton, *Time Measurement* (London, 1914).

Middle Ages with very little change. Indeed, it may almost be claimed
that in principle it has persisted even to modern times, for, after all,
apart from the addition of telescopic vision and refinements of adjustment and workmanship and graduation, the dioptra of the Greeks,
with its levelling-staff accessories (as already described in some detail
on p. 159) has virtually become the theodolite and the levelling instrument of today. It was certainly the theodolite of the fifteenth
century. It should be remarked, however, that it is by no means clear
from the obscure records which exist whether Hiero of Alexandria did
in fact utilise the toothed half-wheel A in Fig. 13 (p. 159) as a means
of obtaining elevation. It is certain that they used this wheel for
adjustments to obtain a true horizontal, and it is probable that the
fifteenth-century engineers used it for the measurement of angles of
elevation. The true inventor of the modern theodolite (he was the
first to use the term "theodolitus") was Leonard Digges (1510–1558),
the essentially new features in his instrument being: (*a*) the attachment
of a magnetic compass for control in orientation; and (*b*) a definite
mechanism for elevation control and measurement.[1]

Some very interesting notes by Leonardo da Vinci on altimetry

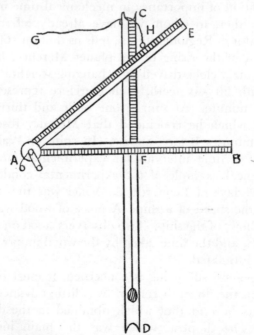

Fig. 24.   Leonardo's apparatus for estimating
the height of a mountain.

[1] See Thomas Digges, *Pantometria* (London, 1571). Thomas was a son of Leonard Digges.
Also see R. C. Skyring-Walters, *Transactions of the Newcomen Society*, vol. ii (1921–1922),
p. 45; also E. A. Reeves, *Maps and Map Making*, pp. 9–30.

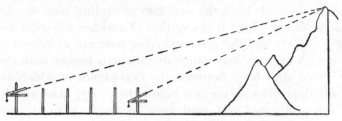

Fig. 25. Estimating the height of a mountain.

and levelling are to be found in the *Codex Atlanticus*.[1] For example, in order to find the height of a mountain Leonardo devised an instrument, a sketch of which is here shown (Fig. 24). Supported on a vertical rod *FC* (there are prongs at *D* to enable the instrument to be stuck into the ground) at a height of about two yards is a horizontal graduated measure *AB*, about three yards long. This is hinged at *A* to a similar rule *AE*, whose angle *EAB* can be varied. Behind *AE* and also resting on *FD* is an upright rule *CF*, notched at the top. *AE* can be swung into any desired position by means of the waxed thread *GCH* working over a pulley at *C*. Leonardo illustrates the method of applying this instrument to the determination of the height of a mountain by means of the sketch (Fig. 25) here shown. Angles of elevation are taken from two positions at a known distance apart and the required result is calculated by trigonometry.

A similar procedure is used for the normal process of levelling. "If you wish to level a plain of many miles accurately, then set about it in the way here indicated," he writes.[2] His sketch shows a series of alignment poles at 400 braccia intervals, the first of them being placed at a distance of 200 braccia from the levelling instrument (obviously a sort of dioptra). A further diagram (Fig. 26) shows by its details of the poles that the observations are to be taken by night. Mounted on the alignment poles are oil lamps, and Leonardo ensures that the lights from all these lamps are maintained at the same height by the simple device of an oil feed. This consists of an oil vessel above each lamp, from which oil flows, drop by drop, into the lamp at a rate which exactly compensates for the consumption in the lamp. In another note-

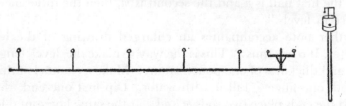

Fig. 26. Alignment poles with oil lamps for night observations.

[1] *Codex Atlanticus*, 131 r.a.   [2] *Codex Atlanticus*, 131 r.a.

book[1] Leonardo deals with the problem of finding how much higher
the elevation of one plane is above that of another adjacent to it. The
sketch (Fig. 27(A)) and the accompanying note are as follows:

"If you wish to know how much one plane is higher than the other,
do thus: Place your level between the two planes of which you wish
to know the depression of the one below the other; place on the lower
position the graduated rod, and raise or lower it until your eye *a*

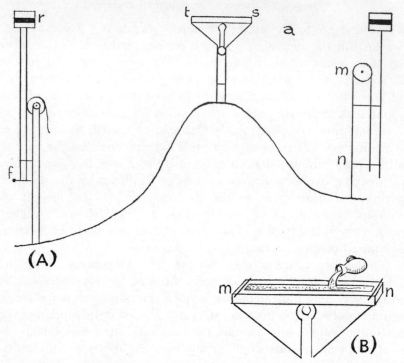

Fig. 27.   Measuring elevations on either side of a mountain peak.

and the two ends *s* and *t* are in the same horizontal as the upper black
bands made on the drum *r*.   Mark the rod below, at the point *f*, with
a nail.   Then carry the rod to the other side and do the same as at
first.   Look through the instrument the other way *ts* and put in another
nail.   If the first nail is *n* and the second is *m*, then the difference is the
difference in levels."

A further note accompanies an enlarged drawing of the level *st*.
(Fig. 27(B)). It reads thus: "This is the way to make the 'level' length two
braccia and thickness of one pouce square. Make a channel of thickness
and depth one finger. Fill it with water. Dip first one end, then the
other. At the ends place two rods *m* and *n* at the same horizontal level to
view from either end."

[1] MS. *B*, 65 v.; see also *Codex Atlanticus*, 436 v.b.

This, then, was the general atmosphere of instrumental science in da Vinci's day. It was scarcely calculated to encourage the would-be experimentalist unless he were a genius. But Leonardo da Vinci was just that. He could and did rise superior to the mechanical deficiencies of his day, and in the succeeding pages we shall consider, against the background of his times as we have reviewed them, the general nature of his own contributions in the fields of mechanical science, engineering and aeronautics.

PART TWO

LEONARDO—
MAN OF SCIENCE, ENGINEER AND
DREAMER OF FLIGHT

VI

THE STORY AND CHARACTERISTICS OF LEONARDO'S NOTEBOOKS

1. THE DISPERSAL AND RECOVERY OF THE MANUSCRIPTS

We may now review briefly the circumstances of the loss and subsequent recovery of Leonardo da Vinci's notebooks. It will be recalled that his last years were spent at Amboise, in the south of France, following an invitation early in the year 1516 from Francis I. These last three years of his life must have been both peaceful and happy. Francis treated him well and enjoyed many an hour in almost daily conversation with him. Under such pleasant conditions the urge to fill more notebooks or to undertake more works of art must have diminished. Some evidence exists to show that he was actively interested in canal problems on the Loire; and there is some less specific evidence of an interest in architectural problems. But in the main these were progressively less creative years—they were rather the final period of a well-earned peace.

Physically all was not well with Leonardo. Judging by an account of a visit paid to him by Cardinal Louis of Aragon in October 1517, he had seemingly suffered a minor paralytic stroke. A record of this visit has been left by the cardinal's secretary, Antonio de' Beatis. Following his account of three pictures which Leonardo had shown to the cardinal, he writes: ". . . but, indeed, on account of a certain paralysis having seized him in the right hand, one cannot expect more fine things from him."

Leonardo died at the Castle of Cloux on 2nd May 1519. Nine days earlier he had signed a will, "duly considering the certainty of death and the uncertainty of its time" and commending his soul "to our Lord, Almighty God, and to the glorious Virgin Mary, and to our Lord Saint Michael, to all blessed angels and Saints male and female in Paradise". Leonardo appointed as sole executor the faithful friend and companion of his old age, Francesco Melzi, who was with him until he died.

Melzi wrote from Amboise on 1st June 1519 to Leonardo's brothers in Florence, informing them of his death and reporting that he had bequeathed to them his estate at Fiesole, together with his savings held to his credit with the Treasurer of Santa Maria Nuova at Florence. Melzi's letter went on to say, "To me he was like the best of fathers for whose death it would be impossible for me to express the grief I have felt. . . . It is a hurt to anyone to lose such a man, for nature cannot again produce his like."

Leonardo was buried in the cloister of the Church of St. Florentin at Amboise and was described in the register as "Me. Leonard de Vincy, noble Milanese, first painter, engineer and architect to the King, State mechanist, and sometime director of painting of the Duke of Milan".

For us the important item in the will is that which reads thus: "The aforesaid Testator gives and bequeaths to Messer Francesco da Melzi, nobleman of Milan, in remuneration for services and favours done to him in the past, each and all of the books the testator is at present possessed of, and the instruments and portraits appertaining to his art and calling as a painter."

Melzi returned to his home in Milan, carrying this bequest with him; and here, in his villa at Vaprio, the manuscripts were guarded with tender and jealous care for the next fifty years.[1] Melzi, however, died in 1570, and it is from this time onwards that the tragic dispersal of the manuscripts may be said to have taken place. Approaches had been made to Melzi from time to time during his lifetime for the purchase of the notebooks (notably by Alphonso I of Ferrara and by Vasari, Leonardo's earliest biographer). Vasari, for example, visited Melzi in 1566 and speaks of him as a "beautiful and gentle old man". Apparently the compilation of notes spoken of as the *Treatise on Painting* had gone by then to a nameless Milanese painter. But, apart from this, Melzi had consistently rejected these various offers. But now, after his death, they were renewed and this time with some success.

Francesco's heir to the notebooks was Orazio Melzi, who had little or no interest in science, art or letters. Taking advantage of this, the family tutor, Lelio Gavardi di Asola, conceived the idea of disposing of some thirteen volumes of the manuscripts. He met with little difficulty. However, the Grand Duke Francesco of Florence, to whom it was intended to sell these volumes, died at this juncture and Lelio Gavardi took them instead to Pisa. Fortunately, the man whom he next approached, a law-student of the University of Pisa named Ambrosio Mazzenta, dissuaded Gavardi from pursuing his opportunist intentions and the latter left the volumes with Mazzenta to be restored

---

[1] The account which follows is largely based upon the detailed history of the subsequent dispersal of the notebooks, given as an appendix to Vol. II of Jean Paul Richter's *Literary Works of Leonardo da Vinci* (2nd Edition, London, 1939). The writer is glad to acknowledge his indebtedness accordingly.

to the Melzi family. Orazio Melzi, the rightful owner, in his lack of interest, however, not only permitted Mazzenta to keep the volumes as a reward for his trouble but told him further that he could help himself to any of the remaining bundles of matter lying about the attics at Vaprio.

Others, too, had heard of the spoils to be gathered from these attics and they readily availed themselves of Orazio's free invitations of "help yourself". Amongst those seeking to acquire Leonardo's manuscripts was Pompeo Leoni, a sculptor and friend of Philip II of Spain. It was his plan to seek favour from his royal master in exchange for these manuscripts, and accordingly he approached Orazio Melzi with promises of reward from King Phliip if he would secure the return of the thirteen volumes given to Mazzenta. But Ambrosio had by now (1590) taken vows with the Barnabite Order and had passed on his thirteen volumes to his brother Guido. It was Guido, therefore, who was approached by Orazio Melzi, and as a result seven of the volumes were returned and handed on to Leoni. Of the remaining six, three were subsequently acquired by Leoni on the death of one of the Mazzentas and another volume was given in 1603 to Cardinal Federico Borromeo, the founder of the famous Ambrosian Library at Milan (1609). The remaining two have long been completely lost sight of. It is known that one of them had been given to Ambrogio Figino, a painter, and has subsequently been traced through various owners up to 1759; and the other was given to Duke Charles Emmanuel of Savoy, and was probably destroyed in an outbreak of fire at the Royal Library at Turin about the year 1667.

Actually Pompeo Leoni never carried out his original intention of giving the manuscripts to King Philip II of Spain. Not only did he keep them himself until his death but he went so far as to cut out portions of them to form, together with a number of loose drawings, a single large volume which, on account of its size (it contains 402 sheets and more than 1700 drawings and sketches), he called the *Codice Atlantico* (*Codex Atlanticus*). Leoni died in 1610 and the manuscripts passed into the possession of his heir, Polidoro Calchi, who, in his turn, sold some of them, including the *Codex Atlanticus*, to Count Galeazzo Arconati in 1625. Arconati kept these until 1636, in which year he presented to the Ambrosian Library at Milan the *Codex Atlanticus*, together with eleven other volumes of da Vinci's manuscripts, thus making, together with the original volume presented by the founder of the library in 1603, a collection of thirteen volumes. To these a further one was added in 1674 by Count Orazio Archinti. One was probably subsequently stolen, since its description coincides with that of a volume bought, long after, in 1750 by Carlo Trivulzio. The period of restoration may now be said to have begun.

In Arconati's deed of gift, making over these volumes to the library, we find the first authentic record of the existence of a manuscript on the flight of birds.[1] Inside the cover of the third volume of the gift we read: "At the end of this book is another little volume of various mathematical figures and of birds, of eighteen pages sewn in the same page in parchment."[2]

For the next chapter in the story of the wanderings of these manuscripts we come to the year 1796, when Napoleon Buonaparte, during his invasion of Italy, commandeered for despatch to France various works of art, including the thirteen volumes of Leonardo's manuscripts. The *Codex Atlanticus* was removed to the Bibliothèque Nationale, whilst the other twelve volumes were transported to the library of the Institute of France in Paris, where, according to the official records, they arrived on 25th November. Here the volumes were carefully examined by Venturi and to him the world is indebted for the first real description of the manuscripts.[3] For purposes of reference Venturi assigned to each of the twelve manuscripts a capital letter beginning with A, and this nomenclature has since received general acceptance.

In the year 1815, consequent upon political changes, representations were made to France on behalf of Lombardy for the return of da Vinci's manuscripts to Milan. For some reason or other, although France consented to this restoration, only the *Codex Atlanticus* (which alone of all these volumes, it will be remembered, was housed in the Bibliothèque Nationale instead of in the library of the Institute of France) was returned to the Ambrosian Library, and the remainder have been kept in Paris ever since.

The particular volume to which we have already referred as containing an appendix of the notebook *On the Flight of Birds* was lettered "B" in Venturi's series. Venturi, however, subsequently considered the notebook of sufficient importance to be regarded as a separate volume in itself and he lettered it "N" accordingly (Plate 39).

The later history of this small notebook is interesting. In the year 1848 it was discovered that certain manuscripts, and amongst them the appendix to Manuscript B, were missing. That they were stolen is fairly certain, and that the culprit was Professor Guglielmo Libri is indicated—first by the fact that prior to 1848 he had had frequent access to these manuscripts, and secondly that he was in undoubted possession of them in 1867. In December of that year Count Giacomo Manzoni of Lugo, whilst on a visit to Florence, was shown the manuscript amongst others "acquired" by Libri and bought it from him

---

[1] Discussed in some detail in Chapter X.
[2] I Manoscritti di Leonardo da Vinci: *Codice sul Volo degli Uccelli*, etc., Pubblicato da Teodoro Sabachnikoff. Trascrizioni e note di Giovanni Piumati, pp. 28 and 29 (Paris, 1893).
[3] J. B. Venturi: *Essai sur les ouvrages physico-mathematiques de Léonard de Vinci* (Paris, 1796).

a year later. Libri also disposed of some of the manuscript to Lord Ashburnham in England, but these latter were returned to France in 1888.

On the death of Manzoni in 1889 the notebook *On the Flight of Birds* passed to his heirs and they disposed of it in 1892 to M. Theodor Sabachnikoff. The notebook has since passed into the possession of the Library of Turin.

Two other "fragments" of manuscripts are held in the Bibliothèque Nationale which call for special mention. They are catalogued as Nos. 2037 and 2038 and in fact were originally parts of Manuscripts B and A respectively. No. 2037 comprises twenty-six pages and No. 2038 sixty-eight pages, and their dimensions (approximately $5\frac{1}{2}$ inches by $7\frac{1}{2}$ inches) and the nature of their contents clearly indicate their original place in the notebooks. Indeed, from the description in the Arconati deed of gift of 1636 it would seem that, even allowing for the MS. Nos. 2037 and 2038, there are still some sheets of MSS. A and B of the Institute of France unaccounted for. Their mutilation, first discovered in 1848, was almost certainly the work of Count Libri, who disposed of MSS. Nos. 2037 and 2038 to Lord Ashburnham in 1875, probably at the same time as the deal referred to above.

All the notebooks so far mentioned have been published in facsimile form—the *Codex Atlanticus*, with Italian transcript in addition to the old Italian text, under the direction of the Accademia dei Lincei;[1] and the Parisian notebooks, printed with the old Italian text together with a French translation, rendered in six large volumes that include the MSS. Nos. 2037 and 2038 referred to above.[2]

By the nature of the circumstances of its compilation, the *Codex Atlanticus*, unlike the other notebooks, represents a cross-section of Leonardo's sketches and notes drawn from various periods of his life, extending from 1490 onwards to his last years. The sheets are large, so that the standard references not only give the sheet number and the suffix "recto" or "verso" for front or back, but also indicate by the further letters a, b, c, d, according to which of the four quarters of each sheet the reference applies.

The notebooks A to N, on the other hand, are self-contained and in some cases can be related to specific dates in Leonardo's life. They vary greatly also in the size of sheet used—some approximate to the quarto size of modern usage, some to quite small pocket-book size ($2\frac{1}{2}$ inches by $3\frac{3}{4}$ inches), and less frequently (e.g. MS. C) to foolscap size. The earliest notebook was probably B, dating from 1488. Other

---

[1] *Il codice atlantico di Leonardo da Vinci nella Biblioteca Ambrosiana di Milano*, riprodotto e publicato dalla Regia Accademia dei Lincei. Trascrizione diplomatica e critica di Giovanni Piumati (Milano, 1894–1904).

[2] *Les Manuscrits de Léonard de Vinci*, par M. Charles Ravaisson-Mollien (Paris, 1881–1897).

known dates are C (1490), A (1492), H (1494), I and M (1498), L (1502), F (1508) and E (1513).

2. THE ENGLISH NOTEBOOKS

Not all the notebooks and sketches are confined to France and Italy. Fortunately, some very important manuscripts have a permanent home in England. These comprise (*a*) the Windsor manuscripts; (*b*) the Forster collection at the Victoria and Albert Museum; (*c*) the Leicester collection at Holkham Hall; and (*d*) the British Museum volume.

Both James I and Charles I in their time had made attempts to acquire some of the notebooks, but the actual circumstances under which the manuscripts and sketches now in the royal possession came to Windsor Castle are shrouded in uncertainty. John Evelyn was unsuccessfully involved in 1646, whilst Addison, who visited the Ambrosian Library at Milan in 1701, records that King James unsuccessfully bid 3000 Spanish pistoles for one of the notebooks (see below).

It is most probably this particular volume which, according to Charles Rogers,[1] "was deposited by King Charles himself in a large chest, in which it lay unobserved and forgotten for 120 years . . . until the beginning of the reign of his present Majesty" (i.e. George III). Rogers described the volume as "strongly bound in calves leather, with the inscription: DESEGNI DI LEONARDO DA VINCI. RESTAURATI DE POMPEO LEONI".

In 1812 it was described by J. Chamberlaine in his *Original Designs of the most Celebrated Masters in His Majesty's Collection* thus: "It is rather probable than certain that this great curiosity was acquired for King Charles I by the Earl of Arundel when he went as Ambassador to the Emperor Ferdinand II in 1636."

An inscription over the place where the volumes are kept states that King James offered 3000 pistoles for one of the volumes. The oldest inventory in Windsor Castle, called "*Catalogue of Drawings and Prints, George III*, mentions: "The Drawings of Leonardo da Vinci arranged by Pompeo Leoni (Sculptor to Philip II of Spain) and interspersed with a great number of original manuscript notes which, being written with inverted characters, are not legible unless reflected by a looking-glass."

It is clear, therefore, that some of the Windsor collection had been first acquired by Lord Arundel, the Earl Marshal, and that some had formed part of the original Pompeo Leoni collection. A note in an inventory found by Richter in the Manuscript Department of the

---

[1] Charles Rogers, *A Collection of Prints in Imitation of Drawings*, 1778, i, p. 5.

British Museum states that some drawings of Leonardo da Vinci, marked with a cross, were delivered to Her Majesty's use in 1728. Generally speaking, it would seem that the Windsor collection must have been acquired bit by bit from various sources from Pompeo Leoni onwards. These, in the main, relate to Leonardo's notes on anatomy, and facsimile reproductions have been rendered, with transcripts and translations, by Piumati and Sabachnikoff (Fogli A in Paris in 1898, and Fogli B in Turin in 1901); and by Vangestan, Fonahn and Hopstock (the *Quaderni d'Anatomea* in six volumes, at Oslo from 1911 to 1916). In addition, a catalogue of the Windsor Castle drawings was undertaken by Sir Kenneth Clark and published in 1935 by the Cambridge University Press.

The volume of notes now housed in the British Museum is known as the Arundel MS. No. 263. Beyond the fact that it was derived from the Arundel collection, its previous history is not known. The Earl of Arundel was in his day an avid hunter after antiquities and works of art in general and manuscripts in particular, and he employed numerous agents in the task of collection. Much of this was, in fact, acquired by the earl in 1636 at Nuremberg, which appeared to have been a natural focus for the disposal of works of art in those days.

The three small notebooks housed in the Forster Collection at the Victoria and Albert Museum were acquired in Vienna at a relatively trifling cost by the first Lord Lytton, who in his turn presented them to Mr. Forster. Again, of the Leicester collection at Holkham Hall, it is known that it once belonged to the painter Giusseppe Ghezzi, who lived in Rome early in the eighteenth century. The first Earl of Leicester spent some years in Rome previous to 1775 and brought many art treasures back with him. The Leicester collection includes Leonardo's notes on the project of a canal at Martesana, and many other studies on the principles of hydraulics and a number of sketches to illustrate their applications to various projects for wheels and mills and engines for both the regulation of water flow and for the raising of water from one elevation to another.

Some reference should be made to the alleged book by Leonardo da Vinci on the *Treatise on Painting*. This was in fact a compilation and collection of his many relevant notes on the subject, first published in Paris in 1651 by Rafaelle du Fresne, and followed almost immediately by a French translation by Roland Fréard of Chambrai. A later, and more complete, edition of the treatise was issued by Guglielmo Manzi in 1817, derived from a manuscript in the Vatican Library which, however, was originally the property of the Dukes of Urbino. This is a more complete text than that issued by du Fresne. Nevertheless, the most complete study of the Vatican manuscript is in German, by H. Ludwig in 1885.[1] It still remains open to serious doubt, however, as to whether Leonardo developed this treatise into final shape from his admittedly extensive notes. The suggestion, though consistent with the general and oft-expressed intentions of Leonardo, is nevertheless inconsistent with the normal fate of the notebooks.

In the light of the foregoing, the necessary references to Leonardo's notebooks have taken on a generally accepted pattern in most of the serious studies and commentaries that have appeared from time to time. This is given in Appendix A to this book and has been followed in these pages.

3. THE CHARACTERISTICS OF THE NOTES

Although, presumably, Leonardo wrote in a normal manner whenever he had occasion to communicate with others by letter, the notes he wrote in his manuscripts were anything but normal. Curiously enough, no one seems to possess a letter which Leonardo may have written during his lifetime. There must have been many such, yet even the famous letter commending himself to Ludovico Sforza (p. 22) has not been found. As already stated, the draft on fol. 391 r of the *Codex Atlanticus* is not in his own handwriting and it is not known who wrote it. But it must be said of all the thousands of sheets of notes written by Leonardo throughout his life that he could scarcely have made them more difficult to decipher if he had deliberately intended so to do. From the outset of his "note-taking" career he had cultivated the habit of writing his notes not from right to left, as is normal to all European scripts, but from left to right, inverting each letter in a "mirrored" style which was to prove a sore trial and puzzle for many years to those who tried to decipher them. Jean Paul Richter, who spent many valuable years on this task, points out that the sheer physical strain of studying the manuscripts by holding them up to a mirror is only possible for very short periods. One simply has to learn to read them mirrorless, as they were written—and the ability so to do has come to very few persons. The difficulties are further aggravated by the fact that Leonardo freely omitted punctuation and introduced tricks both of abbreviation and the occasional combining of two or three words into one.

These latter devices are, of course, habits of scribbling common to most prolific note-takers and they have no special significance. They are used for the benefit of the note-taker himself. But what are we to make of the major habit of right-to-left "mirrored" writing? The first thought that inevitably suggests itself is that Leonardo desired

---

[1] Leonardo da Vinci: Das Buch von der Malerei (Bd XV–XVIII of Quellenschriften für Kunst-Geschichte, etc. Edit. R. Eitelberger v. Edelberg). Vienna, 1882, and Stuttgart, 1885.

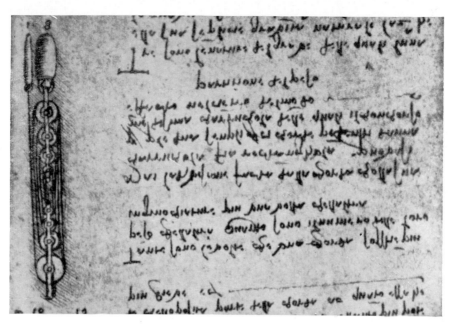

Plate 54—An example of Leonardo's use of sheaves of pulleys.

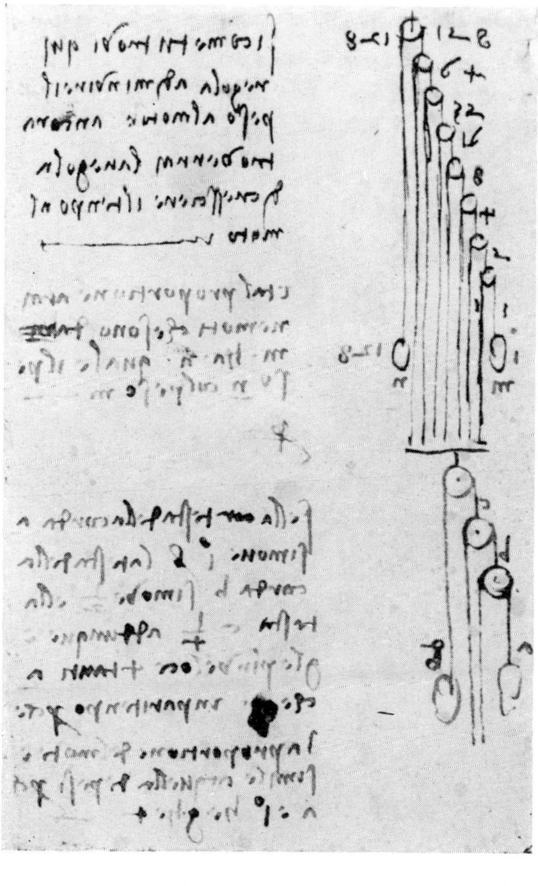

Plate 55—Pulley system indicating link between "velocity ratio" and "mechanical advantage" (C.A. 120 v.c.).

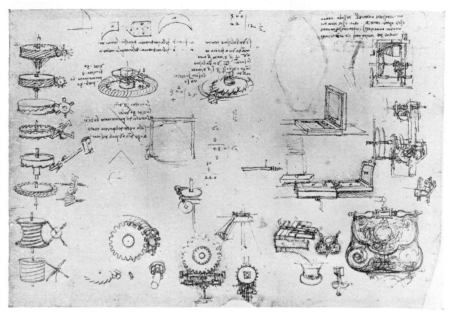

Plate 56—A sheet of sketches of various forms of toothed gearing (C.A. 372 r.b.).

Plate 57—Power transmission in a nap-raising machine
(C.A. 38 r.a. and I.B.M., New York).

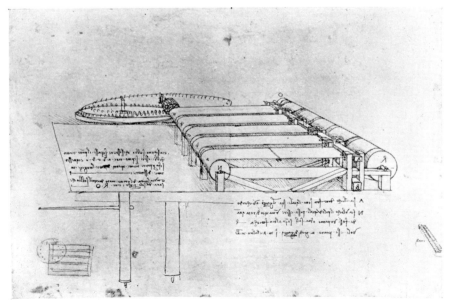

secrecy—either against plagiarism, or as a defence against the possible consequences of displeasure, either from his powerful patrons or from the disciplinary authority of the Church. Superficially there is plausibility in any or all of these suggestions. We know Leonardo was always frank and uninhibited in writing whatever he felt. Throughout the political changes of his times the authority of the Church was an element of importance. Though less effective in some areas than others, it was, generally speaking, sufficiently adequate for it to be unwise to make statements or express opinions contrary to Church doctrine. Leonardo never, in fact, associated himself with the Church and, indeed, he held himself aloof from it. But he may have felt, particularly in his younger years when he first began to fill his notebooks, that some of his comments might lead to troublesome consequences. Yet spontaneity of expression was instinctive in him. The comments had to be made, so presumably he might well have felt it to be wise to ensure that they were not easy to decipher.

As to the fear of plagiarism, there is very little, if any, evidence that he ever showed his notebooks to his friends. Even if he had done so, they would obviously have been hard put to it to read them. Nor, interestingly enough, is there any evidence in the notebooks themselves of any personal discussions with interested colleagues regarding their contents or the pros and cons of the many problems they dealt with. Obviously, such discussions must have occurred, as, for example, with such specialists as Fra Luca Pacioli on mathematical topics in his earlier years, and with della Torre in later years on anatomical and biological studies, but they are not in fact recorded. The names of contemporaries are usually mentioned in relation to the day-to-day round of life and living rather than to matters involving scientific discussion and opinion. Names relating to such matters do occur, but usually they concern writers and thinkers of the past whose books Leonardo had read and studied.

On the other hand, there is ample evidence that Leonardo intended sooner or later to make an attempt to sort out his notes and perhaps recast them, as and where necessary, into a form suitable for publication. The quotation given on p. 19 of this book is an obvious indication of this. The care and the regard for logical sequence with which Leonardo lays down procedures for this purpose is quite unmistakable. For example, in the British Museum manuscript he proposes a discussion on the problems of fissures in walls. "First write the treatise on the causes of the giving way of walls and then, separately, treat of the remedies."[1] Very many other examples may be quoted, all pointing to his intention of future publication, and it is plausible to

[1] Brit. Mus., 157 a.

N

believe that, until such time as publication under his own signature could give him the undisputed title to originality, there was some need to protect his notes from would-be copyists by devices of caligraphy such as he in fact employed.

Some of the notebooks contain actual letters, or portions of letters, to named individuals[1] or to collective bodies[2]—but obviously, since these were both tucked away in pages of the notebooks *and* written in his characteristic right-to-left and mirrored style, they were but drafts from which, presumably, the actual letters will have been written.

The problem of *why* Leonardo wrote thus, therefore, still remains one of pure conjecture. Most students of his notebooks agree, however, that the answer is closely related to the extreme probability that he was naturally a left-handed writer and painter. Fra Luca Pacioli was known to have referred to this, and another contemporary of Leonardo, named Saba da Castiglioni, states in his *Ricordi* (Bologna, 1546) that Leonardo was *mancino* (i.e. left-handed) and that he not only wrote but drew and sketched with his left hand. Jean Paul Richter suggests that he may have been "deprived of the normal use of his right hand by an accident or in a fight",[3] but this, after all, though possible, is again conjecture. The only really indisputable evidence of a disability in Leonardo's right-hand is that of the minor stroke suffered in his later years in 1517 (see p. 108), i.e. two years, in fact, before he died.

On the other hand, positive evidence of Leonardo's use of his left hand (though not necessarily arising from a disability) is to be found in the shade lines so often met with in his sketches. The person who is normally right-handed instinctively shades from right to left diagonally downwards, thus: /////, whilst the naturally left-handed person instinctively shades from left to right diagonally downwards, thus: \\\\\. It is this latter type which is met with predominantly in da Vinci's sketches and the inference is permissible that this is because he was born "left-handed". In this connection there is a drawing in the *Codex Atlanticus*[4] (Plate 40) showing a left-hand holding a pencil. One would suppose that a normally right-handed person would in such circumstances have portrayed a right hand.

But, of course, even a left-handed person conforms inevitably to the normal practices of handwriting to which he is brought up. Whether left-handed or right-handed, Leonardo must have been taught

[1] E.g., Bernado di Simone (CA. 4 v.b.); My most beloved brother (probably Domenico b. 1484) (CA. 202 v.a.); Ludovico Sforza (several references); and others.
[2] E.g., My most illustrious Lords (i.e. of the Venetian Senate) (CA. 234 v.c.); My Lords, Fathers and Deputies (CA. 270 v.c.); Illustrious Commissioners of Buildings (CA. 323 v.b.).
[3] J. Paul Richter, vol. i, p. 110.
[4] *Codex Atlanticus*, 283 v.b.

and trained to the normal practice of writing from left to right, without tricks or devices of any kind. Nevertheless, all children and young persons experiment on paper in one way or another if only as part of the "play instinct" natural to all youth. It is therefore extremely probable that Leonardo as a youth must have discovered the ease and, no doubt, the pleasure of writing from right to left and to have found, in so doing, that his caligraphy tended to be of the "mirrored" type. The reader, whether naturally right- or left-handed, can satisfy himself that this is true by trying it out for himself. Let him take pen or pencil in the left hand and, without attempting to think about the process of what he is doing, go straight to the top right-hand corner of a sheet of paper and start writing some such simple and easy phrase as "Dear Sir" or "How do you do?" It is important that the experimenter should do this without trying to analyse what he is doing *while he is doing it*—otherwise the fact that what he is doing is contrary to conventional writing obtrudes itself upon the experiment and defeats it. The reader who tries this out will find that he is, in fact, writing in "mirrored" style.

Interesting publicity was given to this self-discovered proclivity for mirrored writing by a London daily newspaper. This paper published in 1949 the facsimile of a letter from a reader (Plate 41) which excellently illustrates the point made above. But actually what this writer found to be instinctive and easy is at least not difficult for anyone to cultivate for himself, as the preceding paragraph will have indicated.

It is therefore plausible to presume that Leonardo discovered this trick quite early in his youth and that it pleased him sufficiently to practise it and cultivate it until it became completely natural and straightforward to him. When, therefore, he began the serious practice of recording his thoughts, feelings, experiences and experiments, he may by then quite naturally have begun the practice of mirrored writing and, from sheer consistency, to have made this a life-habit.

On the other hand, Capener has argued on medical and neurological grounds,[1] that he was not a "right-cerebral-hemisphere-dominant" individual (as he would need to be if naturally left-handed). He draws attention to the deformity of the middle finger of the left hand shown in Plate 40 in support of Richter's story of the accident or fight (quoted above), and suggests that although normally right-handed, this "temporary but serious incapacity would lead a man of Leonardo's character and interests immediately to learn to use the left hand, which he would find most easy to do in mirror fashion . . . if he were previously right-handed." Capener also expressed the view that the hand shown in

---

[1] Norman Capener, F.R.C.S., "Leonardo's Left Hand", *The Lancet*, p. 813 (April 19th, 1952).

Plate 40 was a self-portrait of Leonardo's right hand as seen through a mirror, and drawn with his left hand.

Riffling through the hundreds and hundreds of pages comprising the various notebooks of Leonardo da Vinci one meets an occasional entry—seldom more than a word or two—in orthodox style from left to right. Several examples are found in the *Codex Atlanticus* and quite obviously (e.g., as in fol. 35 v.a.) the handwriting is definitely not his own but that of some subsequent possessor of the notes. On the other hand, a left-to-right normal note in fol. 79 r.c., and another in fol. 172 r.b., offer some puzzling resemblance to Leonardo's own handwriting, which suggests the rare occasion when he "lapsed"—if the term is permissible—into the normal and conventional mode of writing, such as obviously he must have done in communications to other persons.

In his standard book on *The Literary Works of Leonardo da Vinci*, to which we have referred from time to time, Jean Paul Richter summarises the caligraphy of the notebooks by showing the letters of the alphabet and the numerals as Leonardo scribbled them. The reader who is interested may refer to these in Appendix B.[1]

4. LEONARDO'S SCIENTIFIC METHOD AS REFLECTED IN HIS NOTES

What do the notebooks of Leonardo da Vinci reveal as to the scientific method of his approach to the variety of problems and topics over which they range? If we are to do justice to this question and to the writer of the notes, it is essential to reiterate what we have already stressed—that the whole collection of notes is not merely a day-to-day compilation made, as he points out in the extract quoted on p. 19, "without order, drawn from many papers that I have here copied", but also the accumulated writings of nearly fifty years of one life. Scientific discussions rub shoulders with odd references to daily budgetary problems and memoranda; sketches appear without "text", and "text" without sketches, and, again, more happily, sketches with an accompanying text. Such an accumulation must at least in their aggregate build up for us an intimate and an accurate picture of the man himself. They reveal his thoughts, his way of life, his abilities, his weaknesses, his repressions. We have summarised these sufficiently in the opening chapter of this book. What we are now concerned with is an analysis of his method of pursuit of any given range of topics.

Clearly this involves for us much of the operation he intended himself—to sort and sift and put in some sort of order. Much that he wrote must, in fairness, be discarded from our consideration. For

[1] These are also described in detail by G. Calvi, *I Manoscritti di Leonardo da Vinci* (Bologna, 1925). (Fig. 3—"Prospetto di carratteri e segni Vinciani".)

example, since our special interest in this particular study is in Leonardo's mechanical science and engineering, a first survey is necessary to sort out and separate, so to speak, his writings and sketches on these topics. But it becomes quickly evident that much of these notes and comments must be put aside, either because they are difficult to follow or because they repeat again and again in varied forms what has been previously stated, or because they are patently fallacious, or even because they cannot be understood. So long as what remains leaves an impression of pertinence, consistency and an ordered sequence of sound discussion, we are doing reasonable justice to the writer of the notes. In a series of scribbles it is not just to hold out against a writer the sort of entries that he would himself be the first to reject when he makes the attempt to "reduce them to order" for the purposes of publication.

It is for that reason that the patient work of years of such men as J. Paul Richter and Edward McCurdy in sorting out and rendering into English Leonardo's most important writings over a selected variety of topics and subjects must arouse our admiration and gratitude, particularly having regard to the difficulties of caligraphy in the original vernacular of fifteenth-century Italy in which the notes were written.

As an illustration of the sort of general impression created by the scanning of a notebook, let us take as an example Manuscript *F* of the series in the Bibliothèque Nationale. This book, whose pages measure approximately $5\frac{1}{2}$ inches by 4 inches, contains 96 leaves (i.e. 192 pages). Leonardo records for us that the book was "Begun at Milan, on the 12th day of September 1508", and it was probably completed a few years later, perhaps in 1513. The topics within these pages include light and shade, hydraulics, biology (fossil studies), bird flight, mathematics, and notes on centres of gravity.

But the entries on the inside cover afford a special interest. They give us a vivid picture of some of the classical writers and scholars whose works he either studied or wished to study, and some of his own contemporaries whom he mentions by name. And mixed up with these are (on the right-hand column of the notes) two memos relating respectively to nude studies and an experiment on the inflation of the lungs of a pig.

The cover reads thus:

Manuscript F—Cover (Verso)

Horace[1] has written:
"Of the speed of
the sky"

Concave Mirrors
Books of Venice
Latin and Vulgate Vocab-
ularies
Bohemian Knife
Vitruvius
Meteors
Archimedes: De Centro
gravitatis
The Anatomy of Alessan-
dro Benedetto[2]
The Dante of Niccolo of
the Cross

Aristotle's "Philosophy"
"Messer" Octavien Pal-
lavicimo, for his Vitru-
vius
Go each Saturday to the
hot baths and you will
see the nudes (naked
men)
Inflate the lungs of a pig
and observe whether
they increase in width
and in length or in-
crease in width while
diminishing in length.

Albertuccio[3] and Marliano: "De Calculatione"
Albertus Magnus: On Heaven and Earth, from Fra Bernardino.

The entry relating to the inflation of the lungs of a pig is of additional interest in that it forms the subject of a comment on Leonardo's proclivity for practical joking. One of the earliest biographies of Leonardo was by the Florentine Vasari. He wrote a well-known *Lives of the Painters* in 1550 and in his chapter on Leonardo da Vinci we read: "He used often to cause the guts of a bullock to be carefully freed of its fat and cleaned, and in this way to become so fine that it could be held in the palm of one hand and, having placed in another room a pair of blacksmith's bellows, to which he fixed one end of these guts, and blowing into them, filled the room, which was very large, whereby whoever was therein was constrained to retire into a corner."

It must be confessed, however, that if he was a practical joker there is little evidence of it in the notes, apart perhaps from a short paragraph in Manuscript *N*, *On the Flight of Birds*, which reads: "One will carry snow in summer, taken from the high crests of the mountains, and one will let it fall in places of festival in the summertime."[4]

Returning to the specific question of Leonardo's studies in mechanical science and engineering, the opinion has often been expressed that his approach was essentially practical and experimental—that he worked from practice to theory rather than from theory to practice. The truth is more probably a compound of both.

Consider, for example, the reference previously made (p. 193) to

---

[1] This Horace probably refers to the Papal Secretary of that name to Pope Nicholas V. He was both a poet and a translator of Homer.

[2] Alessandro Benedetto was well known as a student of Greek Medicine. He died *c*. 1525.

[3] Albertuccio. This might have been Albert of Saxony (see footnote 2, p. 224), but possibly it could have referred to Leon Batista Alberti (d. 1484).

[4] *MS. N, Codice sul Volo degli Uccelli*, 14 (13) r.

Leonardo's discussions on the problems of cracks developing in walls. These are discussed in the British Museum notebook, as part of a sequence on the "strength of materials" in their special application to the theory of architecture. Quite obviously he works from the practical to the theoretical in the sense that the problem is created by the actual *presence* of cracks in a wall and by the need to put the matter right. But his approach to it is completely scientific. Some of his notes on the subject are very extended and they soon impress as being based upon his own conception of the relevant principles of mechanics involved. Moreover, they are original. There is no evidence of any earlier writer having attempted a similar serious field of enquiry. We quote some of the note-headings or titles, which speak for themselves. Some are taken from the British Museum manuscript and some from Manuscript *A* of the Bibliothèque Nationale.

"What is the law by which buildings have stability?" (Br.M. 157b.)
"How to prognosticate the causes of cracks in any sort of wall."
(Br.M. 157b.)
"Of cracks in walls, which are wide at the bottom and narrow at the top, and of their causes." (Br.M. 138a.)
"Of arched cracks, wide at the top and narrow below." (Br.M. 138a.)
"Of the causes of fissures in [the walls of] public and private buildings."
(Br.M. 158a.)
"On Fissures in Arches." (Br.M. 158a.)
"On the loading of round arches." (MS. *A*, 50a.)
"On the damage done to the pointed arch by throwing the pressure on the flanks." (MS. *A*, 50b.)
"On the Remedy for Earthquakes." (MS. *A*, 51a.)

Another fundamental point relating to Leonardo's scientific method is that he has at all times a sense of logical classification. This is wholly a modernistic approach. It was also, as we explained in Chapter III, a feature of Aristotle's writings in the field of biology. An excellent example (among very many) may be taken from his frequent writings on the subject of water. What today we would speak of as hydrostatics and hydrodynamics interested Leonardo profoundly, and particularly so as, from time to time, he was concerned, both officially and unofficially, with problems of irrigation, of land drainage, of canal engineering and allied tasks in a country that essentially presented such problems. His writings on the subject occur and recur over and over again throughout the notebooks, but as an illustration of his sense of classification we quote the following from the Leicester manuscript (fol. 15 v.):

Divisions of the Book

Book 1 of the nature of water
Book 2 of the sea
Book 3 of subterranean rivers
Book 4 of rivers
Book 5 of the nature of the depths
Book 6 of the obstacles
Book 7 of gravels
Book 8 of the surface of water
Book 9 of the things that move on it
Book 10 of the repairing of rivers
Book 11 of conduits
Book 12 of canals
Book 13 of machines turned by water
Book 14 of raising water
Book 15 of the things which are consumed by water

Progressively, it will be noticed, he proposes to treat of his subject in a manner that might well have been charted thus:

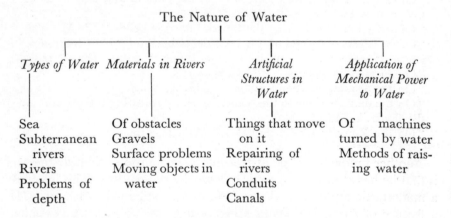

The Nature of Water

Types of Water	*Materials in Rivers*	*Artificial Structures in Water*	*Application of Mechanical Power to Water*
Sea	Of obstacles	Things that move on it	Of machines turned by water
Subterranean rivers	Gravels	Repairing of rivers	Methods of raising water
Rivers	Surface problems	Conduits	
Problems of depth	Moving objects in water	Canals	

Problems of water were of perennial interest to Leonardo. He saw in them something profound. "Water is the driver of nature," he writes[1] and adds: "Water, which is the vital humour of the terrestrial machine, moves by its own natural heat"—though what he meant by this is, of course, anything but clear.

It is, however, the sense of sequence and of classification that is the predominating impression. We meet examples of it over and over again. It must therefore inevitably be claimed for him that his attitude to any subject upon which he was writing was completely scientific in the modern sense of the term. For he brought within the ambit of his work the basic elements of modern scientific methods. These may

[1] MS. *F*, 87 v.

be enumerated as follows: first of all, sound observations; secondly, the instinct for careful classification whenever the subject under discussion lent itself to this; thirdly, he would proceed to a discussion of his observations and develop inferences and theoretical arguments; and, finally, he would, where possible, apply his observations and inferences to what he regarded as the supreme test of experiment. "Experiment," he writes, "never deceives: it is only our judgment which deceives, promising from it things that are not in its power";[1] and, more specifically, he advises: "Before making this case a general rule, test it by experiment two or three times and see if experiment produces the same effect."[2]

One more reference may well be quoted. "The Experiment should be made many times so that no accident may occur to hinder or falsify this proof," he writes, "for the experiment may be false whether it deceived the investigator or no."[3]

Now it must be stressed that this appeal to deduction from direct experiment and observation was something quite new. It simply had no place in his day. Nicholas of Cusa had pointed the way at the beginning of the fifteenth century but none had followed it. As a philosophic approach, the credit for its inception is associated with the name of Francis Bacon; but as a practical doctrine, the first experimental philosophers in the truly modern sense, who by their publications influenced their times and those that followed them, were probably Andrea Vesalius, to whose epoch-making book we have already referred (p. 144); Galileo in Italy; and William Gilbert in England. All these flourished many years after Leonardo's day. Vesalius died in 1564, William Gilbert in 1603 and Galileo died in 1642. Leonardo's world was still firmly dedicated to the absolutism of classical authority and it is difficult for us to appreciate the revolutionary nature of his rejection of this attitude.

One further point must be made. Leonardo was firmly wedded to the notion of mathematics as the foundation of all scientific study. "There is no certainty in science to which one of the mathematical sciences cannot be applied, or which are not in relationship with these mathematics,"[4] he writes—i.e. in order best to understand a happening or phenomenon or observation, it should be capable of measurement. More particularly to the special themes developed in this book, what could be more striking than his assertion that "Mechanics is the paradise of mathematical sciences because here we come to the fruits of mathematics".[5]

---

[1] *Codex Atlanticus*, 154 v.
[2] MS. *A*, 47 v.
[3] Leicester MS., 3 v.
[4] MS. *G*, 95 v.
[5] MS. *E*, 8 v.

Leonardo's notebooks abound with mathematical studies of one kind and another. On the whole, they are mainly arithmetical and geometrical and show practically no algebra. This is understandable. Manuscript M, for example, a pocket-size notebook of 188 pages (i.e. 94 leaves), is predominantly filled with notes on ratio and proportion, on similar triangles, on parallel lines, on problems relating to the circle, and on solid geometry. Some studies on the solid geometry of the cone, pyramid and cylinder, including notes on "plane development", are found in Manuscript G. Da Vinci continually resorts to sketches involving the theorem of Pythagoras, but on the whole there is little in his diagrams to indicate anything more than an elementary level of study. Sometimes it is a little difficult to follow what he is after in some of his mathematical moods and sketches.

Having thus outlined the main foundations of his scientific method, we are now in a position to deal with some of those basic conceptions of mechanical and physical science to be found in Leonardo da Vinci's notebooks, and which we must assume to have provided the foundations upon which so many of the drawings and designs of his many machines and other mechanisms were thought out. But a word of caution is necessary in connection with the general literary style of Leonardo's writings. We shall see that, in the subject of mechanics, for example, many references are to be found to basic notions such as force, motion, mass, inertia, power and work. These are matters that call for very specific wording because each has a specific meaning. Only precise phraseology can do real justice to their treatment. But although the student of Leonardo's notes becomes aware of his appreciation of this, it must be reiterated that Leonardo lacked such preciseness of phraseology. His standards of literary expression were not very high. Indeed, such an authoritative expert as Charles Singer has expressed the view that "the vernacular that he employs is that of a Florentine shopkeeper of the lower class".[1] This sounds rather harsh judgment, but it is true nevertheless that, although so frequently Leonardo's meaning is clear, the wording is frequently clumsy; and there are other cases when, in matters calling for precision of meaning, we are confronted with paragraphs that are frequently vague and puzzling.

On the other hand, except perhaps in the field of pure mathematics, there was in the fifteenth century no such thing as rigidity of scientific phraseology. It would be asking too much to expect it of Leonardo, particularly in relation to physical concepts about which so little was known in his day. Looseness of expression was a device not unknown to some of the encyclopaedists of the Dark Ages as a means to gloss over ignorance. It was frequently used by the alchemists and astrologers

[1] C. Singer, *A Short History of Science*, p. 172 (Oxford, 1941).

to provide a cloak of secrecy and mystery about their work. But deliberate looseness and vagueness of expression was certainly foreign to the intentions of Leonardo da Vinci. His difficulty was rather, then, the sheer inadequacy of words to convey new ideas for a man who lived years ahead of his times. Bearing this in mind, let us consider some of the fundamental concepts of mechanical and physical science as they appeared to him.

VII

LEONARDO'S STUDIES IN THE
MECHANICAL AND PHYSICAL SCIENCES

1. LEONARDO'S VIEW OF THE COSMOS

Working, so to speak, inwards from without, let us first consider what views Leonardo held regarding the universe as a whole and what place in it the earth itself had in his cosmical picture. It will be recalled that early in the fifteenth century Nicholas of Cusa had pointed out that, from an astronomical point of view, there is nothing unique about the earth—that it is merely one star among so many others. To this point of view Leonardo himself contributed. Most of the worth-while comments on astronomical topics are to be found in Manuscript *F*, but others of importance occur also in the *Codex Atlanticus* and in the Leicester manuscripts; but, of course, additional odd notes, some of major importance, are to be found scattered among many of the others.

As we might expect, his approach is experimental. "Construct glasses in order to see the moon large," he writes;[1] and again, on the same page: "In order to see the nature of the planets, open the roof and note at the base one planet singly; the reflected movement on this base will show the nature of this planet; but arrange that the base reflects only one at a time." Clearly, he tried to set up some sort of observatory under the skylight of his roof, using apparatus which would reflect and focus his celestial objects on a receiving base of some kind.

It is refreshing to see how essentially modern some of his notes appear in respect of the sun and the moon. Of the sun he writes: "The sun has substance, shape, movement, radiance, heat and generative power; and these qualities all emanate from itself without its diminution."[2]

A modern lecturer might easily make similar assertions regarding the sun and be regarded as approximately correct, if a trifle clumsy in his choice of words.

Of the moon he writes thus: "The moon has every month a winter

[1] *Codex Atlanticus*, 190 r.a.   [2] Ibid, 270 v.b.

and a summer. And it has greater colds and greater heats and its equinoxes are colder than ours."[1] And again: "The moon has no light of itself but so much of it as the sun sees, it illuminates. And of that illuminated part we see as much as faces us."[2]

Leonardo realised, therefore, that the moon shines by light reflected from the sun, and he entered into interesting speculations as to the existence of continents and seas on the moon's surface. Some of his most interesting observations on the moon are to be found in the Leicester manuscript. Here he discusses the existence of a sort of lunar force of gravitation.[3] He argues that the moon, being spherical, is like the earth and therefore is dense and consequently has weight. How then, he asks, can the moon sustain itself in its place in space? If there is no such thing as a force of gravity (Leonardo did not, of course, use this term) on the moon such as prompts the body to fall to itself, as would a stone to the earth, then the seas on the moon, for example, would of necessity fall to the earth. But they do not do this, and so Leonardo concludes that such a tendency exists for the moon in the same way as for the earth.

It was mentioned above that to Leonardo the earth is just a star among many. "All your discourse," he writes, "points to the end that the earth is a star almost like the moon and thus you will prove the glory of our universe; and thus you must make a discourse about the size of various stars according to the authorities."[4] Earlier in the same notebook we read: "If you look at the stars without their rays—as may be done by looking at them through a small hole made with the extreme point of a fine needle and placed so as almost to touch the eye— you will perceive these stars to be so small that nothing appears less; and, in truth, the great distance gives them a natural diminution, although there are many there which are a great many times larger than *the star which is our earth*, together with the water. Think, then, what this star of ours would seem like at so great a distance, and then consider how many stars might be set longitudinally and latitudinally amid these stars which are scattered throughout this dark expanse."[5] The reader will surely agree that this is much the sort of picture of the skies about which we read in the books of today.

But we must not assume that Leonardo had completely rejected the astronomical picture of classical tradition. The four basic elements of earth, air, fire and water must, by implication, have had some reasonable meaning for him and specific references to this geo-physical picture are met with from time to time. Thus we meet approaches to it in a long note which is headed "Element of Fire: Middle Region

---

[1] *Codex Atlanticus*, 303 v.b.　　[2] Brit. Mus., 94 v.　　[3] Leicester MS., 36 v.
[4] MS. F, 56 r.　　　　　　　　　　　　[5] MS. F, 52.

of the Atmosphere"; which begins thus: "The atmosphere interposed between the fire and the water participates in the water and the fire but so much more in one than the other as it is nearer to one than the other."[1] A similar inference may be drawn from a later note in the same manuscript as follows: "You may see that the beating of its wings against the air supports a heavy eagle in the highest and rarest atmosphere close to the sphere of elemental fire."[2]

The Leicester manuscript, however, also comes near to a specific reference to Leonardo's acceptance of the scheme of the four basic elements of earth, water, air and fire, in the course of Leonardo's discussions on the moon above referred to. In fol. 36 v. he argues that there is water on the moon, and included in his note there occurs the following: ". . . if there is water on the moon there is also earth there upon which the water supports itself and, consequently, the other elements: and water is supported up there *among the three other elements*, as down here our water is among its accompanying elements."

There is one other link with the cosmology of Greek tradition to which we should refer. This relates to the Pythagorean doctrine of the harmony of the spheres, and of the heavenly music produced by the friction between the successively rotating spheres containing the various planets. Leonardo discusses and discards this doctrine in a note which is headed: "Whether the friction of the heavens makes a sound or no."[3] He points out that friction consumes the bodies which are rubbed and he enquires into the effect which the revolving of the concentric system of spheres would have if each member were rubbing against its neighbour day by day for centuries. How, he asks, could they persist without being used up? He even goes so far as to point out that, whereas the linear velocity of rotation is zero at the poles of the spheres and maximum at their "centre", i.e. the equatorial region, the friction at the equators would be of enormous proportions and the system could not persist.

Some controversy has been directed towards the question of whether or no Leonardo believed in the diurnal rotation of the earth on its axis. There is a note in Manuscript *G*[4] in which he discusses the spiral motion of a falling body. He develops brilliantly the deduction that as a falling body approaches the earth it acquires a spiral path of fall. It is difficult, therefore, to believe that he would have propounded this problem at all unless he accepted the idea that the earth is rotating on its axis, since it is by virtue of this rotation that the falling body acquires its spiral movement. This, however, in its turn brings up the question of his attitude to the view that the earth was the centre of the

---

[1] *Codex Atlanticus*, 75 v.a.
[2] Ibid., 372 r.a.

[3] MS. *F*, 56 v.
[4] MS. *G*, 54 v., 55 r.

universe. After all, the orthodox opinion was that the earth was at rest, with all the heavenly bodies revolving around it daily. Was Leonardo a Copernican? There is a famous line in the Windsor manuscript which reads: "The sun does not move."[1] We must not deduce from this that he was aware of or influenced by Copernicus, whose epoch-making book *De Revolutionibus* could not have been completed before 1529 (see p. 142)—i.e. ten years after Leonardo's death—and was not published till 1543. Yet, on the other hand, there is a note in Manuscript *F* which reads: "How the earth is not in the centre of the circle of the sun, nor in the centre of the universe, but is in fact in the centre of its elements which accompany it and are united to it."[2] On balance, we must believe that Leonardo was at least on the track of the truth and that, at any rate, he had come to reject the Ptolemaic doctrine of a geocentric universe.

As a final thought before we leave this aspect of his writings, let us reflect upon the fact that nearly a century after Leonardo wrote the significant phrase "Il sole non si muove" ("The sun does not move"), Giordano Bruno, an eminent philosopher, was burnt at the stake in 1594 for saying the same thing; and that when the great Galileo also came into the open as a Copernican, he was haled before an ecclesiastical court in 1632 to be condemned as a heretic for saying so. He only saved his life by the famous act of recantation.

2. LEONARDO'S COMMENTS ON THE STRUCTURE OF THE EARTH

Leaving Leonardo's observations on the universe as a whole, let us consider next, very briefly, the general trend of his comments on the structure of the earth itself. Most of Leonardo's observations on geology are to be found in the Leicester manuscript and in the *Codex Atlanticus*, and some of them strike a distinctly modern note. There naturally had been available to Leonardo some, though not much, earlier work on geology. It was a subject that was bound to receive the attention of scholars, if only because of the violence and destruction accompanying some forms of geological phenomena. Floods, landslides, earthquakes and volcanic eruptions are, by their very nature, self-assertive, and offer lessons in geological change "before your very eyes". The Mediterranean area was and is rich in such incidents, and some of the early philosophers and writers of Greece and Rome inevitably gave them some attention. Aristotle, for example, was quick to establish a connection between earthquakes and volcanic eruptions, and his view, accepted for centuries after, was that the ejection of hot materials in a volcano is the result of severe earthquake, following which the subterranean wind rushes out violently and causes the

---

[1] Windsor MS., 12669 r. [2] MS. *F*, 56 v.

surrounding country to be buried under ash and cinders. Subsequent writers took up the theme in varying form. Lucretius recognised some of the causes of earthquakes as the subsidence of mountainous rock masses, with consequent propagation of earth tremors of wide extent; and the geographer Strabo cited examples of both widespread and local subsidences of land and of the raising in places of the sea bottom.

Perhaps the most detailed discussion of earthquakes in classical times is to be found in Seneca's *Questiones Naturales*. He had met and questioned survivors of the great earthquake of February, A.D. 63, and the attendant eruption of Vesuvius in the Naples area; and on the whole he supported the "orthodox" theory of subterranean wind which, struggling for an outlet through the cracks and chasms, came into violent contact with stores of sulphur and other combustible materials, which are thus set on fire by friction.

The more placid geological processes, on the other hand, not unnaturally received far less notice from the philosophers of antiquity. Two such phenomena, however, did receive some attention and comment. Rivers, for example, have at all times been so intimately related to the welfare of communities that such attendant observations as their erosive effects, accompanied by the deposition of silt (sometimes in great quantity), were bound to receive notice; and Herodotus, Aristotle and Strabo all commented upon them. Strabo, in particular, was interesting in his discussions relating to the slow carving out of alluvial plains and of the formation of deltas at the mouths of river estuaries.

The second group of phenomena connected with the more placid geological processes was the finding of shell and fossil remains in what geologists speak of as the tertiary and post-tertiary deposits of the Mediterranean area. These, too, are referred to by the earlier philosophers, and the inference that the sea once existed where there was now dry land, and vice-versa, had been duly noted.

Paradoxically, centuries later, following the revival of learning in the late Middle Ages, geological discussion was no longer able to receive the freedom it had enjoyed in classical times, because Church dogma had decreed that land and sea were duly separated on the third day of creation, that animal life was created on the fifth day, and that all this occurred some six thousand years ago. The geological admixture of dry land, made up in part of rock formed in the sea, together with the evidences of fossiliferous remains found in rock strata, were held inadmissible and contrary to Church teaching. There was, however, a sort of compromise permission to take into account the possible geological implications of the advent of the Deluge in biblical times. As a consequence there was little room for progress in geological knowledge.

Plate 58—Working model of a flyer spindle. For Leonardo's original drawing see Plate 59 (I.B.M., New York).

Plate 59 — Leonardo's sketch of a flyer spindle (C.A., 393 v.a. and I.B.M., New York).

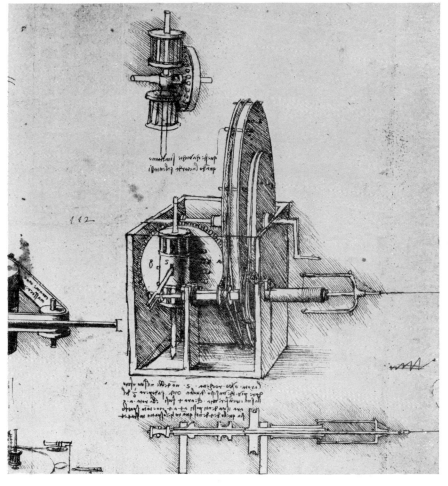

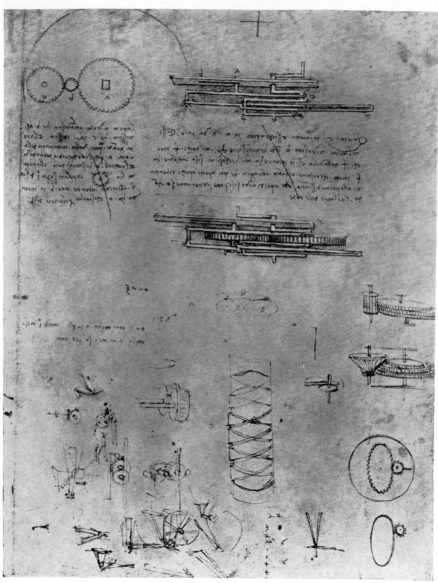

Plate 60—Sheet of sketches showing a variable-speed gearing device (C.A. 27 v.a.).

Readers will, however, have realised that Leonardo could have no such inhibitions. In a note in the *Codex Atlanticus*, headed "Doubt",[1] he writes: "Here a doubt arises, and that is as to whether the flood which came in the time of Noah was universal or not, and this would seem not to have been the case for reasons which will now be given. We have it in the Bible that the said Flood was caused by forty days and forty nights of continuous and universal rain, and that this rain rose ten cubits above the highest mountain in the world. But consequently, if it had been the case that the rain was universal, it would have formed in itself a covering around our globe which is spherical in shape; and a sphere has every part of its circumference equidistant from its centre and, therefore . . . it becomes impossible for the water on its surface to move, since water does not move of its own accord unless to descend. How then did the waters of so great a Flood depart if it is proved that they have no power of motion? If it departed, how did it move unless it went upwards? At this point natural causes fail us, and therefore, in order to resolve such a doubt, we must needs either call in a miracle to our aid or else say that all this water was evaporated by the heat of the sun."

He was very specific in appreciating the significance of fossil remains found at great heights above sea-level, and he attacked the theory of the advent of the Deluge by pointing out that the geological processes of change on the earth are ever present and that they tend to be gradual; and that great violence in nature is comparatively rare and is insufficient to explain the phenomena of fossils.

Nor could he show patience with a belief encouraged by the Church that fossils have their origins under the influence of the stars. "And if you wish to say that the shells are produced by nature in these mountains by means of the influence of the stars, in what way will you show that this influence produces, in the very same place, shells of varying sizes and varying in age, and of different kinds?"[2]

On the contrary, Leonardo maintained that they had once belonged to living organisms and that, therefore, what is now land was formerly covered by the sea; and that successive inundations produce successive layers of earth, imprisoning the organic remains within them. Consider, for instance, the following passage: "When nature is on the point of creating stones, it produces a kind of sticky paste which, as it dries, forms itself into a solid mass together with whatever it has enclosed there, which, however, it does not change into a stone but preserves within itself in the form in which it has found them. This is why leaves are found whole within the rocks which are formed at the bases of the mountains, together with a mixture of different kinds of

---

[1] *Codex Atlanticus*, 155 r.　　　　　　　　[2] MS. *F*, 89 v.

o

things, just as they have been left there by the Floods from the rivers which have occurred in the autumn seasons; and there the mud caused by the successive inundations has covered them over, and then this mud grows into one mass, together with the aforesaid paste, and becomes changed into successive layers of stone which correspond with the layers of the mud."[1]

In most of these observations Leonardo was dominated by an intense interest in the movements and flow of rivers and all problems relating to the power of moving water. He wrote constantly about them and spent much time during his travels in making careful observations of the countryside about him. These coloured his notes on geological and geographical processes. "In every hollow at the summits of the mountains," he writes, "you will always find the folds of the strata of the rocks."[2] And again he writes: "The lowest parts of the world are the seas where all the rivers run. The river never ceases its movement until it reaches the sea; the sea is therefore the lowest part of the world. Water does not move from place to place unless it is drawn by a lower position. Lowness, therefore, serves as a magnet for water."[3]

He is very clear on the subject of land erosion. "The water wears away the mountains and fills up the valleys and if it had the power it would reduce the earth to a perfect sphere," he writes;[4] and later, "All the plains which lie between the seas and the mountains were once covered by the salt waters. Every valley has been made by its river and the proportion between valleys is the same as that between rivers";[5] and his obsession on the topic of rivers even persuades him to continue: "The greatest river in the world is the Mediterranean, which is a river that moves from the source of the Nile to the Western Ocean."

We conclude this section of Leonardo's studies with a quotation from Manuscript E[6] on the subject of the dual role of silting and erosion by rivers: ". . . Where the river flows swiftly it washes away the soil, and where it delays there it leaves its deposit, and both for this reason and because water never travels so slowly in rivers as it does in the marshes of the valleys, the movement of the waters there is imperceptible. But in these marshes the river has to enter through a long narrow winding channel and it has to flow out over a large area of but little depth . . . because the water flowing in the river is thicker and more laden with earth in the lower than in the upper parts. . . . So the conclusion is that the marsh will be destroyed because it is receiving turbid water below, while above, on the opposite side of the same

---

[1] MS. *F*, 80 r.
[2] MS. Brit. Mus., 30 v.
[3] *Codex Atlanticus*, 63 r.
[4] Ibid., 185 v.
[5] Ibid., 328 v.
[6] MS. *E*, 5 r.

marsh, only clear water is flowing out, and consequently the bed of the marsh will of necessity be raised by means of the soil which is continually discharged into it."

3. BASIC CONCEPTIONS IN MECHANICS—THE DOCTRINE OF INERTIA

At the root of all the physical sciences must lie the fundamental conceptions relating to matter and its movements in and through space. These involve, therefore, an understanding of the terms mass, motion and force. The reader will know that these constitute the foundations of that branch of modern mechanics known as "dynamics", and that they find their expression in what are generally spoken of as Newton's "Three Laws of Motion". Sir Isaac Newton was not himself the author of these laws, but he was the first formally to set them out collectively, in his famous *Principia*. The first two deal with the conception of force and the principle or doctrine of inertia, and the third is the law of reactions. For the benefit of the reader who may not be familiar with these fundamental principles of mechanics, and in order to enable him the better to appreciate the nature of Leonardo's notes on the subject, we venture to enlarge on this.

We all use the terms force, weight and motion in our everyday life, but, curiously enough, we much less frequently use the term "mass". Yet "mass" is the more fundamental in the sense that it relates to the measure of the amount of matter in any given body. A man of science will know that he cannot speak of the *weight* of such a body without first introducing the conception of the term *force*—and, indeed, that particular brand of force which we call gravity.

This will become clearer if we point out that the basic principle in nature regarding matter is that it cannot, of its own volition, so to speak, either move itself if it is at rest, or alter its motion (e.g. speed itself up, or slow itself down, or swerve from its previous path) if it is already moving. Only an external agency that we call *force* can do this to a body. So we have, at one and the same time, what is called the "doctrine of inertia", and the definition or meaning of the term "force".

The doctrine of inertia tells us that no body can of itself change its own state either of rest, or of uniform motion in a straight line. Indeed, these are the two *natural* conditions of all bodies. They either tend to be *motionless* (i.e. at rest), or to be moving all the time in the same direction in space and at the same speed. The external agency that will *compel* the body to alter this state of rest or of uniform motion in a straight line, we call *force*.

Actually, too, the tendency in nature is for all bodies to tend to *resist* change. It is because of this innate *inertia* in all bodies, for example, that when one injudiciously applies the force of the brakes to a fast-moving motor-car to compel it to a sudden reduction in speed, the unwary passenger is thrown forward, sometimes with dangerous consequences. And, similarly, if a car is suddenly jerked into a forward movement by the force of its engine, the passenger is jerked backward. In each case the car and the persons it carries all tend to persist in the previous state of rest or motion in accordance with the doctrine of inertia.

There are several ways in which forces may be exerted on a body to alter its movements. Some are applied to a body directly, and these may be *pulls* or forces of tension, and *pushes* or thrusts, which usually cause compressions; or again, there are *twisting* forces which produce torsion. Another group of forces are called *attractions* and *repulsions*, and these refer to forces which exist between bodies which are separated from each other by space. Electrical and magnetic forces are of this kind.

But the most important case of attraction is the *force of gravity*, which exists mutually between all bodies in the universe. Sir Isaac Newton established that the amount of this force of gravity is directly proportional to their masses but inversely proportional to the square of the distance between them. More particularly, the earth attracts all bodies on it. It is the earth's force of gravity that pulls on a body that is "up in the air" and makes it fall straight down (i.e. towards the centre of the earth) with a speed that increases or accelerates by approximately 32 feet per second every second. And when we speak of the *weight* of a body, what we really refer to is the amount of gravitational force that the earth exerts on it. The further "up" a body is, the greater is its distance from the centre of the earth and therefore the less is the force of gravity on it. That is why a body (whose *mass* is of course always the same) weighs *less* the higher up it is. Its *mass* is the same all the time because *mass* measures the amount of stuff or matter of which it is composed—but get it somehow far enough away from the earth and its weight will become less and less until right out in space it will become weightless.

Let us now turn to Leonardo's notes on these subjects. Speculations and pronouncements regarding the related conceptions of weight, force, motion and gravity, are to be found more or less liberally dispersed throughout his notebooks. They represent his thoughts on the subject throughout the years of his adult life. He never used the term "mass", and referred, on the whole, to "movement" rather than "motion". His notes show him to be obsessed with the idea that, fundamentally, what he refers to as the four powers of nature are weight, force, percussion and movement. "Speak first of the movement," he writes, "then of the weight because it is produced by the movement, then of the force which proceeds from the weight and the movement, then of the percussion which springs from the weight, the movement, and often from the force."[1] There are also discussions of varied length on each of these separate factors, most of which are couched in phraseology that makes it difficult really to comprehend his meaning—and, of course, some notes seem at variance with others. A typical example reads as follows: "I find that force is infinite together with time; and that weight is finite together with the weight of the whole globe of the terrestrial machine. I find that the stroke of in- divisible time is movement, and that this movement is of many varieties, namely natural, accidental and participating, and this participating movement ends its greatest power when it changes from the accidental to the natural, that is in the middle of its course; and the natural is more powerful at the end than in any other place; the accidental is strongest in the third and weakest at the close."[2]

Or again, consider this passage: "Weight, force, a blow and impetus are the children of movement because they are born from it. Weight and force always desire their death, and each is maintained by violence. Impetus is frequently the cause when movement prolongs the desire of the thing moved."[3]

It would be easy to take these words literally and to deduce that Leonardo attached "personal" and "animate" qualities to inanimate objects when he used such phrases as "the desire of the thing moved". But this would almost certainly be doing him an injustice. Prolific writer that he was, he was nevertheless clearly circumscribed by the paucity of words to convey concepts which were largely new to his contemporaries. He was, in fact, groping for phrases to describe the inherent property of matter we now call "inertia". And occasional notes are fortunately refreshingly clear on such points.

We are therefore entitled to seize upon those notes which, whether by a flash of genius or as part of a process of thought in which his notions derived from classical and medieval tradition are blended with his own original ideas, bring us right into the forefront of the ideas of modern physics and mechanics. In Manuscript A, for example, we read: "Nothing whatever can be moved by itself, but its motion is effected through another. This other is the force."[4] We have here, at one and the same time, a conception of the term "force" which is completely valid today—and, implicit in it, we also have the principle of inertia. It is by no means the only example. That force was to Leonardo a non-material concept is clear from the following: "Force I define as a spiritual power, incorporeal and invisible, which with brief

[1] *Codex Atlanticus*, 155, v.b.
[2] Ibid., 117 r.c.
[3] Ibid., 123 r.a.
[4] MS. *A*, 21 v.

life is produced in those bodies which, as the result of accidental violence, are brought out of their natural condition and state of rest. I have said spiritual because in this force there is an active, incorporeal life; and I call it invisible because the body in which it is created does not increase in weight or size, and of brief duration because it desires perpetually to subdue its cause, and when it is subdued it kills itself."[1]

Of course, much of this is difficult to follow. It is naturally not the language of modern science. Nevertheless, it breathes the whole spirit of modern science. When he speaks of the "weight or size" he clearly is referring to the mass of a body; and his analysis of what he regarded as the three "properties" of force—spirituality, invisibility, and brevity of duration—and his common-sense deduction that the weight (meaning the mass) of a body during, before and after the action of a force, remains unaltered, are of a standard far beyond his days.

We have already mentioned the implication of the principle of inertia in Leonardo's understanding of the term "force". He says that a body which is at rest cannot move of itself. We meet the phrase often. In the *Codex Atlanticus* there is one particular note of some length which reads like an extended paean of praise to force; and one line of this reads: "Without it [i.e. force] nothing moves."[2] Again, in Manuscript *A*, which we have already quoted, there also occurs the following note: "No inanimate object will move of its own accord; consequently when in motion it will be moved by unequal power, unequal that is in time and velocity, or unequal in weight; and when the impulse of the first motive power ceases, the second will cease abruptly."[3]

Another passage which strikingly shows Leonardo's appreciation of a profound and basic distinction between a non-material "force" and a material "weight", and the imposition by the force of an internal effect contrary to the inertia of the "weight", occurs in the *Codex Atlanticus* and reads thus: "Force is spiritual essence which by accidental violence is united to weighty bodies, restraining them from following their natural inclination; and here, although of short duration, it often shows itself of marvellous power."[4]

But a most striking evidence of Leonardo's modernity of outlook in this basic doctrine of inertia comes from a note in his small book *On the Flight of Birds* (also known as *N* in the Bibliothèque Nationale series), which shows that he realised that the principle of inertia applies as much to *moving* bodies as it does to bodies at rest. In the course of a discussion on the sudden turning of a bird on to its side, he writes: "And because all movement tends to maintenance, or rather all moved

[1] MS. *B*, 63 r.   [3] MS. *A*, 22 v.
[2] *Codex Atlanticus*, 302 v.b.   [4] *Codex Atlanticus*, 253r.

bodies continue to move as long as the impression of the force of their motors remains in them." [1] Here, surely, we have a real flash of the scientific genius which, unknown to the world of science for so long, forestalled Galileo by more than a hundred years.

We have referred to Newton's three famous laws of motion as the basis of modern mechanics. The first two concern the definition of force and the doctrine of inertia; whilst the third is known as the "law of reactions"—i.e. to every action there is an equal and opposite reaction. When the reader sits on a chair, he applies the external force of his own weight on the chair, and if this were the *only* force it would inevitably produce motion in the direction of the force, i.e. downwards. But there is no such motion. The reader remains safely balanced on his chair because there is instantaneously brought into being by the chair an equal and opposite (i.e. upwards) force of reaction which exactly balances out the downwards weight of the occupant of the chair. This, too, Leonardo understood. In the *Codex Atlanticus*, in the course of a note on the parachute (see p. 322), we read: "An object offers as much resistance to the air as the air does to the object." [2] Of course, the statement here takes the form of a particular application, but its specific character must leave us in little doubt as to Leonardo's appreciation of a general law of action and reaction. A similar reference occurs later in the same manuscript. [3]

But let us turn to the problem of the *measure* of the effect of a force on a body. We have seen that Leonardo foresaw what we now speak of as Newton's "first law of motion"—that, in effect, it both defines what we mean by force and enunciates a principle of inertia. The reader may know that Newton's "*second* law of motion" carries this one step further and tells us that the amount of change that takes place in the movement of an inanimate object depends upon the amount of force which is applied to it—that if, for example, the force is doubled, the *change* in the body's motion is similarly doubled. Leonardo understood this clearly enough—since, in any case, it is in accordance with common sense. But what he did *not* understand was the *nature* of the change in the body's motion. This is not one of speed or velocity, as Leonardo assumed it to be, but of *acceleration of speed*, which is a very different matter. An oft-repeated note [4] reads: "If a power moves a body through a certain space in a certain time, the same power will move half the body in the same time through twice the space." The reader who is familiar with the elementary formulae of kinematics and dynamics will immediately note the fallacy of this conclusion. Leonardo was here, however, following and accepting the teachings of

---

[1] *On the Flight of Birds*, 13 (12) r.
[2] *Codex Atlanticus*, 372 b.
[3] Ibid., 1158 b.
[4] E.g., MS. *F*, 26 v. and also 51 v.

Aristotle, and one feels that his own observations of what is, after all, a matter of day-to-day experience, should have taught him better.

4. LEONARDO ON GRAVITY

It is but one step from the general discussion of forces to the particular case of the force of gravity and its effect on falling bodies. This is extensively discussed in a series of notes in the manuscript in the British Museum, one of which says: "Why does not the weight O remain in its place? It does not remain because it has no resistance. Where will it move to? It will move towards the centre [of the earth]. And why by no other line? Because a weight which has no support falls by the shortest route to the lowest point, which is the centre of the world. And why does the weight know how to find it by so short a line? Because it is not independent and does not move about in various directions."[1]

Here we have, clearly, a concise statement of Leonardo's philosophy of the falling body. We are told of Galileo, more than a century after the death of da Vinci, that he startled the world of philosophers of his day by his simple experiment of dropping a heavy and a light weight simultaneously from the leaning Tower of Pisa. Such an experiment was a challenge against the authority of the Ancients. Yet Leonardo, the experimentalist, emerges continually through his scattered notes. "If a weight of a hundred pounds falls ten times from the height of ten braccia to one spot, and sinks one braccia," he writes, for example, "how much would it sink in falling from the height of one hundred braccia?"[2]

We mentioned above that Leonardo had not fully realised the importance of the acceleration factor in discussing the effect of a force on a moving body. In the case of a falling body, however, he was on surer ground. Here is definitely realised the fact that such a body does gain speed as it falls, i.e. it is accelerated. In Manuscript M we read: "In the air of uniform density, the heavy body which falls at each stage of time acquires a degree of movement more than the degree [of movement] of the preceding time."[3] Thus the idea of an acceleration is very clearly brought out. Later in the same manuscript we read: "If after the descent of a braccia by one ball you let fall another, you will find that at each stage of the fall the proportion of their velocities and powers will change."[4]

Interestingly enough, in the same manuscript another passage[5] makes it clear that da Vinci was aware of the influence of the air. He discusses the fall of two equal weights, the one vertically above the other,

---

[1] Brit. Mus., 175 a.   [2] MS. *A*, 3 r.   [3] MS. *M*, 44 v.
[4] MS. *M*, 61 r.   [5] MS. *M*, 43 v.

and notes that the distance between them steadily diminishes as they fall until the bodies touch, his explanation being that, owing to the screening effect of the lower body upon the upper one, the resistance of the air retards the motion of the former but not of the latter.

Leonardo da Vinci definitely sought to discover the true law of accelerations for falling bodies. In one note, for example, he enunciates his problem thus: "If a weight falls a distance of two hundred braccia, by how much would it fall quicker in the second hundred braccia than in the first?" Unfortunately, he failed to find a correct answer to his question. The correct law for falling bodies is, of course, that the fall is proportional to the square of the time, but Leonardo concluded that the function was linear. In Manuscript *M* we find the following passage, a portion of which has already been quoted above: "In the air of uniform density, the heavy body which falls at each stage of time acquires a degree of movement more than the degree (of movement) of the preceding time, and likewise a degree of velocity more than the degree (of velocity) of the preceding time. *Then to each quantity doubled in time the length of the descent is doubled, likewise the velocity of the movement.*"[1]

We see from the sentence in italics that da Vinci regards (1) the velocity as proportional to the time (which is correct; cf. the formula in kinematics, $v=gt$), and (2) the height of fall as also proportional to the time (which is incorrect since it is proportional to the *square* of the time). Additional interest is lent to the above passage by a sort of graphical representation of a velocity-time scheme adjoining it, with a time scale shown horizontally, and a velocity scale vertically, somewhat as follows:

```
   1     2     3     4     5     6     7     8     9     10
   o     o     o     o     o     o     o     o     o     o
   o     .     .     .     .     .     .     .     .     .
         o     .     .     .     .     .     .     .     .
               o     .     .     .     .     .     .     .
                     o     .     .     .     .     .     .
                           o     .     .     .     .     .
                                 o     .     .     .     .
                                       o     .     .     .
                                             o     .     .
                                                   o     .
                                                         o
```

The note against this scheme reads thus: "Here is shown how such a proportion as one quantity of time with another will have a quantity of movement with the other, and a quantity of speed with the other."

[1] MS. *M*, 44 v.

From some points of view it may fairly be claimed that this was the earliest example of the graphical method in the history of the mathematical sciences and, as such, it calls for our respectful admiration.

5. LEONARDO ON THE PARALLELOGRAM OF FORCE AND ITS CONVERSE

In the course of his investigations on the falling of heavy weights Leonardo shows us a very brilliant example of sound scientific deduction. We referred to this earlier in this chapter (see p. 205) in discussing Leonardo's views on the diurnal rotation of the earth on its axis. He dropped a number of heavy weights from the top of a tower and noticed that they did not meet the ground absolutely vertically beneath the starting point. There was, he thought, a small easterly

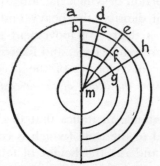

Fig. 28.   Descent of a falling body in
relation to the earth's rotation.

deviation and this he proceeded to explain by its true cause, namely, the rotation of the earth on its axis.

Actually, it seems impossible that in the relatively small fall of a body from the top of a tower such a deviation is capable of observation. The probability is that Leonardo *thought* he saw it, and was thus started on a train of thought which led him to believe that there *must* be such a deviation, so that it would never afterwards occur to him to doubt the accuracy of his observations. This, after all, is not an isolated example of the part played by the imagination in scientific discovery. Centuries after, for example, Dalton offered another instance in the train of ideas and impressions that led up to his enunciation of the atomic theory. In Leonardo's case the passage in question occurs in Manuscript *G* of the collection at the Institute of France and is illustrated by a diagram similar to Fig. 28.

"Let '*A*' be the body [he says[1]] which falls from the highest point of the sphere of fire[2] in order to come to the midpoint of the earth *m*.

---

[1] MS. *G*, 54 v. and 55 r.

[2] Leonardo refers here to the elemental spheres of earth, water, air and fire surrounding the "globus mundi", the sphere of fire being outermost and therefore the "highest up" from the centre of the earth.

I say that this weight, descending in a spiral, will not leave the straight line which follows its way towards the mid-point of the earth, because if the body goes from *a* in order to reach *b*, so will it go towards *b* and come to the position *c*. The point *a* in turning reaches *d*. If we now consider the position of the body, we see that it is always found in the straight line which, originally at *a* and now at *d*, joins it to the mid-point of the earth at *m*. If the body goes further towards *f*, then the point *d* will at the same time go to *e*. During the descent from *f* towards *g* the rotation of *e* is brought into the position *h*. Thus the body descends to the earth, always out of the starting-point. This is an accumulative movement. It is a combination of a straight line and a curved line. It is a straight line because the body is always found on the shortest line which joins it from *a* to the centre of the earth. It is a curved line in itself and in every point of the path. Therefore, a stone thrown from the height of a tower does not strike the wall of the tower until it reaches the earth."

6. THE COMPOUNDING OF FORCES AND MOTIONS

We make no apology for quoting this extensive discussion by Leonardo in full. It is surely difficult to withhold our admiration for the progressive logic of his argument and for the wholly modernistic line of thought which it indicates. Apart from the astronomical bearing which prompted our earlier reference to this passage, there is implied in the argument a definite example of an important basic operation in the mechanics of motion, namely, the compounding of two velocities, motions or forces (as the case may be) in different directions which, when imposed simultaneously upon a body, produces a single equivalent or, as it is called, a *resultant* velocity, motion or force. All schoolboys will recognise this as the principle of the parallelogram of velocities or of forces, according to which is relevant. It would perhaps be straining the facts to suggest that Leonardo was aware of this precise principle. That he was groping his way to the facts is, however, undeniable.

Not surprisingly, Aristotle in his day had attacked this problem in the particular case in which two forces are applied simultaneously upon a body at right angles to each other. His argument was clumsy but in his *Questiones Mechanicae* he showed[1] the example, so well known, that if two forces can be represented by two straight lines in the direction of the two forces so that their lengths are proportional to their magnitudes, then the diagonal of the completed rectangle will represent, both in direction and length, the equivalent single resultant force.

Leonardo went further. He did not confine himself to the special case of the right angle but considered any two forces at any angle

---

[1] See translation by E. G. Forster (Oxford, 1913), cap. i, 848 b.

whatsoever to each other. We meet it in his small notebook, written in 1505, *On the Flight of Birds* in a passage which reads thus: "The bird being in the act of falling in the direction of its open wing with a force of 4 [Fig. 29], and the wind which strikes it underneath with a force of 2, makes its course straight: we will say then that the descent of such a bird will be by the mean line, between the levels of the course of the wind and the obliquity in which the bird was with the force 4. As: let the obliquity of such a bird be the line *adc*, and let the wind be *ba*: I say, if the bird *adc* had a force 4, and the wind *ba* had a force of 2, that the bird would not go in the direction of the wind in *f* nor by its obliquity in *g*, but would fall by the mean line *de* and one proves it thus."[1]

The reader will note that, in spite of the characteristically clumsy language, Leonardo marshals his points clearly and cogently. He

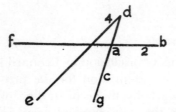

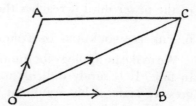

Fig. 29.   Leonardo's approach to the problem of the parallelogram of forces.

Fig. 30.   Converse of the principle of the parallelogram of forces.

displays here an insight into a truth of fundamental importance in mechanics. It is true that he neither constructs nor mentions a parallelogram, and in this respect he obviously fell short of the formal principle. But he does definitely speak of a resultant "effect" (he mixes his references to forces and "movement" quite freely) intermediate between the two separately imposed forces.

There is, of course, a converse to this principle of the compounding of forces and movements into a single equivalent resultant. It is a matter of common sense that if two forces or velocities acting simultaneously on a body at *O* (Fig. 30) can be represented on paper in magnitude and direction on some suitable scale by two lines *OA* and *OB*, so that their resultant in magnitude and direction becomes the diagonal *OC* of the parallelogram as shown, then similarly a *single* force (or velocity) *OC* could be replaced by the two simultaneously equivalent forces (or velocities, as the case may be) *OA* and *OB*, provided that *OA* and *OB* are the "arms" of the parallelogram of which the original single force (or velocity) *OC* is the diagonal.

We speak of this principle in modern mechanics as the *resolution*

[1] *Codice sul Volo degli Uccelli*, 6 (5) r.

or *resolving* of forces (or velocities), just as its converse is called the *compounding* of forces (or velocities). Was Leonardo aware of this converse principle? References in Manuscript *G* are illuminating in this connection. In the course of a discussion on the motion of a weight sliding down an inclined plane, we read: "The weight which descends obliquely divides its weight in two different aspects. One proves it thus: Let *ab* [Fig. 31] move according to the obliquity *abc*. I say that the weight of the body *ab* divides its gravity in two aspects, that is, according to the line *bc* and according to the line *mn*. Why and how much the weight is greater for one than for the other aspect, and what obliquity is that which divides the two weights in equal parts, would be in the weight of the body."[1]

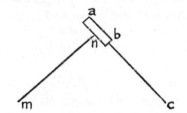

Fig. 31.　Resolution of forces down
inclined plane.

It is difficult to deny for Leonardo, in the face of this note, an understanding of the resolving of a force into two components in different directions; but again we are unable to say that he knew in the complete form of today the "principle of the resolution of forces", either as such or as a converse of the "principle of the parallelogram of forces".

6. THE PRINCIPLE OF WORK AND PERPETUAL MOTION

The reader will know that the term "work" has a special meaning in mechanical science apart from the day-to-day use of the term. Whenever a force acts upon a body and moves it, we say that "work" is done by the force on the body, and we measure the amount of this work by multiplying the mass of the body by the distance through which it moves. The engineer's unit of work in this country is called the foot-pound. Now Leonardo had his own understanding of this matter. The term "work" in the field of mechanics is relatively modern and da Vinci never used it in his notes—and certainly he had no very clear ideas as to the importance of the product of the acting force and the distance through which it moves the body concerned. What he spoke of was what he called the *achievement* of a force, and he certainly

[1] MS. *G*, 75 r.; 76 r.

appreciated the fact that this represented a term which has a value and which is capable of measurement. In Manuscript *F* there occurs this passage: "If a force carries a weight in a certain time through a definite distance, the same force will carry half the body in the same time through double the path."[1]

This is one of many similar pronouncements. They point to an appreciation of the fact that a given effort (i.e. by a given force) produces just so much effect and no more. It may move a smaller body through a greater distance, or a larger body through a lesser distance, but never a larger body through a larger distance. So he writes, for example, about the use of a machine for the movement of heavy bodies: "When the moving parts exert more movement in the same time than the moved body, then it [i.e. the 'force' or 'power'] has more force than the moving body and it will move more quickly than the body itself. When the part which is the moving part has less speed than the moved part, then it will have the less force than the moved body."[2]

There is therefore, in effect, a limitation imposed by the principle of work. It ties up, in fact, with the doctrine of inertia, since just as surely as no object can start moving of its own volition, so equally surely is it impossible to get any more work out of a machine than is put into it by the action of external forces. That this was clear to Leonardo one can see from the following note: "No inanimate object will move of its own accord; consequently when in motion it will be moved by unequal power, unequal that is in time and velocity, or unequal in weight; and when the impulse of the first motive power ceases, the second will cease abruptly."[3]

Yet one of the characteristics of medieval gullibility, on a par with the fortune-telling astrologers and the alchemists who claimed to produce gold artificially and to be able to prepare the "elixir of life", was a belief in the possibility of setting up machinery that would be capable of perpetual motion. To them it was useless to argue that if the principle of work be true, then the achievement of perpetual motion was impossible. We need scarcely be surprised, therefore, that Leonardo da Vinci writes "*Satanasso*" against "perpetual motion" comments in his notes, and that he consigns the "perpetual motion" dreamers with a gesture to their true place among the large army of necromancers, seekers of the philosopher's stone, and similar quacks of those times. "Oh speculators on perpetual motion," he writes, "how many vain projects of the like character you have created! Go and be the companions of the searchers after gold!"[4]

[1] MS. *F*, 51 v.   [3] MS. *A*, 2 v.
[2] *Codex Atlanticus*, 185 r.   [4] MS. *E*, 20 r.

7. LEONARDO ON FORCES OF "PERCUSSION"

We conclude our survey of Leonardo's treatment of that branch of mechanics we speak of as dynamics (i.e. the relations between forces and bodies and the movements the one produces on the other) with a brief comment upon his notes on what he called *percussion*, but which we speak of in modern mechanics as *impulsive* forces. Leonardo realised that these forces of percussion were different from forces in general, but there was certainly something more in his understanding of this class of forces than the bald fact of their existence.

He frequently speaks of differences between the terms "weight", "force" and "percussion". "Deal first with weight, then with its supports, then with friction, then with motion, and lastly with percussion,"[1] reads one note, whilst another says: "Weight, force, together with percussion, are to be spoken of as the producers of movement."[2]

It is evident from his references in the *Codex Atlanticus*[3] and elsewhere that he carried out a number of experiments both upon the collision of bodies and upon the recoil of spherical bodies when dropped upon plane (i.e. flat) surfaces. His two chief conclusions are on the subject of the glancing impact of smooth spherical bodies on smooth planes. The first is that a blow applied normally (i.e. at right angles) to a plane surface has a greater effect on the plane than one applied at an angle, and that of two such inclined blows the one whose angle of incidence is the smaller produces the greater effect. "The blow," he writes, "will be less powerful than its impulse according as the angle of its percussion is nearer the right angle."[4]

The second conclusion is that, for a rebounding body, the angle of incidence is equal to the angle of rebound. This is embodied in a note in Manuscript *A* headed "Percussion", which reads as follows: "The line of percussion [incidence] and that of rebound [reflection] are placed at the middle of equal angles. All blows struck on an object rebound by an angle equal to that of the percussion. This proposition appears clearly; in effect, if you strike a wall with a sphere, it will rebound behind by an angle equal to that of the percussion. Thus if the ball *b* [Fig. 32] is thrown on *c* it will return by the line *cb*, because it is constrained to fall on the wall *fg* at equal angles [i.e. normally]; and if you throw it by the line *bd*, it will return back by the line *de*, and thus the line of percussion [incidence] and the line of rebound

[1] In a collection of sheets with annotated drawings in the Academy at Venice.
[2] MS. Brit. Mus., 184 v.
[3] E.g., *Codex Atlanticus*, 28, 47, 64, etc.
[4] MS. *A*, 21 v.

make an angle on the wall *fg* situated at the middle of two equal angles as one sees the angle *d* between the angles *m* and *n*."[1]

We have thus passed in review the chief contributions of Leonardo da Vinci to one of the two main branches of the science of mechanics. It will be seen in what follows that the field of statics, the second of the two branches, claimed even a larger share of his attention. Nevertheless, the reader is reminded that, whereas up to the time of Leonardo the history of mechanics was virtually a history of statics (i.e. of forces in a state of balance or equilibrium), the study of bodies in motion was almost entirely a new one.[2] In this respect, as in so many others, our philosopher was a true pioneer. Dynamics had made such very little headway since the Greek days of speculation upon theories of gravity largely because the influence of the Peripaticians was against

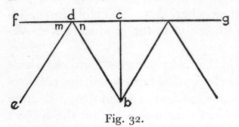

Fig. 32.

experiment—a situation with a distinct element of irony in view of the fact that their great master, Aristotle, was himself so keen an observer of nature. From this attitude, as we have seen, Leonardo broke completely away. Paying due respect to the wisdom of the ancients, who indeed influenced his views very profoundly in many respects, he yet insisted upon the test of experiment. Naturally a genius, professionally an artist and an engineer, he was bound to break new ground. To those who, surveying the subject matter of the previous pages of this chapter, are tempted to regard the dynamics of Leonardo as superficial and bare, we would answer that the wonder is not that he did so little but that he accomplished so much. For of the whole of it, it may justly be said that it constituted pure speculation and research in a virgin field.

8. LEONARDO DA VINCI ON CENTRES OF GRAVITY

Da Vinci's notes on what today we speak of as *Statics* cover a very wide field. In a sense this is not surprising. Unlike dynamics, the way had been indicated by his predecessors. He had at hand, as was shown in Chapter IV, the earlier writings of Aristotle, of Archimedes, of

[1] MS. *A*, 19 r.
[2] Aristotle, as we saw in Chapter IV (p. 120), did interest himself in the problems of motion and gravity, and later Albert of Saxony followed this up. Both are referred to in Leonardo's notebooks—e.g., *M* and *I*—but Leonardo himself went much further. It should be noted that there was a considerable body of serious study in the mathematical and dynamical writings in the fourteenth century by Jean Buridan (d.c. 1358), John of Dumbleton (late 14th Century), Marsilius of Inghen (d. 1396), Nicole Oresme (d. 1382), Richard Swineshead (fl.c. 1350), and William of Heytesbury (1313–72). Moreover, many of these became available in printed form during the sixteenth century, mainly after Leonardo's own lifetime. There is certainly no evidence that he was directly familiar with their writings.

Plate 61 — Working model of Leonardo's variable-speed gearing device (I.B.M., New York).

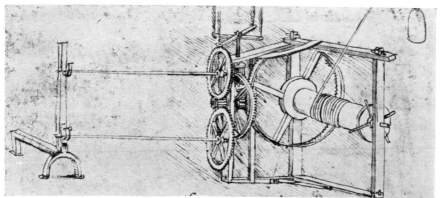

Plate 62 — Mechanically operated turnspit. Compare this with Plate 45 (C.A. 5 v.a.).

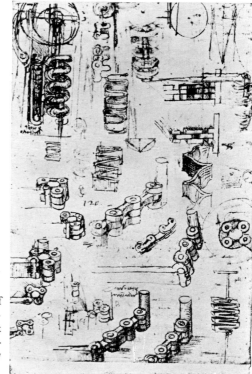

Plate 63 — Drawings of chain links, probably devised for the wheel-lock mechanism for breech-loading guns (C.A. 357 r.a.).

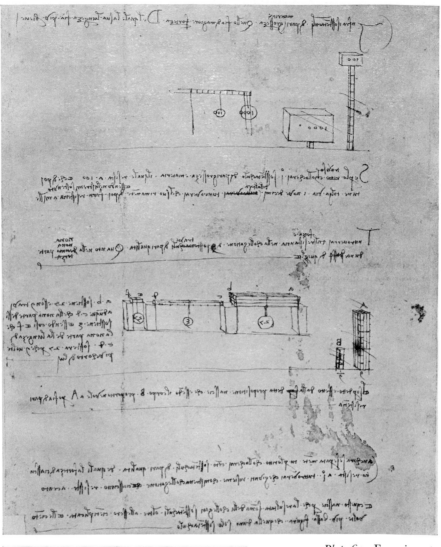

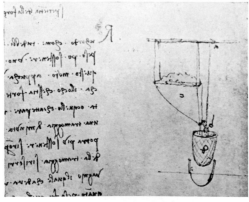

Plate 64—Experiments on the strengths of struts and loaded beams (MS. A. 49 r.).

Plate 65—"Test to find the load an iron wire will carry" (C.A. 82 v.b.).

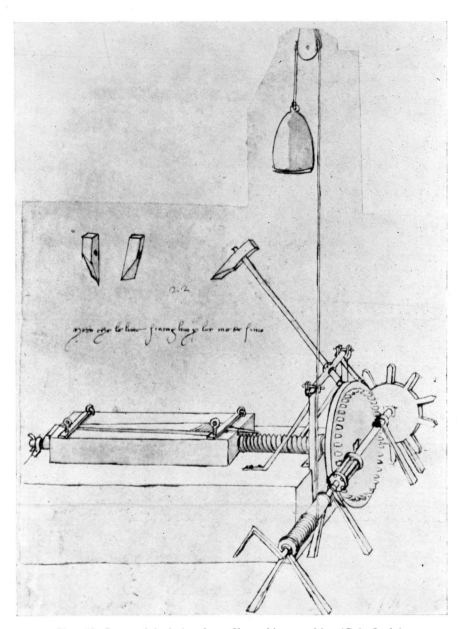

Plate 66—Leonardo's design for a file-making machine (C.A. 6 r.b.).

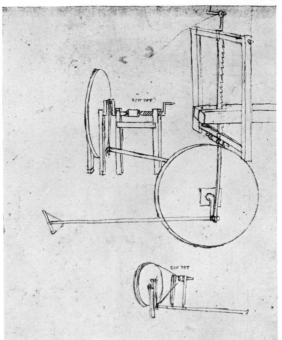

Plate 67—Treadle-operated lathe and mechanical saw (C.A. 381 r.b.).

Plate 68—Sheet of sketches to show a screw-cutting machine (MS. G. 70 v.).

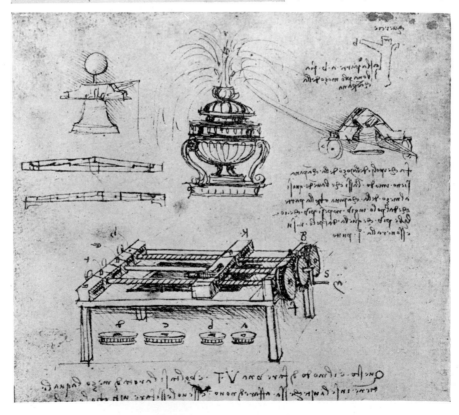

Jordanus Nemorarius and of others; and he applied these materials in his own way with his usual vigour and independence. If the range of da Vinci's statics was wide, it was also, within the possible limits of his days, thorough. Nevertheless, in turning to Leonardo's notes on this second of the main branches of mechanics the same prefatory caution is needed as was offered earlier regarding his limitations of language and nomenclature.

Referring back to the account given in Chapter IV[1] of the contributions to mechanics by Aristotle and Archimedes (the latter of whom, by virtue of the scientific superiority of his work in this field, is the more important of the two), it will be noted that these centred chiefly round two themes—the laws of the lever and the balance, and the conception of centres of gravity. This naturally set the pattern of approach to the whole subject by all subsequent writers, and in this respect Leonardo was no exception.

The law of the balance, imperfectly presented by Aristotle, received its real scientific blessing at the hands of the great Syracusan philosopher, Archimedes. Its demonstration was based on certain definitions and axioms, amongst which is the statement that in every body there is a definite point called *a centre of gravity*, at which we may suppose the weight of the body to be collected.

A consideration, therefore, of Leonardo's notes on centres of gravity makes a suitable starting-point for our study. This was a subject of peculiar importance and interest to da Vinci. It touched upon matters vital to his professional career. As an engineer he realised its importance in connection with the stability of structures and of the machines he was called upon to devise; as an artist he was constantly concerned with the balance of the human frame. References to the centre of gravity are therefore plentiful.[2] Yet it is difficult to find any actual attempt at formal definition. This, however, is not surprising. The conception of the centre of gravity of a body is one which has grown up literally through the ages. It had penetrated all existing writings on mechanics. It was, so to speak, a commonplace of ancient and medieval science. Nevertheless, that Leonardo regarded the conception of centre of gravity as fundamental to mechanics is clear enough from his remark that "mechanical science is very noble and useful beyond all others, for by its means all animated bodies which have movement perform their operations; which movement proceeds from their centre of gravity. This is situated at the centre, except with unequal [distribution of] weight."[3]

---

[1] See pp. 120 et seq.
[2] E.g., *Codex Atlanticus*, 86 r.a.; MS. *A*, 5 r.; MS. *G*, 78 v.; MS. *H*, 105 r.; MS. *M*, 37 r.
[3] *Sul Volo degli Uccelli*, 3 r.

P

There is an interesting link in the mind of Leonardo da Vinci between the conception of the centre of gravity of a body and its relationship to the centre of the earth. "Every gravity weighs through the central line of the universe," he writes, "because it is drawn to this centre from all parts."[1] And he continues: "A central line of the universe to that which arises from the centre of the world and ends in the centre of gravity of every body."

It is clear, too, that he studied the subject experimentally. The basis for his procedure presumably arises from two notes. The concluding sentence of one reads: "The centre of natural gravity is that which divides a body into two parts of equal weight and quantity,"[2] whilst the other, in Manuscript *I*, says: "The centre of every suspended gravity stops below the centre of its support, therefore: The central

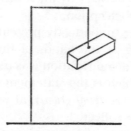

Fig. 33.   Centres of gravity.

line is the name given to what one imagines to be the straight line from the thing to the centre of the world."[3]

In Manuscript *B* is shown a sketch of a suspended weight (Fig. 33) with the note: "The centre of all suspended weights is established under its support,"[4] and in a similar sketch of a suspended artificial bird we read: "This is done to find the centre of gravity of a bird."[5] A number of da Vinci's notes on this subject occur as incidental to his studies on the poise of the human figure. They bring out his appreciation of the need for a due distribution of weight about the "axis" (i.e. the vertical line through the centre of gravity) under such varying circumstances as standing, sitting, kneeling, walking up and down hill, mounting stairs and ladders, and so on. The following is quoted as a typical example: "A sitting man [we read] cannot raise himself if that part of his body which is in front of his axis does not weigh more than that which is behind that axis without using his arms. A man who is mounting any slope finds that he must involuntarily throw more weight forward—that is, in front of the axis and not behind it. Hence a man will always involuntarily throw the greater weight towards any

[1] Brit. Mus., 195 r.   [3] MS. *I*, 22 v.
[2] Ibid., 123 r.   [4] MS. *B*, 18 v.
              [5] *Sul Volo degli Uccelli*, 16 (15) v.

Fig. 34. Centre of gravity of a
plane irregular figure.

point whither he desires to move than in any other direction. A man
who runs down hill throws the axis on to his heels and then on the
points of his feet."[1]

Those readers who have some familiarity with the subject will know
that in the case of irregularly-shaped bodies whose weight is concentrated largely to one side, the position of the centre of gravity is cor-
respondingly found in almost unpredictable points. Leonardo was
aware of the possibility of the centre of gravity of a body being actually
outside itself. Thus, in the course of a long note in the *Codex Atlanticus*
attached to a sketch (Fig. 34) we read: "Occasionally the centre of
gravity is to be found outside of the body, that is to say, not within the
weight of the matter, that is to say, in the air."[2]

So far, of course, apart from the experimental aspect, we see here
little that is really an advance on what had been done before. There
is one aspect of the problems of centres of gravity, however, in respect
of which Leonardo did do pioneer work. This was in the determination
of the centres of gravity of solid figures. Archimedes had made a
thorough study of the centres of gravity of *plane* surfaces in his *Treatise
on the Equilibrium of Planes and of their Centres of Gravity*, deducing his
results on Euclidian lines. Up to the time of da Vinci, however, no
one appears to have considered mathematically the problem of the
centre of gravity of the solids. It is of peculiar interest, therefore, to
find in Manuscript *F* the following note accompanied by a sketch of

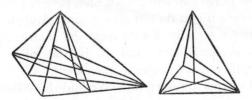

Fig. 35. Centre of gravity of a pyramid and
tetrahedron.

[1] MS. *A*, 28 v.   [2] *Codex Atlanticus*, 153 v.b.

two figures (Fig. 35) from which it is clear that Leonardo certainly considered the case of the tetrahedron: "The centre of gravity of a pyramid is in the fourth of its axis, towards the base, and if you divide the axis in four equal parts, and as you cut between two of the axes of this pyramid, one such intersection comes out at the above-mentioned quarter."[1]

Apart from this note on the two figures we have no further guide as to how da Vinci arrived at his result. The treatment appears to be modern enough and it embodies a result which formal history has hitherto attributed to Commandin and Maurolycus later in the middle of the sixteenth century.

We have from time to time referred to the misfortune that, following the vicissitudes of Leonardo's notebooks after his death, his writings could have little or no influence on the work of those who followed him. A case has, however, been made out by Duhem, a distinguished authority on Leonardo's work, that his studies on centres of gravity did at least bear some fruit.[2] Duhem claims that the sixteenth-century philosopher Jean Baptiste Villapond (1552–1608) somehow had access to Leonardo's notes on the subject and borrowed freely from them, though without acknowledgment. If this claim by Duhem is justified, then indeed Leonardo's work bore fruit, since Villapond's writings were freely quoted in their turn by a well-known and widely read sixteenth-century commentator named Father Mersenne in his *Mechanicorum Libri*.

9. THE PRINCIPLE OF THE LEVER

We turn next to the second of the two chief legacies of antiquity to the study of "Statics" in the Middle Ages, namely, the principle of the lever. Historically, this topic is associated with the name of Archimedes, and Leonardo was most deeply influenced by him in his own treatment on the subject.

As an introduction to Leonardo's conception of it, let us first note an entry in Manuscript *A* which interestingly links the ideal of the lever principle with what he wrote on centres of gravity. The note reads thus: "The perfect sphere placed on a perfect plane will have no movement whatever if you do not give it any. And the reason of it is that all its parts are equally distant from the centre; consequently, it always remains in equilibrium, and the balance of its equal arms of weight and length remain without movement."[3]

But what if the arms are unequal? We find this stated by Leonardo

---

[1] MS. *F*, 51 r.
[2] Duhem, *Etudes sur Leonardo da Vinci* (Paris, vol. ii, p. 80).
[3] MS. *A*, 21 v.

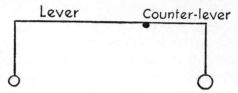

Fig. 36.   Lever and counterlever.

in its simplest form in a later note in Manuscript *A*.[1] Here he speaks
of the long arm as the lever and the shorter arm as the counterlever.
The note is accompanied by a diagram (Fig. 36) and reads as follows:
"The weight attached to the extremity of the lever made of any
material whatever will lift up at the extremity of a counterlever a
weight superior to itself by the same proportion as is the counterlever
to the lever."

It is clear that da Vinci was appreciative of the direct consequences

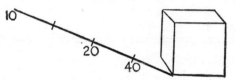

Fig. 37.   Practical utility of the lever.

of the principle of the lever. In Manuscript *A* there is a sketch illustrating its practical utility (Fig. 37) with the remark: "10 pounds at
the end of a lever will do the same as 20 pounds at the mid-point and
as 40 pounds at the fourth part."[2] Again, in the same notebook, a
note accompanying a sketch (Fig. 38) reads: "I ask, if the two arms
of the balance are divided in equal parts, and if one pound be placed
at each of the points *abcde*, what weight would resist their combined
effect at *f*? You make it thus: *a* gives a resistance of one pound;

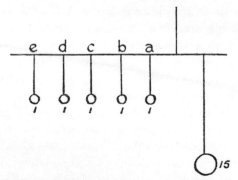

Fig. 38.   Application of the principle of the lever.

[1] MS. *A*, 47 r.   [2] MS. *A*, 5 r.

b makes a resistance of 2, c of 3, d of 4, e of 5, so that the sum gives a resistance of 15 pounds placed at f."

A problem suggested by this note, among others, is whether Leonardo was familiar with the idea of *moments* as we use it in modern mechanics. Readers will know that we measure the turning effect of a force about a fulcrum or point of suspension by the product of the force and the distance of its line of action from the fulcrum. In Fig. 38, for example, since it is clearly intended that a, b, c, d and e are progressively equally separated by the same distance as is f on the other side of the point of suspension, the turning effect on the left of the fulcrum is $(1 \times 1)+(1 \times 2)+(1 \times 3)+(1 \times 4)+(1 \times 5)$, which amounts to 15. Hence the balancing weight at f must also be 15 lb. It would seem natural to suppose that the *idea* of a moment is inherent in the above-quoted note, but the note accompanying a similar sketch (Fig. 79)[1] throws doubt on the matter. It affords an illustration of the occasional blunders made by Leonardo on relatively simple points.

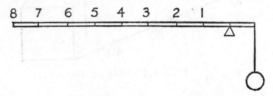

Fig. 39.   Leonardo in error—a steelyard type of balance.

The sketch reminds us in appearance of the steelyard—on the one side of the fulcrum is a short arm, at the extremity of which is a suspended weight, and on the other side there is an arm eight times as long, with divisions marked as shown. The lever is assumed to be heavy and the problem Leonardo sets himself is to ascertain what weight he must suspend at the extremity of the short arm in order to counteract the effect of the heavier arm, given that each section of the balance weighs 1 lb. A simple calculation shows the result to be $31\frac{1}{2}$ lb. and the fault of his argument lies in the unfortunate view that the weight of each section acts at the *outer end* and not at the mid-point. On this basis, he says, in effect, that the weight of the short arm is cancelled out by section 1 of the long arm, so that the weight must equal the sum of 2 lb (to balance the 1 lb of section 2 at twice the distance) and 3 lb (to balance the 1 lb of section 3 at three times the distance) and so on to the 8th section at eight times the distance, i.e. $2+3+4+5+6+7+8=35$ lb. Happily, this clearly did not satisfy the philosopher, since a later sketch is accompanied by the correcting remark that the weight must act in the middle of each portion.

[1] MS. *A*, 57 v.

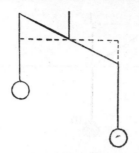

Fig. 40.   The "potential"
arm.

But whether or no Leonardo knew of the conception of moments
as a measure of the turning effect of a force around a point of suspension, there is ample evidence that he did appreciate the significance
of the measurement of the perpendicular distance of the force in
question from the fulcrum. This arises because, as the unequal arms of
a lever from the ends of which two weights are suspended swing about
the fulcrum, the perpendicular distance between the fulcrum and the
line of the weight naturally shortens. Leonardo spoke of this as the
potential arm. A note in Manuscript *E*, accompanied by a sketch
(**Fig.** 40), reads: "The junction of the appendices of the balances
with the arms of these balances is always a potential rectangle and is
not able to be real if these arms are oblique."[1] And again: "The
real arms of the balance are longer than the potential arms and as
much more as they are nearer the centre of the world" (i.e. nearer
the vertical through the fulcrum); and again later on: "And always
the real arms will not have in themselves the potential arms if they
are not in the position of equality."[2] Something surely of the modern
conception of the moments of a force about a point of swing is inherent
in these notes.

Indeed, they led Leonardo to his next step in a seemingly logical
sequence of studies. This concerns what, in effect, is the modern bent-
arm lever. So far, the lever or balance has been straight and the
weights perpendicular to it. What if one arm is now bent relative to
the other so that the corresponding weight is inclined to it at some
angle? The fundamental experiment upon which Leonardo bases this
problem has often been quoted and is illustrated in Fig. 41.[3]

A bar *at* is pivoted at *a*, and has a weight *m* suspended from *t*.
A second weight is also attached to *t* by means of a horizontal cord
tn passing over a pulley *n*. The problem is to find the ratio of the
weights depending from *t* and *n* for the equilibrium of the rod *at*.

Leonardo regards this, in effect, as a lever problem in which the

[1] MS. *E*, 64 r.   [2] MS. *E*, 65 v.   [3] MS. *E*, 65 r.

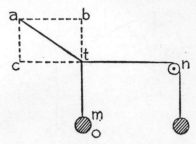

Fig. 41.   The bent-arm lever.

lever arm for the weight *m* is not *at* but what he calls the *potential arm or potential lever ab*, and for the weight at *n* the lever arm is the potential arm *ac*. He also speaks of these potential arms as *real* (i.e. in the sense of effective arms), and the lines *ctn* and *btm* (i.e. the real lines with the cord extensions) as *semi-real*. Alternative terms used by Leonardo are "spiritual lines" and "corporeal lines". Leonardo's conclusion, therefore, becomes that, as with the simple balance, the ratio of the two weights will be inversely as the ratio of their potential arms.

Actually, the nearest we get to the idea of moments in Leonardo's notebooks is in the use of this perpendicular—the potential arm. A device he uses from time to time in this connection is his employment of what he calls the "circumvoluble"—a tangential circle drawn from the fulcrum as centre. Thus, in Manuscript *M*, for example, there is a diagram[1] (Fig. 42) of a lever *fm* having a weight of 4 lb suspended vertically from *m*, and one of 8 lb held at an inclined direction *fp* through the use of the pulley *p*. Leonardo clearly indicates his use of the perpendicular to the line of action of the force by his employment of the "circumvoluble". This Leonardo stresses by a

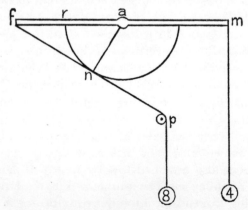

Fig. 42.   The device of the circumvoluble.

[1] MS. *M*, 40 r.

variety of conditions, one example of which is illustrated by Fig. 43,[1] against which we read: "In some part as would be, for example, the cord *nc*, it makes no difference because one always employs a line which falls perpendicularly from the centre of the balance and the line of the cord, i.e., the line *mf*."

It clearly emerges from all the above that Leonardo da Vinci appreciated the significance of the perpendicular on to the line of action of the force. Nevertheless there is no evidence that Leonardo used the product of force and distance, or attached to this product any significance as a measure of the turning power of the force about the fulcrum. As a matter of simple theory the alternatives of treatment are really as between the general use of *either* the factor of proportion *or* of the product of force and distance. The former embodies the

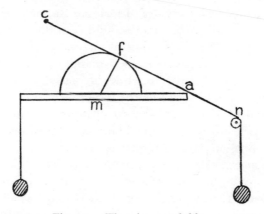

Fig. 43. The circumvoluble.

principle of the balance to the effect that for equilibrium the *ratio* of the weights is inversely as the lengths of the arms (or of the potential arms in the case of inclined forces). The principle of moments applied to the balance would express the fact that the *product* of the weight and the length of the arm is the same on both sides. Leonardo employs the ratio factor and not the product factor, and hence it is difficult to believe that he was aware of the conception of moments as it is understood today.

10. APPLICATIONS OF THE LEVER PRINCIPLE

Let us next consider some of the ways in which Leonardo applied the principle of the lever to mechanisms in general. As an introduction to this theme let us consider his treatment of the problems of the inclined plane. In the field of dynamics, this has always been an

[1] MS. *M*, 50 v.

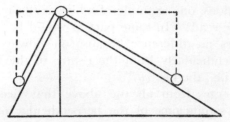

Fig. 44.   The double inclined plane.

important variant of the problems of falling bodies. The interposition of a smooth slope means that the body rolling or sliding down it is prevented from developing the full acceleration of a freely-falling body (i.e. of an increase of speed of approximately 32 feet per second every second), and the amount of this restriction depends naturally upon the slope of the incline. The greater the slope, the nearer we get to the conditions of "free-fall". But in the field of statics we are concerned with the problems of the balancing of forces. To illustrate this let us consider the case of the *double-inclined* plane, on each slope of which is a weight connected to the other by a cord passing over a pulley at the top. Orthodox history records Simon Stevinus of Bruges (1548–1620) as the first to investigate this most important range of problems, and Stevinus, in his turn, influenced Galileo later in his own important experiments. But, in fact, Leonardo, some 70 or 80 years before Stevinus, had also tackled the problem. He shows little more than a few detached notes and sketches, and his treatment is incomplete and undoubtedly lacks the thoroughness of his Dutch successor. But it was pioneer work none the less. Here and there throughout the notebooks we find sketches, some with and some without accompanying notes, showing a double-inclined plane with the two weights connected by a pulley at the top. And the clearest indication that he linked up this problem with that of the lever is given in Manuscript G^1 (Fig. 44) in which we see the addition of the dotted lines showing what we might call the equivalent simple lever, the two weights being common to the two systems. Clearly he regards the ratio of the weights for equilibrium as being equal to the ratio of the two bases.

We turn next to the application by Leonardo of the lever principle to some simple mechanisms. For instance, there is a reference in the *Codex Atlanticus* to the Chinese windlass. Against the sketch (Fig. 45(*a*)) Leonardo writes: "If one pulls at the arm of the windlass *ac* with the cord *bc*, it is just the same as turning the balance *ab*";[2] and on the same page (Fig. 45(*b*)) he shows a diagram of a windlass in which a heavy load of 400 lb is raised by means of a lever at the end of which

[1] MS. *G*, 49 r.; and also MS. *E*, 1 v.   [2] *Codex Atlanticus*, 25 r.b.

a force of 20 lb is applied. The length of the lever is twenty times that of the radius of the drum. In effect the problem is equivalent to that of a lever with unequal arms in the ratio of 20 to 1, producing what we call a "mechanical advantage" of 20. It is normally a basic element in the design of all mechanisms to produce a big mechanical advantage, i.e. to overcome a big load by the application of a small force or effort. Nature, however, always demands its toll, and the price of a high mechanical advantage is slowness of working. The effort of 20 lb, for example, has to be exerted over the long distance represented by the large circle of which the lever arm is the radius in order to lift the

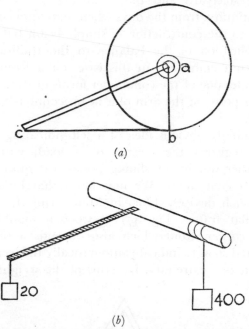

(a)

(b)

Fig. 45. Application of the lever principle to simple mechanisms.

400 lb load very slowly upwards through one-twentieth of the distance moved by the 20 lb "effort". This is in accordance with what we call the "principle of work". Technically, work is measured by the product of the force applied and the distance through which it moves; and since, as a matter of common sense, one cannot get more work out of a mechanism than one puts into it, the work done (in the above example) *by* the force of 20 lb at the end of the lever must equal the work done in lifting the 400 lb load. Therefore the lift can only amount to one-twentieth of the distance of swing of the 20 lb force.

One obvious practical application of the balancing of objects on either side of a fulcrum is the weighing machine. Although the device

Fig. 46.   The yoke in antiquity.

of a steelyard itself is not to be found in Leonardo's notes, he did interest himself in the problem of a self-registering instrument for weighing. Both the steelyard and the balancing scales were inventions dating from antiquity, from the days when man applied the idea of the yoke (Fig. 46) to the construction of simple-beam balances. Plate 42 shows the application of the balance to the traditional symbol of Justice and Truth embossed, in this case, on a Roman coin, whilst Plate 43 illustrates one of the commoner forms of Roman steelyard, in which a sliding poise on the arm of a beam counter-balances the load to be weighed.

Yet the seemingly obvious idea of a self-indicating machine which automatically registers the weight of a load, without having to manipulate either weights or sliding poises was quite unknown until comparatively recent times. We now know that Leonardo da Vinci wrote of two such devices. One, in Manuscript A,[1] shows an equilateral triangular frame (Fig. 47) of wooden mouldings suspended from the top corner, from which also depends a plumb-line. The base is graduated so as to indicate automatically the weight of an object m suspended at one extremity, in terms of the weight n at the other

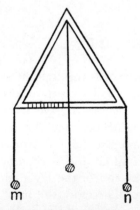

m   n

Fig. 47.   Leonardo's device of a self-
indicating balance.

[1] MS. A, 52 r.

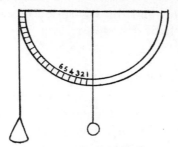

Fig. 48. Self-indicating device with semi-
circular frame.

extremity, i.e. when *m* is applied, the triangle swings over and the plumb-line reading is taken. The second form of this device is to be found in a self-explanatory sketch[1] in which the triangle is replaced by a semicircular frame (Fig. 48), with the right-half presumably weighted to counteract the effect of the scale-pan suspended from the left extremity of the diameter. The left quadrant is again graduated to give a direct reading of the load as the scale swings down over the plumb-line.

The same principle was used by Leonardo in his notes on hygrometry. The hygrometer is the instrument used by physicists to measure the moisture content of the atmosphere. As a topic and a problem it was not new to Leonardo. Nicholas of Cusa had studied the matter earlier in the fifteenth century in Germany, and hygrometers had been designed in Italy by Leon Battista Alberti. But neither showed the ingenuity of Leonardo. His designs were based upon the fact that a cotton wad or "bullet" is heavier when it absorbs moisture from a very humid atmosphere than when it is quite dry. Two designs are shown in the *Codex Atlanticus*.[2] One takes the form of an orthodox balance with a bullet of wax in one pan and a bullet of cotton in the other. Both balance in a dry atmosphere, but the pan with the cotton wad is depressed in humid weather. In the second form (Fig. 49) a balanced rod carries the absorbent bullet on the left extremity and the

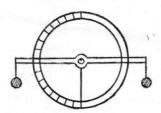

Fig. 49. Leonardo's hygrometer.

[1] MS. No. 2038 Bibliothèque Nationale.
[2] *Codex Atlanticus*, 18 v.; and 249 v.

dry bullet on the right, and the absorption of moisture during humid weather draws the left arm down over the graduated quadrant of a circle.

11. SOME NOTES ON HYDROMECHANICS

It will be remembered that much of Leonardo's professional work was concerned with structural engineering. In this connection he was constantly involved in such operations as drainage and canalisation. This sort of work almost certainly gave him great pleasure. It fitted in with one of the absorbing topics of his life—the physical phenomena relating to water. Its movement, the power to be derived from it, the innumerable factors governing its behaviour—these matters were of unending interest to him, and few of his notebooks are free from references to them.

He was, as we may expect, always interested in the writings of earlier workers in this field; and in Manuscript *M*, for example, his notes on water and its movements refer to Aristotle, Albert of Saxony and a later writer, Richard Suisset (called the "Calculator"), to whom Leibnitz subsequently referred as having introduced mathematics into scholastic philosophy.

Records of Leonardo's observations on water behaviour in nature alternate from time to time with suggestions for laboratory experiments of the kind that have become normal to the modern textbook. His approach to these problems was that of the experimental scientist. "Remember," he cautions, "when discoursing about water to use first experience and then reason."[1] We see this particularly in his notes "On the Nature, Weight and Movement of Waters" in the Leicester Manuscript at Holkham Hall. Let us first see him in the mood of the interested observer. "I have seen," he writes, "in the case of two small canals each of a breadth of two braccia, which serve as a line of demarcation between the road and the estates, how their waters clashed together with unequal force and then united, and bent at a right-angle, and passed underneath a small bridge by this road and continued their course. But what I want to refer to in them is the fact that they formed there a flow and ebb, with a height of a quarter of a braccio, caused now by one, now by the other canal, as will be stated. The first canal, being the more powerful, subdued the onrush of the water of the opposite canal, and, by adding to it from the opposite direction, caused it to swell up, and then the water coming above this from the swollen river, rose up in such a way as to acquire so much power of the water which at first was more powerful and so drove it back with fury; and consequently the victor, redoubling the

[1] MS. *H*, 90 (42) r.

impetus of its movement, entered with an undulation extending over more than a hundred feet into the more powerful canal, which at that time retarded and held up such of its waters as were at the boundary of the conquering wave. And from this wave upwards the river massed together so much water that, after the end of the aforesaid impetus of the wave, these waters gained the victory and drove back the said waters; and so they continued in succession, without ever retarding the movement of that third canal in which they were united under the aforesaid bridge." [1]

We can picture the fascination with which Leonardo spent his hours at this bridge watching, speculating, wondering. To him water seemed alive, and the link it seemed to provide with the ancient doctrine of macrocosm and microcosm was a compelling one. In Manuscript A we read: "Man has been called by the ancients a world in miniature and, indeed, the term is rightly applied, seeing that if

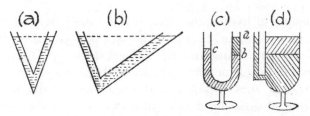

Fig. 50.   Leonardo's experiments on the balancing of liquid columns.

man is compounded of earth, water, air and fire, this body is the same; and as man has within himself bones as a stay and framework for the flesh, so the world has the rocks, which are the supports of the earth; as man has within him a pool of blood wherein the lungs as he breathes expand and contract, so the body of the earth has its ocean, which also rises and falls every six hours with the breathing of the world; as from the said pool of blood proceed the veins which spread their branches through the human body, in just the same manner the ocean fills the body of the earth with an infinite number of veins of water." [2]

But although Leonardo had these roots in the doctrines of the past, he could nevertheless continue to keep his head reasonably cool and his thoughts objectively dispassionate. "Water will not move from one spot to another unless to seek a lower level," he tells us, "and in the natural course of its current it will never be able to return to an elevation equal to that of the spot whence it first issued forth from the mountains and comes into the light." [3] So he enunciates the funda-

[1] Leicester MS., 35 r.   [2] Ms. A, 54 v.   [3] MS. A, 56 r.

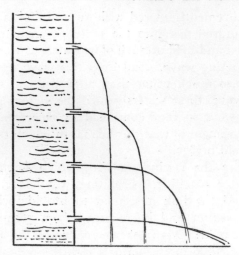

Fig. 51.   Liquid pressures proportional to depth.

mental principle of hydrostatics that water "finds its own level" and that "from its nature, no sheet of water can be lower than the surface of the sea." And in Manuscript E[1] we meet sketches of the well-known experiments of the elementary physical laboratory of the schools of today illustrating these fundamental principles by the balancing of liquid columns of differing density in order to show that the levels of two different liquids are in inverse proportion to their densities (Fig. 50). Here, too, are sketches showing in varying form the standard experiment of a deep vessel filled with water and fitted with orifices at varying levels (Fig. 51), to illustrate by the varying shape and penetration of the issuing streams that the pressure of the liquid is proportional to the depth.

Archimedes, is of course, a constant stand-by for Leonardo, and we find him, in Manuscript H, referring in effect to the famous Principle of Archimedes in the note: "The water that is expelled from the spot which the vessel occupies weighs as much as all the remainder of the ship which displaces it."[2]

From time to time Leonardo also interested himself in the familiar problem of raising water from one elevation to a higher one. The method of the Archimedean Screw was well known to him. In effect this was a pipe twisted in the form of a spiral screw. It was held inclined with one end dipping below the water which was to be pumped up. By turning a windlass or some equivalent device, the screw was then made to revolve about its axis, thus drawing the water up at each successive winding of the "screw" until it came out at the top. Plate 44

[1] MS. E, 74 v.   [2] MS. H, 69 (21) r.; see also 92 (44) r.

Plate 69—Mechanical rollers for "the art of making a thin and even tin-plate" (MS. J. 48 v.).

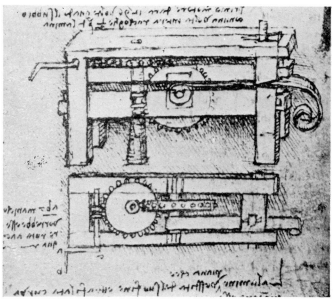

Plate 70—Mechanism for stretching and rolling copper strips (MS. G. 70 v.).

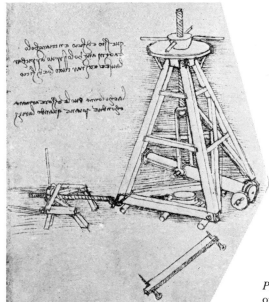

Plate 71—Lifting device mounted on sheer-legs (C.A. 49 v.a.).

Plate 72—Portable lifting mechanism on wheeled carrier and overhead guide wires (C.A. 49 v.a.).

Plate 73—Scheme of twin cranes for raising large stone blocks.

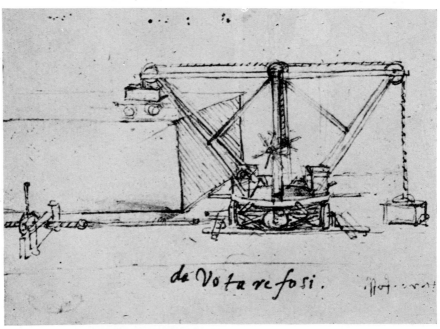

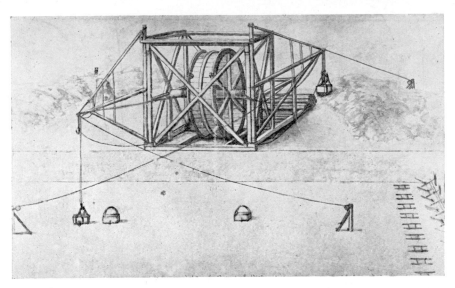

Plate 74—Twin cranes for canal construction.

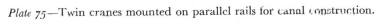
Plate 75—Twin cranes mounted on parallel rails for canal construction.

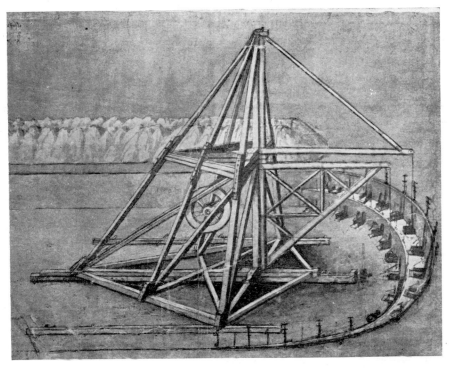

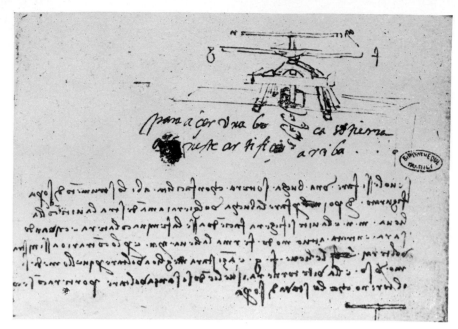

Plate 76—Out-door boring machine for drilling into the ground (MS. B. 65 r.).

Plate 77—"A borer to drill into the ground to find water" (C.A. 9 v.b.).

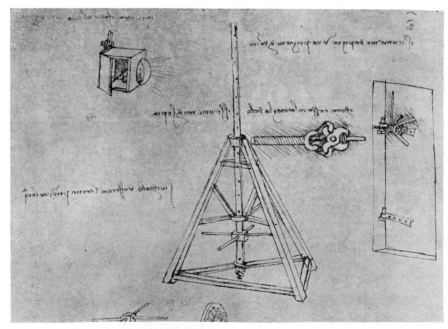

is a reproduction of Leonardo's design of such a screw,[1] including his suggestions for a geared-wheel system to apply the power.

Leonardo understood and used the principle of the siphon, and also that of the centrifugal pump. These are described in Manuscript *F*: "If the water in a half-filled vessel is stirred with the hand, a whirling current is produced which will expose the bottom of the vessel to the air; and when the force that produced it is no longer applied, the current will continue in motion but will continually diminish in speed until the impetus given by the force ceases."[2] Leonardo applied this practically to the design of a large-scale pump for the purpose of the draining of swamp waters, details of which are given in the next chapter (p. 286).

In some of Leonardo's comments on hydraulic phenomena we occasionally meet with notions characteristic of the medieval mind. These sometimes led him into futile speculations. For instance, in asking himself what force impelled waters on occasion to well up—as happens with springs, for example, at the sources of rivers—he sought for the answer in terms of heat, a subject upon which little had been written (p. 247). But he accepted the Middle Age idea that heat was an agency of elevation—"Where there is life there is warmth and where there is the warmth of life one finds a movement of saps."[3] It seemed a good basis for a solution of his problem. So he continues: "As the sun warms the man's head the amount of blood there increases, and it grows to such an excess there with the humours as to overload the veins and frequently to cause pains in the head. It is the same with the springs which ramify through the body of the earth and, by the natural heat which is spread through all the body that contains them, the water stays in the springs and is raised to the high summits of the mountains."[4]

But at least, if these ideas were classical and medieval in origin and flavour, they were not entirely without scientific profit, since they also provided a basis for his discussions on cloud formation on a more modernistic note.[5] "Where there is life there is heat and where there is vital heat there is movement of vapour. This is proved because one sees that the heat of the element of fire always draws to itself the damp vapours, the thick mists and the dense clouds which are given off by the seas and other lakes and rivers and marshy valleys. And drawing these little by little up to the cold region, there the first part halts, because warm and moist cannot exist with cold and dryness; and this first part having halted receives the other parts, and so all the parts joining together one to another form thick and dark clouds."

"And," Leonardo continues, "these are often swept away and

[1] *Codex Atlanticus*, 7 v.
[2] MS. *F*, 13 r.
[3] MS. *A*, 55 r.
[4] MS. *A*, 56 r.
[5] MS. *A*, 54 v.

carried by the winds from one region to another until at last their density gives them such weight that they fall in thick rain; but, if the heat of the sun is added to the power of the element of fire, the clouds are drawn up higher and higher and come to more intense cold, and there become frozen and so produce hailstones."

Although based upon the ancient conception of the four primary elements and humours we have virtually in this description a summary of some of the elements of meteorology as we know them today; and following our survey of Leonardo's observations on hydromechanics, this affords a fitting introduction to his notes on physical science as distinct from mechanical science, and to this we next proceed.

12. LEONARDO'S GENERAL PHYSICS

Physics is usually considered to embrace the subjects of heat, light, sound, magnetism and electricity. On the whole, very little had been done prior to the fifteenth century to establish physics as a science, with the possible exception of the subject of light. Here, as we have seen, following early speculations by Plato and the Pythagoreans, some serious beginnings were made by Ptolemy and Euclid in the classical period, and later by El Hazen in the Arabic East and by Roger Bacon and Witello in the Christian West. It is perhaps natural that, of the various physical phenomena, those associated with vision would attract most attention; and the two queries "What is light?" and "How do people see?" were frequently propounded through the ages. In the Greek era two theories were developed, but they were neither experimentally based nor theoretically proved. They were, in fact, simple speculations.

The Pythagoreans regarded the eye as throwing out minute particles which, impinging on a given object, "seize it", so to speak, and hence "see" it. According to Plato, on the other hand, the act of seeing depended upon a somewhat complicated triple reaction as between the sun (or other luminous body), the eye, and the object seen.

Leonardo was, of course, interested in this, and his notes on optics and such related topics as "light and shade" and "perspective" were voluminous. They date from 1489 onwards, and they fitted in naturally with his role as a painter. Yet, prolific as they were, we cannot say that the notes contributed much that was new. They are better described, in the main, as a refreshing restatement of ground already covered. Leonardo had dissected the eye because he wanted to know how it worked. In Manuscript K he gives this description:

"The pupil of the eye is situated in the centre in the eyeball, which is of the shape of part of a sphere, which takes the pupil at the centre of its base. This eyeball, forming part of a sphere, takes all the images of the objects and transmits them by the pupil within to the place where the vision is formed.

"In the anatomy of the eye, in order to be able to see the inside well without spilling its watery humour, you should place the complete eye in white of egg and make it boil and become solid, cutting the egg and the eye transversely so that no part of the middle portion may be poured out."[1]

And on the previous page to this he advises: "In order to see what function the eyeball serves in the pupil, cause a thing resembling the eyeball to be made out of glass."[2]

Leonardo was familiar with the structure of the eye as including the iris, the pupil, the pigment layer and the crystalline lens. All these, except the last, had been previously known to his predecessors —but the first published account of the crystalline lens was by Maurolycus in 1575.

It would be too much to expect that Leonardo understood the actual physiological mechanism of the nervous system of "rods and cones" for varying the curvature of the "crystalline lens" of the eye as it successively observes objects at varying distances. Nevertheless, he writes vividly on the "accommodation" of the pupil as it "works" in varying conditions of brilliance and darkness. "The pupil of the eye," he writes, "changes to as many different sizes as there are differences in the degrees of brightness and obscurity of the objects which present themselves before it . . . Nature is here establishing a continual equilibrium, perpetually adjusting and equalising by making the pupil dilate or contract in proportion to the aforesaid obscurity or brightness which continually presents itself before it."[3]

On the whole, therefore, we may take it that Leonardo saw the principal member of the eye as a lens which was connected by nerves to the brain; and of course he knew the refractive or bending properties of the lens. Indeed, he also appreciated how sight could be artificially aided or reinforced where necessary by spectacles. Let us follow him on the subject as he writes in the *Codex Atlanticus*: "A proof of the manner in which glasses aid the sight. Let *ab* be the glasses and *cd* the eyes, and suppose these to have grown old. Whereas they used to see an object at *e* with great ease by turning their position very considerably from the line of the optic nerves, but now by reason of age the power of bending has become weakened, and consequently it cannot be twisted without causing great pain to the eyes, so that they are constrained of necessity to place the object farther away, that is from *e* to *f*, and so see it better but not in detail. But through the interposition of the spectacles the object is clearly discerned at the

[1] MS. *K*, 119 (39) r.   [2] MS. *K*, 118 (38) v.   [3] MS. *D*, 5 v.

distance that it was when they were young, that is at *e*, and this comes about because the object at *e* passes to the eye through various media, namely thin and thick, the thin being the air . . . and the thick being the thickness of the glass of the spectacles, the line of direction consequently bends in the thickness of the glass, and the line is twisted, so that seeing the object at *e* it sees it as though it was at *f*, with the advantage that the position of the eye with regard to its optic nerves is not strained and it sees it near at hand and discerns it better at *e* than at *f* and especially the minute portions." [1]

Leonardo accepted the current view of his times, that *seeing* was a matter of perception and not of projection—and that all bodies had certain qualities whereby they were able to transmit their form and peculiarities to the sense organs. Such visible bodies were constantly emitting palpable thin shells from their external visible surfaces and these met with the visual emanation from the eye. These two elements, the emanation from the eye and the "species" (as the palpable thin shells from the external body were called), then combined together and passed back to the eye as images. It will be noticed that, involved and somewhat complicated as this picture appears to be, there is implied in it the conception that *seeing* is a phenomenon due to light falling on the eye, and to that extent it is a rejection of both the Pythagorean and the Platonic theories or speculations referred to above.

"It is impossible," writes Leonardo, "that the eye should itself project by visual rays the visual virtue, since as soon as it opened the front door which would give rise to the emanation, it would have to go forth to the object, and this it could not do in that time." [2]

There is even a note in Manuscript *A* which, taking into account also the emanation of the "species" or "thin palpable shells" referred to in the note previously quoted, suggests the basis of an undulatory or wave theory for both light and sound. It reads as follows: "Any body placed in a luminous atmosphere" (i.e. exposed to light), "diffuses itself in circles and fills the surrounding air with infinite images of itself." [3] The implication is that images of the luminous object are sent out in a succession of circular ripples—"just as a stone flung into the water becomes the centre and cause of many circles, and as sound diffuses itself in circles in the air". Leonardo frequently gives this sort of picture in his notes.

We may summarise their general trend by saying that he understood and accepted the principle of the rectilinear propagation of light. As a consequence, he worked out innumerable and elaborate shadow schemes showing both umbra and penumbra phenomena. He was familiar, too, with the sort of experiment we speak of as photo-

---

[1] *Codex Atlanticus*, 244 r.   [2] MS. *I*, 32 v.   [3] MS. *A*, 9 v.

metry, the purpose of which is to make qualitative comparisons of the relative intensities of different light-sources. (Yet the Rumford photometer, using the same principle, was not to appear for another three centuries.) Leonardo, of course, well understood the law of reflection of light and he was able to apply it to the focal property of a concave mirror. He also appreciated the advantage of using the eyes simultaneously to produce stereoscopic vision. "Things seen with two eyes will appear rounder than are those seen with one eye," he commented.[1]

On refraction he was much less precise. He was quite clear as to the principle of refraction itself, however, and, as we have already seen, he understood the main properties of spherical lenses and spectacles. To sum up, we may say of his notes on optics that they gave clear evidence of a groping after a better theory of vision than was current in his day.

Finally, we should mention Leonardo's understanding of the property we speak of as the "diffusion" of light by the atmosphere. In a discussion on why stars are not visible in daylight, he writes: "The stars are visible by night and not by day owing to our being beneath the dense atmosphere which is full of an infinite number of particles of moisture. Each of these is lit up when it is struck by the rays of the sun and consequently the innumerable radiant particles veil these stars; and if it were not for this atmosphere the sky would always show the stars against the darkness."[2]

We turn naturally from Leonardo's work in optics to his studies in acoustics, because to him they were related phenomena. We have already met a reference to this in the quotation on page 244. Both light and sound are propagated by wave motion, a theme which he develops by the analogy of wave motion in water. Consider the following: "Just as the stone thrown into the water becomes the centre and cause of various circles, and the sound made in the air spreads out in circles, so every body placed within the luminous air spreads itself out in circles and fills the surrounding parts with an infinite number of images of itself, and appears all in all and all in each part."[3] And from this to the systems of wave motion proceeding from more than one source, giving the phenomena known in modern physics as "interference" note the following: "Although the voices which penetrate the air proceed from their sources in circular motion, nevertheless the circles which are propelled from their different centres meet without hindrance and penetrate and pass across one another, keeping to the centre from which they spring."[4]

It is, however, very important that we should appreciate not only

[1] MS. *H*, 49 r. [2] MS. *F*, 5 v. [3] MS. *A*, 9 v. [4] MS. *A*, 61 v.

that Leonardo regarded both sound and light as analogous to water in the setting up of an outward developing sequence of circular (or spherical) waves but also that he appreciated that, in fact, this propagation was producing not a forward movement but a *vibration* of the medium. Let us note how the above-quoted passage continues: "Since in all cases of movement water has great conformity with air, I will cite it as an example. I say, if at the same time you throw two small stones on a sheet of motionless water at some distance from one another, you will observe that round the two spots where they have struck, two distinct sets of circles are formed, which will meet as they increase in size and then penetrate and intersect one another . . . and the reason of this is that although apparently there is some show of movement there the water does not leave its places because the openings made there by the stones are instantly closed again and the

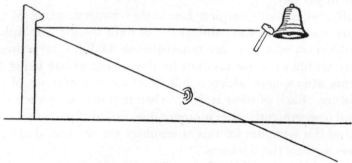

Fig. 52.   Reflection of sound.

motion occasioned by the sudden opening and closing of the water causes certain shakings which one would describe as a tremor rather than a movement."

We might well be reading a modern popular account of the mechanics of wave motion in this passage, which further proceeds as follows: "Watch the pieces of straw which, on account of their lightness, are floating on the water and are not moved from their original position by the wave that rolls beneath as the circles reach them. The impression on the wave therefore, being a tremor rather than a movement, the circles . . . transmit the tremor from one place to another without changing their place. For as the water remains in its position it can easily take this tremor from the adjacent parts and pass it on to other adjacent parts, its force steadily decreasing until the end." And, by analogy, argues Leonardo, so it is also with sound tremors.

Leonardo has some idea of the reflection of sound and the production of echoes. In Manuscript *C*, for example, he sketches a bell being struck by a hammer (Fig. 52), and the resulting sound is reflected back from an obstructing wall, to be received by the ear of the listener. "I say," reads the note, "that the note of the echo is cast back to the ear after it has struck, just as the images of objects strike the mirror and are thence reflected back to the eye. And in the same way as these images fall from the object to the mirror and from the mirror to the eye at equal angles, so the note from the echo will strike and rebound within the hollow where it has first struck, at equal angles to the ear."[1]

And in Manuscript B[2] another sketch (Fig. 53) shows how a multiple echo is set up between two sets of steps by a man blowing a blast on a horn.

His appreciation of the instantaneous speed of light as compared with the speed with which sound is propagated through the air is illustrated by a note on the distance of a clap of thunder from the

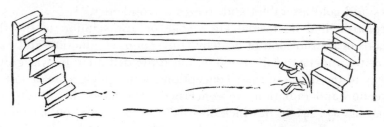

Fig. 53.   Echoes by multiple reflection.

observer: "It is possible," he says, "to recognise by the ear the distance of a clap of thunder on first seeing its flash, from its resemblance to the note of the echo."[3]

He is interested, too, in the greater speeds of propagation of sound through media denser than air. "If you cause your ship to stop," he writes, "and place the head of a long tube in the water and the other extremity to your ear, you will hear ships at a great distance from you. You can also do the same by placing the head of the tube upon the ground and you will then hear anyone passing at a distance from you."[4]

We next pass to Leonardo's treatment of the subject of heat. His formal references to this are somewhat scanty, but in any case, apart perhaps from Roger Bacon in the thirteenth century, very little had been done by philosophers up to his day towards serious discussion on this subject. Leonardo joined with others in regarding heat as one of three primary products or emanations of the sun's rays which, he tells us, "are made up of three incorporeal forces, namely radiance,

<hr />

[1] MS. C, 16 r.   [2] MS. B, 90 v.   [3] MS. A, 19 r.   [4] MS. B, 6 r.

heat and the image which produces these."[1] And from this he linked
heat with luminosity in general. He also conformed to the current views
of his day in regarding heat and cold as two different "opposites"
and not as varying degrees of the same phenomenon as we now know
to be the case. He does, however, come to the fringe of the more
modern picture when he writes: "I say that cold proceeds from two
causes; the first is from the air being deprived of heat; the second is
from the movement of the air."[2] This tendency to pair up "opposites"
was, of course, a characteristic of medieval days, carried over from the
philosophers of antiquity. So we get "wet and dry", "gravity and
levity", and now "hot and cold". "Heat and cold," writes Leonardo,
"proceed from the propinquity and remoteness of the sun. Heat and
cold produce the movement of the elements."[3]

This reference to the movement of the elements arising from heat
and cold is one of many. Another reads: "Heat separates and dis-
perses and cold assembles and freezes or condenses."[4]

Leonardo had no formal knowledge or appreciation of the three
methods of transmission of heat by convection, conduction and radiation as we understand them today, but quite definitely he was groping
his way to the fringe of these conceptions, so to speak, at least so far as
convection and radiation are concerned. We have already discussed
the passage (p. 241-2) in which he attributes the formation of cloud and
rain to the effect of heat upon the earth's waters, but he elsewhere
writes on a much more general plane, as when he says: "Every movement of the elements arises from heat and cold."[5] But when he wrote
this he little realised the "molecular" sense in which it was so true.
For on this topic of heat and cold we see in Leonardo the blend of the
modern man of science with the traditional tug of the medieval mind,
always impressed by evidences of nature in its more violent aspects.
So he writes: "And the vital heat of the world is fire which is spread
throughout the earth; and the dwelling place of its creative spirit is in
the fires, which in divers parts of the earth are breathed out in baths
and sulphur mines, and in volcanoes, such as Mount Etna in Sicily,
and in many other places."[6]

The property of the expansion and contraction of substances with
the application of heat or cold was naturally familiar to Leonardo.
He refers to the "greater solidity of the fluids where there is greater
coldness", but his observation is at fault in a sketch[7] (without text)
which shows a thick metal slab heated in front of a fire and bent inwards (i.e. towards the fire) through expansion. Actually, however, it

---

[1] *Codex Atlanticus*, 204 v.
[2] MS. *A*, 20 r.
[3] Brit. Mus., 204 r.
[4] *Codex Atlanticus*, 279 r.
[5] Brit. Mus., 205 r.
[6] Leicester MS., 34 r.
[7] Ash. MS., 4 r.

is the back surface which, being the cooler, expands the less, and the slab must therefore bend outwards.

Leonardo was familiar with the convection effect of heat on air, even if he was hazy on its precise theory, and an example of how he applied this to the arts of the kitchen is given in a sketch in the *Codex Atlanticus*[1] of a roasting spit—at this time a very popular device. He observes, by way of introduction, that when two equally heavy objects are suspended from the two sides of a balance, and the air below one of them is heated, the hot air around it in rising will carry it upwards, causing the colder body to descend at the same time. Leonardo's drawing (Plate 45) shows the meat suspended over a fire from mechanism geared to a set of vanes at the top. The rising current of hot air rotates the vanes, and this rotation is transmitted to the mechanism below, which thus causes the meat also to rotate. Quite clearly, too, we must attribute to Leonardo the beginnings of the experimental work we speak of in the physical laboratories of today as calorimetry—the measurement of quantities of heat involved in the heating of liquids under controlled conditions. More particularly, Leonardo attempted to measure the expansion effect of converting water into steam (although to Leonardo and his contemporaries steam and hot air meant very much the same thing)—an investigation which, after all, is fundamental in the evolution of the steam-engine and steam power. We shall have occasion to refer to this further in the next chapter. Here, however, we are merely concerned with the fact that Leonardo sought to measure the amount by which water expands when heated to boiling point, and the volume of steam produced by the evaporation of a given quantity of water. Readers may know that under normal conditions steam occupies 1,700 times the volume of the water from which it is produced. His note accompanying a sketch (Fig. 54) reads

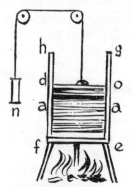

Fig. 54.   Leonardo's calorimeter to measure
the expansive power of steam.

[1] *Codex Atlanticus*, 5 v.a.

as follows: "In order to make an experiment to see how much water grows in bulk when it changes into steam, take the square vessel with an open top *ghef*, and fit into it a bag made of calf-skin. This is very thin and can be treated like bellows—that is to say, it can be stretched out to fit the vessel. On it lay a flat board so wide that it fits the sides of the vessel at *ab*. We now half fill the bag with water so as to half fill the vessel. The other half of the vessel contains air. When the water turns into steam, and the other half of the bag is filled with steam, the cover over the bag is forced upwards, and the counterweight *n* moves downwards."[1] By this means Leonardo was able to measure the amount of expansion.

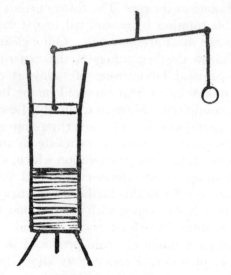

Fig. 55.   Leonardo's improved steam calorimeter.

The experiment was, of course, a crude one, but it is important to note that, probably for the first time in history, a quantitative attempt was being made to measure the expansive power of steam, and also that Leonardo was the pioneer of the device of a piston, i.e. the flat board *ab* working upwards under the control of the counter-weight *n* connected to it by a rope passing over two pulley wheels.

Actually Leonardo must have felt dissatisfied with this particular design of apparatus. A few pages on in the Leicester Manuscript[2] we see Leonardo dispensing with the bag, the water being contained directly in the vessel itself (Fig. 55). It will also be seen that the piston has an actual piston-rod, and that this and the counter-weight are now suspended from a centrally suspended fulcrum.

Reti has recently advanced the view that we have here not only

[1] Leicester MS., 10 r.   [2] Leicester MS., 15 v.

the beginnings of the steam-engine of the future but that Leonardo's work must have been known and followed up by della Porta a century later. We will refer further to this matter in the next chapter (p. 296).

We turn finally to the subject of magnetism. In modern physics we couple this subject with electricity. There was, however, no science of electricity in da Vinci's day and his notes are devoid of references to this phenomenon. Magnetic phenomena had, however, long been known and studied, and by the fifteenth century both the magnetic properties of the lodestone and the directive property of the compass were well known.

Leonardo shows in his sketches that he agreed with the current (but incorrect) notion that the compass property of a magnet was caused by the attraction of the Pole Star. In Manuscript *E* we see a sketch

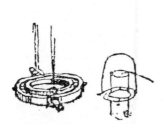

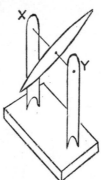

Fig. 56. Ring suspension   Fig. 57. To illustrate the angle of
     for compass.   magnetic dip.

(Plate 46) accompanying a note which reads: "If you wish to find the part of the magnet that naturally turns towards the north get a large tub and fill it with water; in this water place a wooden cup and set in it the magnet without any more water. The magnet will float on it like a ship, and by virtue of its power of attraction, it will immediately move in the direction of the north star [i.e. the Pole Star]; and it will move towards this, first turning itself with the cup in such a way that it is turned towards the star, and will then move through the water and touch the edge of the tub with its north side, as before mentioned."[1]

We may, with some confidence, attribute to Leonardo the device of compass suspension in a form suitable to keep it both steady and horizontal in spite of the movements of the ship. Although this type of suspension was not known in practice before 1571, there is a sketch of such a design in the *Codex Atlanticus*[2] (Fig. 56). Another is shown a few pages later.[3]

[1] MS. *E*, 2 r.   [2] *Codex Atlanticus*, 288 r.   [3] Ibid., 316 r.

Finally, and perhaps most interesting of all, it would appear that Leonardo knew something of the phenomenon we speak of as magnetic dip. In the ship's compass the magnet is suspended on a *vertical* axis, so that it may swing horizontally over a graduated compass-card to indicate the "bearing" of the ship. If, however, we arrange instead to suspend a magnet on a *horizontal* axis (as in *XY* in Fig. 57), provided this axis is left free to rotate, the magnet will not set itself vertically, as would a non-magnetic needle, but is found instead to take up an *inclined* position, as shown in the figure. It is essential, however, that the magnet itself is set so as to swing in the plane of the magnetic

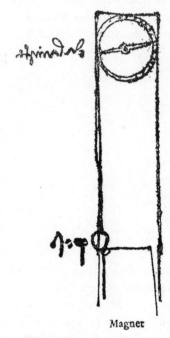

Magnet

Fig. 58.   Leonardo's magnetic dip board.

meridian at the point of observation. The inclination of the needle to the horizontal is known as the *angle of dip*, and readers acquainted with elementary magnetic theory will know that this varies with the magnetic latitude, i.e. it is ninety degrees at the North Magnetic Pole (where it is therefore upright), and zero at the magnetic equator (so that it here swings horizontally). In Manuscript *A*[1] we see Leonardo's design for this measurement (Fig. 58). A vertical board is spiked at the base so that it may be pushed into the ground. At the upper part of the board is a graduated circle carrying a horizontally mounted magnetic needle, shown in Leonardo's sketch as having set itself at its

[1] MS. *A*, 20 v.

appropriate angle of dip. A plumb-line is attached to the apparatus to ensure that the board is vertical.

We must, of course, not make too much of this. It is improbable that Leonardo fully appreciated the significance of the phenomenon of magnetic dip; but the conclusion is unavoidable that he was aware that a magnet mounted to swing in a vertical plane *would* register an angle of dip. In his drawing he could not have fixed the frame in the magnetic meridian, or the angle would of course have been very much steeper—but at least there *is* an unmistakable inclination.

So far as is known, the earliest published version of such a design was by von Hartmann in 1542, and the earliest example of its use in practice was in 1576.

VIII

LEONARDO THE ENGINEER AND
MASTER OF GADGETRY

I. INTRODUCTION

Having regard to the wide activities and interests in which he was gainfully employed, how, professionally, would Leonardo have described himself? There can be little doubt about the answer. Although, like so many others, he had "more than one string to his bow", he almost certainly considered himself first and foremost a professional artist. For this he was trained and in this he excelled. Yet in the aggregate he must have spent more time on his duties as a military and civil engineer, and on the study of the problems and underlying principles upon which these duties were based, than he did on his art.

In the light of this we must recall that although Leonardo had been a formal art pupil under Verrocchio's tuition, he had received no actual training as an engineer. He simply acquired this "as he went along". We have previously commented upon the range of activities that were included in the daily round in Verrocchio's *bottega*, and these must have had a considerable bearing on the extraordinary fact that by the age of thirty Leonardo was in a position to make the many sweeping claims to engineering competence such as were embodied in the famous letter to Ludovico Sforza.

As to how he came to acquire his unique taste for the study and design of mechanical apparatus we can but conjecture. Basically it stemmed from his attitude to his art—to the need for accuracy of observation on the anatomy and physiognomy of man and beast, on the plant life around him, and on the ever-changing landscapes in the varying weather conditions from day to day and from season to season. Gradually the thoughts and ideas engendered by these observations began to dominate him for their own sake, and soon the problems of mechanical science became fundamental to his being. Thus the mechanical bent of his mind and his hands came to be applied to the principles of mechanics and to the practice of mechanical processes as something quite separate from the practice of his art.

Many commentators on the engineering aspect of Leonardo's work have expressed the view that he was primarily an empiricist in his approach. But it would probably be more correct to say that he was both a theorist and an empiricist. Some of his notes and sketches show obvious evidences as inspired "hunches", depicting a Leonardo who is the master of gadgetry rather than the engineer. These were the "brain-waves" of the intuitional empiricist. Some were amusing, and some displayed ideas and suggestions that could never, in his day, find conversion from paper to the finished job; yet all were ingenious.

But these were additional to, and not a substitute for, the more sober achievements of scientifically and experimentally based studies of the sort that so peculiarly differentiates the professional engineer from the practitioner of applied science. Again and again we see how the theoretical aspects of a problem presented themselves to him as the self-imposed challenge of finding basic explanations of observations and experiences as he met them. It was thus that he came to develop the basic principles upon which engineering is founded—as in his studies on the conceptions of force, motion and mechanical work.

We can well imagine the steps that led the young Leonardo on from the "trial and error" beginnings of the observer with a mechanical bent to the scientific technician that he was later to become. He quickly saw that the muscles and bones of the human body had the same functions in relation to the human machine as had the constituent parts of the mechanical tools used by the workmen around him; and that the human frame moved and worked in accordance with the same mechanical laws as were applicable to these tools. We have seen how he was familiarising himself with the laws of the lever and its potentialities to enable man to overcome considerable resistances by the application of relatively small forces ("Give me where to stand and I will move the earth"—see p. 121); and with the pulley as an obvious device of convenience in hauling operations. So he proceeded from the design of improved forms of the various hand-tools of the workman (Plate 48)—the picks and shovels, the pincers and pliers, and so forth—to much more complicated devices as drills for boring, and derricks, cranes and jacks for lifting, hauling, loading and winding; and then to the mechanisms required in machine-shop practice—lathes for turning, mills for rolling, grinding and polishing mechanisms; and from these to a variety of designs covering a wide range of engineering activities.

In the pages that follow we shall first survey what we may call Leonardo's studies in applied mechanics—i.e. the subjects that provide the textbook equipment for the theoretical engineer. These comprise his notes on friction, his studies of various pulley systems, his various lifting devices and their applications in practice, his approach to the problems of power transmission, and finally, his very important work on the strength and testing of the materials of engineering—i.e. of beams, struts, columns and wires. These surely must comprise a formidable sequence of studies in terms of the fifteenth-century world of technology.[1] We shall then pass on to a review of how he applied these studies to the general mechanisms and devices of practical engineering.

2. LEONARDO ON FRICTION

Quite early in his work Leonardo realised the toll on the efficiency of working engendered by the phenomenon of friction. It was an ever-present bogey and it was therefore a necessity to understand it in order to minimise its effect. "Deal first with weight, then with its supports, then with friction, then with motion, and lastly with percussion," we read in a sheet of notes to be found in the Academy at Venice. And in Manuscript *E* he analyses his problem thus: "Friction is divided into three parts: simple, compound and irregular. Simple friction is that made by the thing moved on the place where it is dragged. Compound friction is that which the thing moved makes between two immovable things. Irregular friction is that made by the wedge of different sides."[2] Clearly Leonardo's approach is not that of the modern textbook on the subject. But his main studies on friction are to be found in the Forster notebooks housed in the library of the Victoria and Albert Museum. Here he argues as follows: "The action of friction is divided into parts, of which one is simple and all the others are compound."[3] (Note the simpler classification here of two categories as compared with the three referred to in Manuscript *E*.) "Simple is when the object is dragged along a plain smooth surface without any intervention; this is the only friction that creates fire when it is powerful, that is it produces [generates] fire—as can be seen at a water wheel when the water is removed between the sharpened iron and this wheel" (i.e. the presence of the water acts as a cooling agent diminishing the heat engendered by friction to below "spark" level). The note then goes on: "The other frictions are compound and are divided into two parts: the first is when any greasiness of some thin substance is interposed between the bodies that rub together; and the second is when an additional friction is introduced, as would be the friction of the poles of the wheels. The first of these is again divided

[1] The most extensive treatment of Leonardo's engineering is to be found in the German writings of Theodor Beck as follows: (1) *Beiträge zur Geschichte des Maschinenbaues*, Berlin, 1899, pp. 88–110, 318–364, 411–484. A second edition was issued in 1900. (2) *Zeitschrift des Vereins deutcher Ingenieure*, Band 50, 1906, pp. 524–531, 562–569, 645–651 and 777–784. The whole comprises an aggregate of 175 pages with 604 illustrations.

[2] MS. *E*, 35 r.

[3] MS. *SKM II*, 131 v.

Plate 78—Dredging operations—"An instrument for excavating the earth"
(MS. E. 75 v.).

Plate 79—Dredging operations—"This is how to dredge a harbour"
(C.A. 307 v.b.).

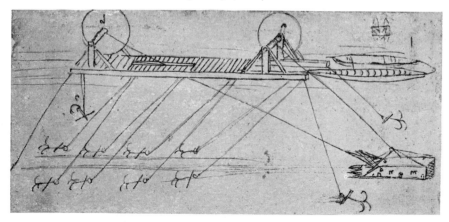

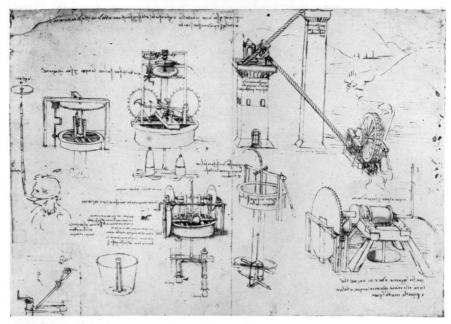

Plate 80—A miscellany of pumping mechanisms for raising water (C.A. 386 r.b.).

Plate 81 — Leonardo's hydraulic screw—a forerunner of the water turbine (Codex Arundel 63 v.). Supplied by the British Museum.

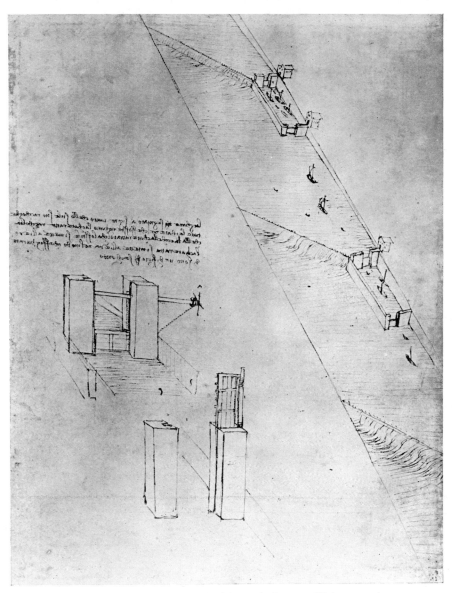

Plate 82—Portion of a canal with two lock gates (C.A. 33 v.a.).

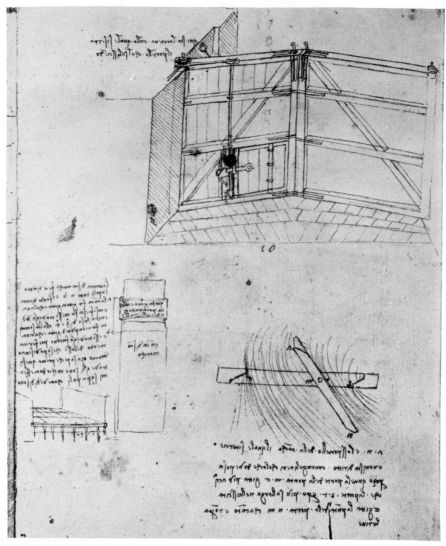

Plate 83—Detail of a canal lock-gate (C.A. 24 r.c.).

Plate 84—Various lock-gate sketches (C.A. 7 v.b.).

into two parts, namely the greasiness that is interposed in the aforesaid second form of friction, and the balls and things like these."

It is not easy to follow Leonardo precisely in this line of thought—but the basic phenomenon is most clearly appreciated. Moreover, there is little doubt but that he must have become growingly aware of the significance of the phenomenon of friction as he came up against the inevitable discrepancies between theoretical results and practical performance in a succession of experiments. He was thus prompted to make direct investigations on the movement of weights over surfaces of varying roughness. "The resistance created by friction to the movement of weights is separate and remote from this weight," he tells us.[1] He then proceeds to explain: "It is clearly seen that the movement by weights along horizontal lines does not of itself offer any other resistance to its mover than its own natural friction which it makes with the surface where it touches it; which movement becomes more difficult in proportion as the surface is more scoured and rough. And in order to see the truth of this, move the said weight upon balls on an absolutely smooth surface. You will see that it will move without effort."

At this point we interpolate the inference that Leonardo was here indicating the very great effect as a "friction-remover" of rolling surfaces like balls, and we shall see this strikingly illustrated in his actual employment of the device of ball bearings in some of his "gadgetry" (see p. 269).

The note goes on, however, to indicate how gravity may be introduced to play its part in overcoming friction by the simple device of inclining the surface upon which the weight rests. "The weight, the movement of which is rendered difficult by the friction which it makes with the smooth surface where it moves, will increase in gravity as it lacks effort in the friction which it has with the smooth surface where it moves. This is shown as it raises itself on a line that has a considerable slant, for as it were its simple weight is in the force of the mover, and the friction is small."

We are now able to follow Leonardo in his laboratory, so to speak, and see how he develops his friction theme experimentally, both with inclined surfaces and with surfaces varyingly lubricated. He records this in an extended note immediately following that previously quoted: "Whoever knows how great a weight raises the hundred pounds upwards over this slope knows the capacity of the screw."[2] (Note here that, theoretically, the screw is a continuous inclined plane.) "If you desire to know truly the quantity of the weight required to move the hundred pounds over the sloping road, you must know the nature

[1] MS. *SKM II*, 85 v. and 86 v.   [2] MS. *SKM II*, 86 v. and 87 r.

R

of the contact which this weight has with the surface where it produces friction by its movement, *because different bodies have different frictions*." The italics are ours, to indicate a fundamental element in Leonardo's observations. The note proceeds: "Thus, if there are two bodies with different surfaces, that is, that one is soft and polished and well greased or soaped, and it is moved over a smooth surface of a similar kind, it will move much more easily than one that has been made rough by the use of lime or a rasping file. Therefore, always when you wish to know the quantity of the force that is required in order to drag the same weight over streets of different slope, you have to make the experiment and ascertain what amount of force is required to move the weight along a level road, that is to ascertain the nature of its friction. . . . Different slopes cause different degrees of resistance at their contact because, if the weight which must be moved is upon level ground and has to be dragged, it undoubtedly will be in the first strength of its resistance, because all of it rests upon the earth (i.e. the ground), and nothing upon the cord which ought to move it. But if you wish to draw it up a very steep road, all the weight which it gives of itself to the cord that sustains it is subtracted from the contact of its friction."

How far was Leonardo aware of what we might call the quantitative laws of friction as we know them today? There are basically two such laws. One tells us that the frictional resistance is independent of the areas of the sliding surfaces in contact with each other, and the other that the amount of this resistance is proportional to the load between them. Leonardo was so specific on both these points that one feels inevitably that he must have tested them experimentally. As to the first of these principles, he writes: "The friction made by the same weight will be of equal resistance at the beginning of the movement, although the contact may be of different breadths and lengths";[1] and the second of the two basic principles is given thus: "Friction produces double the amount of effort if the weight be doubled."[2] So far as the formal history of mechanics is concerned, it was the French engineer Amontons who first enunciated these laws in 1699 to a surprised and somewhat sceptical audience of scientists at the Académie Royale des Sciences.

But on the development from these two principles to the facts relating to what we call the "coefficient of friction", a quantity that naturally differs with the nature of the rubbing surfaces, Leonardo was not so successful. Since the friction is proportional to the load, we define the coefficient of friction as the ratio of *the force of friction to the applied load*; and as examples of its value we may quote ratios of the order of 0·5 for a brick sliding on wood, but as little as 0·1 for a lubricated metal sliding over another metal. But da Vinci gives a uniform value

[1] MS. *SKM II*, 133 r.   [2] MS. *SKM III*, 72 r.

of 0·25 for all such surfaces. ("The friction of a polished smooth surface resists the engine with a force equal to one quarter of its weight.")[1] As a matter of fact, the value is actually 0·25 in the case of dry hardwood on dry hardwood, and it is barely possible, perhaps, that Leonardo may have generalised (somewhat hastily) from experiments on just these materials. But at least we may claim for Leonardo, firstly, that he appreciated the significance of the ratio, and, secondly, that he specified a "polished smooth" surface. (Plate 47.)

There is one further quotation we should note, since it concerns the subject of rolling friction. Leonardo observes that the interposition of round substances between two rubbing surfaces at once diminishes the friction between them and makes the movement of one over the other much easier. This is the basis for the use of roller bearings which he was himself to introduce, and which is now common practice in all modern rotating machinery. "All things . . . however thin," writes Leonardo, "which is interposed in the middle between objects that rub together, lighten the difficulty of this friction . . . and so increasing tiny grains such as millet makes it better and easier and, even more, the balls of wood or rollers, that is, wheels shaped like cylinders, and as these rollers become greater so the movements become easier."[2]

Finally, before we pass from theory to practice, it is curious to note that Leonardo went so far as to discuss the possible influence of friction on the "harmony of the spheres". He poses the query: "Whether the friction of the heavens makes a sound or no."[3] There are two alternatives, he suggests. Either the heavenly boundaries are smooth, in which case "not having air between them" they would make no sound; or else "they are full of lumps and rough and therefore their contact is not continuous". He then argues that, in this case, friction would have rubbed away the boundaries of each heaven so that "the sound would cease and the dancers would stop". He thus provides us with an interesting juxtaposition of ancient and modern, and shows us once again that his mind was never completely divorced from the classical cosmological picture.

Turning from these theoretical considerations to their application to practice, we are able to note some interesting examples of practical devices in which the element of friction is usefully employed. Leonardo interested himself, for example, in the design of grinding machines for the manufacture of optical glass and other purposes. A straightforward illustration is shown in Plate 49,[4] in which we see how the glass to be ground is held in a mounted wooden frame and pressed against

[1] *Codex Atlanticus*, 198 v.   [3] MS. *F*, 56 v.
[2] MS. *SKM II*, 132 r.   [4] *Codex Atlanticus*, 380 v.b.

a vertical grinding wheel manipulated by hand. An interesting variant of this design is seen earlier in the notes[1] with the lens and grinding surfaces reversed (Plate 50). The former is held vertically in the frame *A*, and the grinding surface *B* is rotated horizontally by means of a disc *C*, operated from a handle *D*. *C* is geared to *B* by a driving band.

As a clue to the nature of his grinding and polishing materials, there is an interesting sketch of a more complicated grinding plant (Plate 51).[2] The details of its operation are not very clear, but below the main sketch Leonardo shows an arrangement of the series of separate grinding discs for the plant, which he describes as comprising (*a*) one of walnut wood fitted with strips of thick leather; (*b*) one of willow-wood; and three (*c*), (*d*) and (*e*), also of walnut-wood; and all are treated with oil and emery.

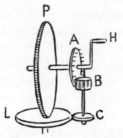

Fig. 59.   Mechanism for polishing lenses.

An ingenious idea devised by Leonardo for polishing lenses is shown in Fig. 59. The polisher *P* is held vertically over the lens *L* to be polished, and its rim is rotated over *L* by rotating the handle *H*. The toothed wheel *A*, on the same axle as *P*, is enmeshed with the horizontal toothed wheel *B*. This, in its turn, rotates *C* and thus keeps the lens *L* turning round under and against the rubbing rim of *P*.

Even more interesting was Leonardo's design for the grinding and polishing of hollow cylinders. It contains one or two ingenious features (Plate 52).[3] The hollow cylinder is held fast by two cheeks, one on each side, each being clamped securely to the wall of the large bracket by a nut and bolt. Filling out the interior of the hollow cylinder are shaped blocks of wood, down the channels and gaps between and around which are poured a mixture of oil and emery. The upper extremity of the projecting blocks of wood is held in the base of a screw, which is prevented from rotating by a rectangular iron block, through which it passes to receive a nut. The nut is free to rotate but not to move up or down. The screw is free to move up or down but not to rotate. Consequently, when the nut is made to rotate, the screw, and therefore the blocks within the cylinder, move up and down.

[1] *Codex Atlanticus*, 320 r.b.   [2] Ibid., 7 r.b.   [3] Ibid., 291 r.a.

The purpose of the mechanism is to create periodic reverses in the direction of rotation of the nut by causing the blocks to move alternately up and down, and so to grind the inside surface of the cylindrical specimen. The device for ensuring this is distinctly ingenious. The nut carries a rack wheel which engages in the teeth. At the same time, above the small horizontal wheel of the nut we have a piece of string wound round, the end being carried to the top of a perpendicularly-fixed spring coming from the base board to the left of the long one. The apparatus now works as follows. The operator turns the large

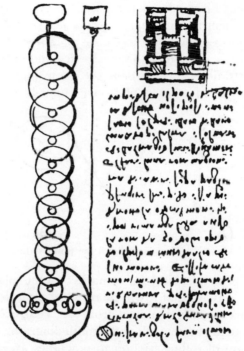

Fig. 60. Scheme for bell mounted on a series of twelve roller bearings.

wheel through half a circle, during which the nut engaging with it will rotate a few revolutions, thus at the same time both winding the string (and therefore pulling back the spring) and causing the wooden blocks to move up. The larger wheel is now let go and the rebound of the spring at once asserts itself. The string unwinds and the previous motion is reversed. The operation is thus repeated indefinitely, the escaping mixture of oil and emery being caught in a receptacle provided below.

It is interesting to note that in the top right-hand corner of the illustration Leonardo develops the idea still further so that by providing

the top half of the larger wheel on the opposite side with another set
of teeth he is able to operate two machines at the same time, and so
when one set of grinding blocks moves up the other set moves down,
and vice versa.

Leonardo was especially happy in his application of rolling friction
to mechanical devices. Since the points of frictional contact are continually changing as the rolling surface moves over the other, the coefficient of friction is naturally enormously reduced. Modern experiments give, for example, a value of 0·0045 for car wheels on rails,
of 0·003 for steel roller-bearings on steel, and of 0·0025 for steel ball-
bearings on steel. Leonardo soon realised the value of roller-bearings
and referred to them in enthusiastic terms as "marvels of mechanical
genius",[1] and he goes on to describe his pleasure at noting that the
revolutions continue even after the mechanical motor has itself stopped.
One of his illustrations (Fig. 60) on the same page shows a scheme
for a bell mounted on a series of twelve roller-bearings, working on

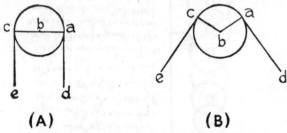

Fig. 61.   The principle of the pulley wheel.

the pendulum principle, and he remarks: "One places the bell on
its pivots in this way, so that it will be rung by a gentle wind, provided
their weights are equally removed from the centre." A plan of the
device is shown to the bottom left of the main diagram. Other examples
of the application of rolling friction to machines are also to be found
in the *Codex Atlanticus*[2] and in Manuscript *B* of the series in Paris.[3]

3. LEONARDO ON PULLEY SYSTEMS

The simple pulley-wheel is so obviously a device of convenience
both in mechanisms and in the day-to-day operations, not only of the
engineer but also of the artisan and the craftsman in a host of crafts—
the builder, the stonemason, the carpenter, the blacksmith, to mention
but a few—that it is not surprising that Leonardo gave it a considerable
amount of attention, both in theory and in practice. In discussing
these, however, we must make due allowance for the fact that he had

¹ MS. *I*, 57 v. and 58 r.   ² *Codex Atlanticus*, 390 v.b.
³ MS. *B*, 70 v.

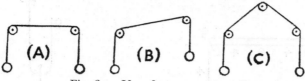

Fig. 62.   Use of two or more pulleys.

at hand a rich store of achievement handed down from the mechanics and engineering of antiquity. Aristotle, Archimedes, Vitruvius, Hiero, Ctesibius, Pappus and others had freely contributed to the subject and Leonardo was acquainted with their work. His own treatment of "pulley" theory is based upon the conceptions of (1) the lever laws and (2) the principle of virtual velocities. This latter is the Aristotelean principle that tells us that the same motive power that moves a heavy body slowly must move a lighter body more quickly, the velocities produced being inversely proportional to the weights. Implied in this is the "principle of work", to which we have already referred (p. 221). We may regard the initial step in Leonardo's study of the pulley as the note which accompanies two sketches in the *Codex Atlanticus* (Fig. 61), which reads: "The line of movement is *ab*, the line of the force is *ad*. The line of the movement in the balance is the distance of the middle points of the pulleys from their circumferences, especially from the direction of the force which acts on the circles as a tangent, i.e. *ab*. At the point of contact of the rope from which the weights act with the circle right angles continually arise between this rope and the radius of contact."[1] The simple pulley is, therefore, a simple balance, as in (*A*), or a virtual balance with potential arms, as in (*B*).

The interposition of another fixed pulley, or even of two, produces no change in the mechanical advantage (a term not, of course, used by Leonardo), and Fig. 62[2] is one of many frequently seen in his notebooks.

We have next to ask ourselves whether Leonardo appreciated the simple function of a pulley as a means of changing the direction of a force. Here, unfortunately, we find him distinctly at fault. Referring

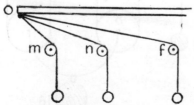

Fig. 63.   Using fixed pulleys for change of direction.

[1] *Codex Atlanticus*, 149 r.a.   [2] MS. *L*, 16 r.

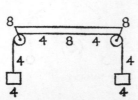
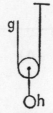

Fig. 64.   The tension in the string.   Fig. 65.   The single movable pulley.

to Fig. 63, he asks: "Which of the ropes *of*, *on* and *om* have more stretch, and further, how much, and why?"[1]   Leonardo must clearly have been confusing this with the problem of the inclined plane. "Because," he must have argued, "with the changing inclination of the plane, the pull on the rope supporting the body on the plane steadily changes, so will the pull on the rope passing over a single pulley change with its angle of inclination to the vertical." This error in reasoning is still more strikingly shown in a sketch (Fig. 64)[2] of a system of two four-pound weights suspended from the ends of a rope that pass over two fixed pulleys, i.e. there is a horizontal portion of rope joining the two pulleys, and two vertical portions. The tension in the horizontal portion of the rope is given as eight pounds, whilst those in the vertical portions are given as four pounds. Yet since it is one continuous rope, the tension in it must, of course, be the same throughout. We are unable, therefore, to say that da Vinci understood fully the simple function of change of direction of a force which all simple pulleys possess.

Let us next consider Leonardo's interpretation of the purpose of the

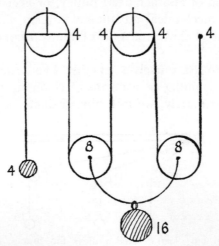

Fig. 66.   Pulley system with two movable pulleys.

[1] *Codex Atlanticus*, 346 v.a.   [2] Ibid., 104 v.b.

movable pulley as against the fixed pulley. Here, happily, we are on more fortunate ground. Attached to a sketch of a single movable pulley in the *Codex Atlanticus* (Fig. 65)[1] is the note: "Pay heed that *g* is the half of the weight *h*, and that the path of *g* is twice as great as that of *h*." Nothing could be more explicit, both from the point of view of mechanical advantage and of velocity ratio.

As a direct application of this property of the movable pulley, we may quote again from the *Codex Atlanticus*, from which Fig. 66[2] is taken. Here we have a system of two fixed and two movable pulleys. Leonardo speaks of the end of the rope carrying the power as the "arganica", and of the end of the rope carrying the cord as the "retinente". Referring to the sketch, he writes: "If one divides the burden lifted through the pulley tackle by the number of pulleys, one obtains a weight that, fastened at the 'arganica', makes equilibrium." Here, then, is the statement regarding the mechanical advantage

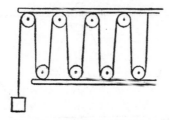

Fig. 67. Pulley system of four fixed
and four movable pulleys.

obtained by this system. In this case he moves a load of sixteen pounds by a force of four pounds, giving a mechanical advantage of four. Continuing, however, he says: "The path of the 'arganica' which lifts the burden is so many times as long as the path of the burden which becomes lifted through the pulley tackle as the number of pulleys," which completes the statement regarding the velocity ratio.

Plate 53[3] illustrates an extreme application of this property of the movable pulley in a pretty scheme of suspension from a framework of two rings of pulleys, the upper set being fixed and the lower movable, producing a very large mechanical advantage.

It is interesting to note, in turning to the various pulley systems with which Leonardo was familiar, that practically all forms of pulley combinations such as are met in the modern textbook are to be found in one place or another among the various manuscripts. Fig. 67 shows a typical example, with four fixed and four movable pulleys, and Leonardo reduces the discussion to the study of the tension in the rope. "The weight divides itself into eight pieces of rope. The ninth

[1] *Codex Atlanticus*, 321 r.a.   [2] Ibid., 321 r.a.   [3] Ibid., 104 v.b.

opposed to this simply holds the equipoise of the eight."[1] A curious case is presented by a note in Manuscript *A* accompanying a sketch of a system of two fixed and two movable pulleys (Fig. 68). The load is twenty pounds and the power should clearly be five pounds. Yet Leonardo makes it six pounds. His note reads: "If the burden borne be twenty pounds, then I say let ten pounds act on the pulley *l* and ten pounds on the pulley *k*, these being the points of suspension of the twenty pounds load. That is to say, that *o* takes off from *l* five pounds, and *p* also takes five pounds from *l*, and five pounds from *k*. Finally, *k* transmits five pounds to *g*. If one wishes to overcome the five pounds, one must apply at *x* an opposing weight of six pounds. So long as one applies six pounds at the extreme point against the five pounds at *x*, and so long as each of the four pieces of string which bear the twenty pounds themselves only experience the five pounds pull, then because the active extra weight on the rope *qx* finds nothing to

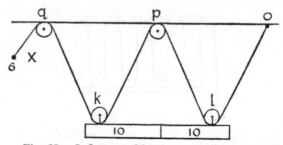

Fig. 68.   Influence of friction on pulley systems.

equal it in the opposing effective pieces of rope, the tension will be overcome and movement will result."[2] Clearly, the point here is that whilst the theoretical value for the power is recognised by Leonardo as five pounds, nevertheless, frictional and other resistances require an addition to this value in order that motion may ensue. At the same time it is just a little difficult to appreciate exactly what was in his mind regarding this extra one-pound pull.

The use of sheaves of pulleys is frequently met with in da Vinci's manuscripts. Plate 54 shows one such example,[3] whilst many other pulley systems are illustrated freely in the *Codex Atlanticus*. One such (Plate 55)[4] is of especial interest on account of the clear enunciation of the relationship between mechanical advantage and velocity ratio given in the text beside the drawing. It will be noticed that the figure, in so far as the scheme of tensions in the ropes and the re-lationship between power and load are concerned, is accurate and

[1] *Codex Atlanticus*, 104, v.b.
[2] MS. *A*, 62 r.
[3] MS. *E*, 54 v.; see also MS. *G*, 82 r.; and *Codex Atlanticus*, 141 v.a.
[4] *Codex Atlanticus*, 120 v.c.

complete. The note reads: "Just as one can here find a rule of diminishing force for the mover, so can one also lay down a rule for the increase in the velocity of the movement. The path of *m* stands in proportion to that of *n* as the weight *n* is to the weight *m*."

As further illustrative of the extent and variety of pulley systems dealt with by Leonardo, we may refer to yet another page in the *Codex Atlanticus*.[1] Here are shown a number of diagrams, self-explanatory (which may possibly account for the fact that they are unaccompanied by notes in the text) giving pulley systems of various complications, in each of which the mechanical advantage is accurately worked out in terms of the tensions in the strings. Some twenty or more variations of pulley systems fill this page of Leonardo's notebook, of which we here show three (Fig. 69).

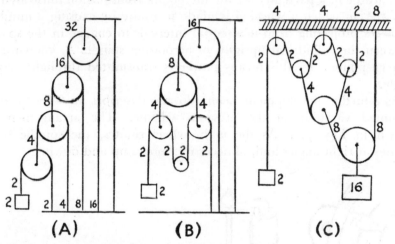

Fig. 69. Various pulley systems.

4. THE TRANSMISSION OF POWER

Turning next to the transmission of power, we come again to a field which by the fifteenth century was already full of historical associations. Indeed, ever since the time when Aristotle had discussed the gearing of three wheels in rough contact, the theory of power transmission, mainly through toothed gearing, progressed rapidly, and was accompanied by an equally rapid development in practice. Hence, not only do we find innumerable examples of machines, structures, cranes and other practical mechanisms sketched and described throughout Leonardo's notebooks, but we also meet with a number of theoretical discussions. The ordinary cases of toothed wheels in gear with each other are naturally very frequent (Plate 56), but, in addition,

---

[1] *Codex Atlanticus*, 153 r.a.

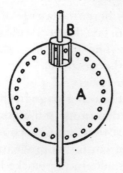

Fig. 70.   Power transmission through
a right-angle.

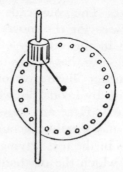

Fig. 71.   Eccentrically-mounted
power transmission.

Leonardo had a partiality for the method of transmission illustrated in Fig. 70[1], in which a wheel *A* is made to rotate by causing a number of pieces projecting from it at equal intervals to engage in the spaces between the cylindrical uprights of a rotating spindle *B*, known as a lantern pinion. By this means power is transmitted through a right angle.

As a further development Leonardo also describes an eccentrically-mounted variation of the previous scheme. The arrangement is shown in Fig. 71[2]. As the main wheel rotates, the spindle both rotates at right angles and, of necessity, moves up and down.

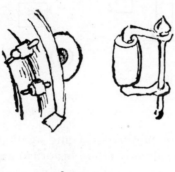

Fig. 72.   Rollers for toothed
wheels to reduce friction.

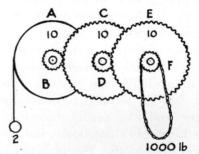

Fig. 73.   Power transmission by
toothed gearing.

[1] MS. *G*, 26 v.   [2] MS. *H*, 86 v.

Before leaving this aspect of our subject, the reader will be interested to note that Leonardo has at least one sketch showing how ingeniously he uses the device of rollers to diminish friction as the wheel to which these are fitted engages with its neighbour. The sketch explains itself (Fig. 72).[1]

As an example of Leonardo's method of discussing theoretically the problems of power transmission by toothed gearing, let us consider Fig. 73, taken from the *Codex Atlanticus*.[2] The scheme is as follows: there are three large wheels, A, C and E, of which C and E are toothed. A has no teeth but carries the power load at the extremity of a cord. The axles B, D and F of each of A, C and E are also toothed, and the radii of the axle wheels B and D are one-tenth of those of the larger wheels A and C, whilst that of F is *one-fifth* of E. F carries an endless

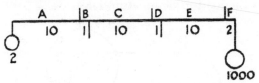

Fig. 74.   Power transmission—the equivalent lever.

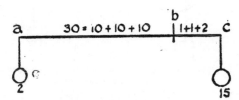

Fig. 75.   The uninterrupted balance.

chain along which the lifted load is distributed. Leonardo's treatment is very simple and is based entirely on the principle of the lever. He reduces the system to what he calls an "interrupted balance", which is really a sequence of equivalent simple levers working from left to right as shown in Fig. 74. In this we see that with a power of two pounds the system AB gives an equivalent load of twenty pounds, the system CD an equivalent load of 200 pounds, and EF a final load of 1,000 pounds. So far the reasoning is perfect. Where, however, Leonardo now goes astray is in introducing the further (and incorrect) notion of an equivalent *uninterrupted* balance (Fig. 75), the left arm of which is equal to the sum of the "interrupted" left arms of Fig. 74 (i.e. 10+10+10=30), and the right arm of which is equal to the sum of the right arms of the "interrupted" scheme (i.e. 1+1+2=4).

[1] Trivulzio MS., Milan, 391 v.
[2] *Codex Atlanticus*, 153 v.d.

This for a power of two pounds, as before, gives a load $\dfrac{2 \times 30}{4} = 15$ pounds. Reverting to the original value of 1,000 pounds, Leonardo now points out that fifteen pounds is contained in the 1,000 pounds $66\frac{2}{3}$ times, and thus concludes that the movement of the heavy weight is $66\frac{2}{3}$ times as slow as that of the power. In view of the fact that Leonardo had shown himself to be quite clear as to the relationship between velocity ratio and mechanical advantage it is difficult to understand why he should have brought in this incorrect and unnecessary notion of the "uninterrupted balance".

We offer one more illustration of Leonardo's applications of the principle of the lever to the transmission of power in Fig. 76.[1] Here we have a combination of two wheels and axles, each of which have radii ratios of three to one. The power being ten pounds, Leonardo readily deduces the load to be ninety pounds.

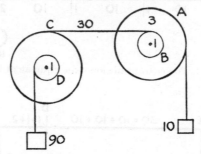

Fig. 76.   Application of the lever principle to
power transmission.

We conclude this section with a brief survey of some examples of "transmission of power" devices either planned by or actually used by Leonardo da Vinci. As a preliminary the reader is referred back to Fig. 59 in the section on friction, as a reminder of a very elegant sequence of linkages used for the purpose of lens polishing; and to Fig. 70, illustrating the simple transmission of power from one wheel to another at right angles to it. An excellent example of this in practice is shown in Plate 57, which depicts a drawing in the *Codex Atlanticus*[2] from which a working model has been reconstructed of a nap-raising machine. Leonardo was very interested in the engineering aspects of the textile industry in Italy, for which he devised a number of mechanisms. In the example here illustrated, the two cog wheels rotating at right angles are shown on the left of the model. This machine was actually designed to operate by water power, and, as the cloth was made to

[1] MS. *J*, 132 r.
[2] *Codex Atlanticus*, 38 r.a. This and other models illustrated here were made for and exhibited at an Exhibition of the Collections of Fine Arts Dept., International Business Machine Corporation, New York, in 1951.

move under the wooden beam by the rotation of the system of cylinders all mounted on one horizontal axis, burrs set on the under side of the beam brushed the nap on the cloth.

Again, referring back to Fig. 71, in which an eccentrically-mounted cage-wheel and spindle produces both a rotating transmission at right-angles to the motive power applied, and a reciprocal up-and-down linear motion of the spindle itself, the reader will note in Plate 58[1] how this, too, was applied by Leonardo to the needs of the textile industry. The illustration shows a working model of a device for distributing the thread over the bobbin as spinning proceeds—a forerunner of Arkwright's spinning machine of 1775. The eccentrically-mounted vertical cage-wheel and spindle is seen on the left. The machine wound thread on a spool by revolving the spool, at the same time moving the guide back and forth. Leonardo's original drawing, from which this model was made, is shown in Plate 59. The flyer itself, however, was not original to Leonardo; it is described in a German manuscript entitled *The Medieval Housebook*, c. 1480.

Since the flyer-wheel converted spinning and winding into a single continuous action, the spinner could be seated. He was thus able to operate the mechanism by using a foot-treadle to drive the wheel—a practice first introduced about the end of the fifteenth century.

One of the most ingenious examples of power transmission devised by Leonardo was for a variable-speed drive of a type that is to be found in our modern automobile. The actual drawing is shown in Plate 60[2] among other sketches of various gearing devices, but again the simplicity of detail is well brought out in the working model illustrated in Plate 61. By meshing three cogged wheels of increasing diameter with the same conical or lantern wheel as shown, Leonardo was able to obtain progressively increasing speeds of rotation.

The reader will recall the device shown in Plate 45 of a turnspit used for roasting meat, driven by a fan at the top of the chimney. The motive power was derived from the current of hot air ascending the chimney, and the device is again a simple example of transmission of power. Above this drawing in the *Codex Atlanticus*, however, is shown another scheme for a mechanically operated turnspit (Plate 62)[3] in which a very elegant sequence of linked toothed gearing is clearly shown. Wound round the drum-axle is a rope carrying a heavy weight over a fixed pulley. The meat to be roasted is fixed to one or both of the horizontal axle projections from the two rotating wheels on the left, and the drive is provided by the fall of the weight. To keep the speed under control uniformly, a braking effect is produced by the air friction set up by the resistance of four goose feathers mounted, as

[1] *Codex Atlanticus*, 393 v.a.   [2] Ibid., 27 v.a.   [3] *Codex Atlanticus*, 5 v.a.

shown at the top left of the diagram. The reader will have no difficulty in following the scheme of linkages between the rotating of the drum and that of the spit.

Finally, before we leave the subject of Leonardo's treatment of power transmission, we should note some remarkable sketches of chain-belting (Plate 63) in the *Codex Atlanticus*.[1] The chain links look, in this very clear series of drawings[2], almost as though they had come from a modern bicycle; and, actually, historical records attribute their introduction to the Frenchman Galle in 1832, more than three centuries after da Vinci's time. Nevertheless, it is not clear, apart from this drawing, to what extent, if any, such chain gearing was actually made and used in Leonardo's day.

5. LEONARDO'S STUDIES IN THE STRENGTHS OF STRUCTURES AND MATERIALS

It is desirable at this stage to turn to another and very important aspect of Leonardo's more purely experimental work in applied mechanics, namely, his investigations into the strengths of structures and the limits of strain to which they could be subjected with safety. Such investigations are a vital necessity both to engineer and architect; and having ascertained both by mathematical theory and by experi-

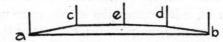

Fig. 77.   Distribution of load on a bird's wing.

mental verification what these limits are, a factor of safety is then usually applied to the results. Factors of safety were not deliberately introduced in Leonardo's day, but then neither were there, apart from his own notebooks, any records of either theoretical or experimental investigations on the subject, at any rate in the modern sense of the term. Actually, however, Leonardo's diagrams and sketches and their attendant notes almost look as though they had come from the pages of a modern textbook on applied mechanics. He deals experimentally with loaded beams, and with the strengths of loaded struts, pillars and columns.

Curiously enough, although Leonardo's interest in these matters was fundamentally as an engineer and architect, he was also brought into contact with this class of problem, surprisingly perhaps, by his studies on the flight of birds. He was curious about the

---

[1] *Codex Atlanticus*, 357 r.a.

[2] It should be noted, however, that Leonardo's sketches of these chain-links appear in conjunction with his preliminary drawings of a wheel-lock device for the breech-loading mechanism of guns. C. Blair claims, in a recent paper, that they were intended as transmission chains for these wheel-lock mechanisms. (C. Blair, "A Note on the Early History of the Wheel Lock", *Journal of the Arms and Armour Society*. March, 1961.)

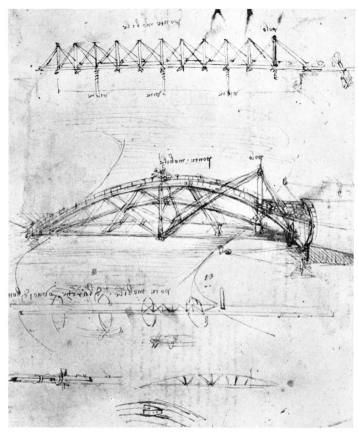

Plate 85—Sheet of designs for three different
swing-bridges (C.A. 312 r.a.).

Plate 86—Model of swing bridge reconstructed from Leonardo's middle sketch
in Plate 85 (I.B.M., New York).

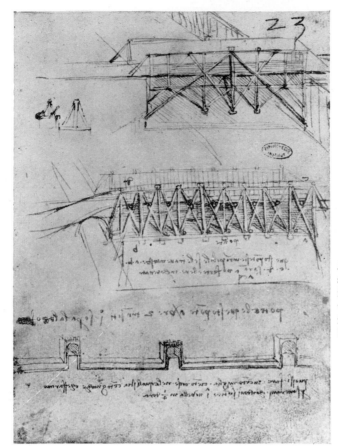

Plate 87—Bridge designs. The centre one is an N-Type bridge with an upper-level for pedestrians (MS. B. 23 r.).

Plate 88—Model of Leonardo da Vinci's N-Type girder bridge (Crown Copyright Reserved. By permission of the Director, Science Museum, London).

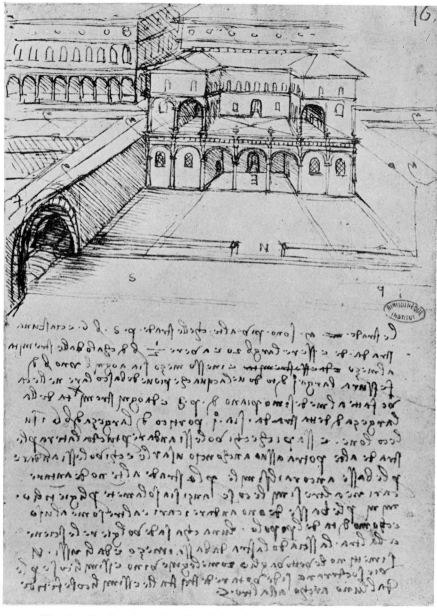

Plate 89—Laying out a city. Road planning at two levels (MS. B. 23 r.).

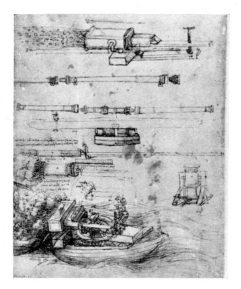

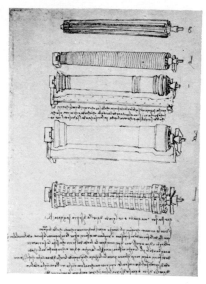

Plate 90—A miscellany of mortars and cannon (see also Plate 3).

Plate 91—Stages in the construction of a gun-barrel (C.A. 19 r.b.).

Plate 92—Wheel-lock device for breech loading (MS. B. 24 v.).

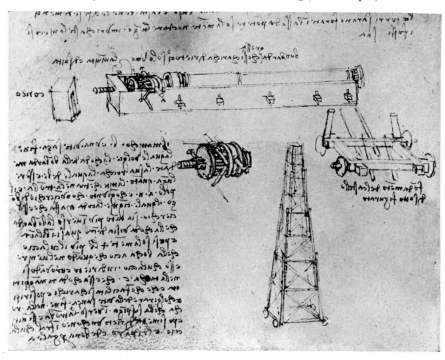

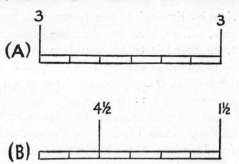

Fig. 78. Reactions on supports of a loaded beam.

distribution of pressure of the relatively moving air in relation to the wing span of the bird in flight. So he asks: "In which part of the under surface of the width of the bird does the wing press the air more than in any other part of the length of the wings?"[1] He is impelled, as a consequence, to discuss the problem of the loading on a rigid structure. He goes on thus: "All bodies which do not bend will exert equal pressures on all supports that are equally distant from the centre of gravity. One proves how the above-mentioned weight exerts equal pressure on its supports: let us assume that it is 4 lb. (I say) and that it is sustained by the support *ab* (Fig. 77). I say that the body being unhindered in its fall except by the two supports *ab*, that these supports will sustain equal parts of this weight that is to say 2 and 2 and the same thing would apply to the 2 supports *cd*, if the 3 other supports were not there: and if the middle one at *e* only remained it would support the whole of the weight."

A similar example is given in the *Codex Atlanticus*.[2] A sketch (Fig. 78(A)) shows a uniform beam of 6 lb weight and the reactions at the ends are given as 3 lb each. Adjoining this[3] he considers what happens when one support is moved inwards two divisions (Fig. 78(B)), and he correctly shows the reactions to be $4\frac{1}{2}$ lb and $1\frac{1}{2}$ lb respectively.

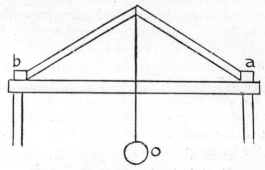

Fig. 79. Problem of the loaded strut.

[1] *On the Flight of Birds*, 4 v.   [2] *Codex Atlanticus*, 101 r.a.   [3] See also *Codex Atlanticus*, 185 r.a.

Standing in a class by themselves are Leonardo's studies of the load which vertical struts, pillars, etc., are capable of sustaining. A characteristic problem he posed is to be found in the South Kensington manuscripts.[1] Accompanying a sketch (Fig. 79) is the query: "If the beams and the weight O are 100 lb, how much weight will be wanted at a and b to resist such a weight, that it may not fall down?"

Most of his notes on this subject, however, are to be found in Manuscript A of the collection at the Institute of France, though others also occur in the *Codex Atlanticus*, and they constitute the first scientific attempt of their kind (Plate 64). All previous efforts were frankly empirical. Of da Vinci's we can at least say that it attempted scientifically to combine theory with practice. He begins early in the former manuscript by pointing out that a number of pillars or supports held together are stronger collectively than a single "equivalent" pillar. "Many little supports held together, i.e. in a bundle," he writes, "are capable of bearing a greater load than if they are separated from each other. Of 1,000 such rushes of the same thickness and length

Fig. 80. Loading on struts.

which are separated from one another, each one will bend if you stick it upright and load it with a common weight. And if you bind them together with cords so that they touch each other, they will be able to carry a weight such that each single rush is in the position of supporting twelve times more weight than formerly."[2]

Turning next to a comparison of the loading capacities of two struts of equal height but of different cross-section (Fig. 80), Leonardo writes: "A support with twice the diameter [width and depth?] will carry eight times as much weight as another, both having the same height."[3] His proof of this is not very convincing, but he concludes in effect that the ability to carry a load is directly proportional to the area of the carrying surface and inversely proportional to the relation of the height to the diameter. We may express Leonardo's results generally by the formula:

$$\text{Possible load} = \frac{\text{carrying surface}}{\text{height}}$$

[1] MS. *SKM II*, 14 v.   [2] MS. *A*, 3 v.   [3] Ibid., 47 r.

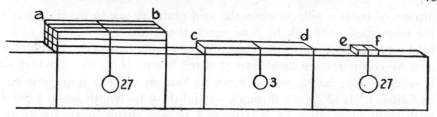

Fig. 81.   Comparison of loaded beams.

Applying this to Fig. 80 we see that there is a factor of four in respect of surface areas and an inverse factor of one-half in respect of the denominator, giving one load as eight times the other. Unfortunately, Leonardo's application of this rule sometimes showed faulty arithmetic. Thus he quotes one example in which the comparison of load shows according to the rule 320: 80, whereas he makes it 320: 60, a note in the text giving the product of 16 and 5 as 60.

Leonardo now passes on to a comparison of the carrying capacities of struts of equal cross-section but of different heights, and concludes that these are inversely as their heights. "So often as the short staff is contained in the longer," he writes, "so much greater is the load which it can carry than the long one."[1]

Next, we may refer briefly to Leonardo's notes, chiefly in the *Codex Atlanticus*, on the subject of loaded beams. On one page[2] we find a sketch (Fig. 81) with the following note: "You will find the same power of support by binding together nine balks as by the ninth part of one of these parts; *ab*, which consists of nine balks, carries twenty-seven units of weight. Further, *cd*, which is the ninth part of the same in cross-section, carries three; thereby can *ef*, which is the ninth part of the length of *cd*, carry twenty-seven units of weight, since it is nine times as short as the former." Whatever else we may say of this result, it does embody certain generally correct features regarding the influence of length, breadth and depth.

Leonardo, however, next proceeds to a discussion of the amount of deflection, or bending, produced in loaded beams. The problem is posed in its simplest form in a note accompanying a diagram in Manuscript *A* (Fig. 82), which reads: "A weight placed on a plank

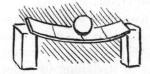

Fig. 82.   Deflection of loaded beam.

[1] MS. *A*, 49; see also 48 v.   [2] *Codex Atlanticus*, 152 r.b.

supported by two pillars causes the said plank to sag in the middle."[1]
He then goes on to ask by how much the beam sags in terms of its
load and the position of the load relative to the supports. In another
note he compares the deflection of three beams (Fig. 83) of which *cd*
is twice as long as *ef*, and *ab* twice as long as *cd*. His note proceeds
as follows: "If *ab* bends through an eighth of its length when loaded
with eight units, then *cd*, if it is, as I believe, twice as strong as *ab*,
will not bend itself through an eighth of its length with a smaller weight
than sixteen units; since it is half as long as *ab*. Similarly, will *ef*, since
it is half as long as *cd*, be twice as strong and will bend one-eighth
of its length with a load of thirty-two units. One must also note that
the beam *cd* which is twice as strong as *ab* on a load double that of *ab*
will not bend one-eighth of its length but, speaking much more exactly,
will bend one-sixteenth of its length."[2]

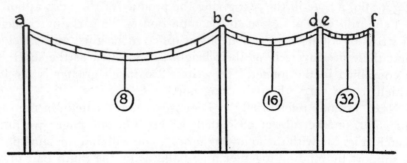

Fig. 83.   Comparison of deflections of variously loaded beams.

Students of applied mechanics will know that the formula for the
deflection *x* of a beam loaded in the middle and supported at the ends
is given by $x = \dfrac{Wl^3}{4\,Ebd^3}$, where *W* is the load, *l* the length, *b* the breadth,
and *d* the depth of the beam. An application of this to the case cited
by Leonardo in Fig. 83 will show that the correction he offers in
the last paragraph of the note is right, the former result being wrong.
We must again stress the point, however, that although he accomplished little in the way of accurate results, he was the first man to
attempt this class of problem scientifically, and to that extent at least
he deserved considerable credit.

Finally in this section we turn to Leonardo's study of the strengths
of metal wires under load. It is a familiar experiment in elementary
physics to subject a length of wire to increasing loads and to measure
the consequent amounts of stretching in order to establish the well-
known Hooke's Law, and one cannot but be particularly impressed by

[1] MS. *A*, 48 r.   [2] *Codex Atlanticus*, 332 r.b.

an example of such an experiment in the *Codex Atlanticus*[1] some two hundred years before Hooke's own experiments were carried out. The art of drawing wire through dies was well understood in Leonardo's day. It actually dated back to the middle of the fourteenth century, when it was first practised at Nuremberg in Germany. The note accompanying Leonardo's sketch (Plate 65) reads: "The object of this test is to find the load an iron wire can carry. Attach an iron wire two braccia long to something that will fairly support it. Then attach a basket or any similar container to the wire and feed into the basket some fine sand through a small hole placed at the end of the hopper. A spring is fixed so that it will close the hole as soon as the wire breaks. The basket is not upset while falling since it falls through a very short distance. The weight of the sand and the location of the fracture of the wire are to be recorded. The test is repeated several times to check the results." Admittedly, the details on the diagram are not very clear in relation to the experiment, but both the intention and the description of the procedure are clear enough and constitute a remarkable example of Leonardo's scientific approach. Obviously, he had in no way anticipated Hooke's Law, but he had certainly anticipated the general nature of the problem of the tensile strengths of wires and the general line of attack for its investigation.

6. THE TOOLS OF WORKSHOP PRACTICE

Let us turn now from these considerations of Leonardo the theorist to Leonardo the practical engineer. In this connection, however, we must again stress that Leonardo was in no sense the originator of engineering practice. As was outlined in some detail in Chapter V, the fifteenth century was in fact heir to a considerable mechanical technology, so that inevitably, in spite of his tremendous fertility of ideas, many of his notes and sketches relate to types of mechanisms already in existence. Almost always, however, he would be found to have indicated some improvements in their design. But apart from these, however, he undoubtedly sketched designs of machines and processes that were exclusively his own creation. Some of them were possibly taken up and brought into subsequent use; others, although probably excellent in theory, would have been beyond the capabilities of construction in his own times; whilst yet others were obviously just delightful brain-waves of impracticable ingenuity.

What did Leonardo contribute, first of all, to the equipment needs of the workshop of his day? In the normal process of machine-shop practice, the usual basic needs for cutting, filing, drilling, turning, planing, and so forth, are all catered for by the special tools and

[1] *Codex Atlanticus*, 8a v b.

mechanisms appropriate to each operation involved. His notebooks show that Leonardo concerned himself with most of these needs.

Since the manipulation of the file is almost the first exercise given to the modern technical apprentice, let us begin the survey by considering Leonardo's design of a file-making machine (Plate 66) taken from the *Codex Atlanticus*.[1] This is of special interest, since, apart from this design, the earliest-known device in the history of engineering practice in actual use for the mechanical processing of files was by du Verger in France in 1735—and his machine was much clumsier than was Leonardo's.[2] The sketch is very clear. The file-blank, a metal strip whose surface is to receive a series of nicks or cuts in order to convert it into a file, is held firmly in the block on the left by two grips at either end of the block. The cuts are made by the successive falls of a hammer at small intervals, created by the traverse of the file-blank holder as the large axial screw passing through it slowly rotates. This main axial screw terminates in a large toothed wheel on the right, geared, as is clearly shown in the sketch, to a small wheel mounted on a drum. Round this drum is wound a rope carrying a heavy weight passing over a pulley. The fall of the weight provides the power which simultaneously both swings the hammer down on to the blank and thus rotates the main screw by a distance equal to half the pitch of the screw thread, to bring the blank into position to receive the next blow. The framework to which the hammer is swivelled is clearly seen to the left of the main toothed wheel; and of course the weight is hauled to the top at the end of each series of blows by hand-rotating the crank operating the drum-winding. To the left of the sketch are shown two hammer-heads with inclined chisel edges, intended for making double cuts.

The mainstay of all mechanical workshops is, of course, the lathe. In its earliest form it was intended for woodwork and was part of the equipment of the carpenter. Rotation was effected by the hand manipulation of a sort of fiddler's bow looped round the specimen. Subsequently, the lathe began to be used for turning the softer metals like tin and lead. Leonardo's design of a treadle-operated lathe, seen in the *Codex Atlanticus*,[3] is shown in Plate 67. The power is applied by a treadle working a crankshaft to which a fly-wheel is added. Treadles were by no means new in the fifteenth century, but the device of the fly-wheel to provide continuous and uniform working certainly was new. The specimen to be turned is held firmly between the two pro-

---

[1] *Codex Atlanticus*, 6 r.b.
[2] An earlier machine for cutting files was described and illustrated by a French locksmith, Jousse de la Fleche, *c.* 1670. He did not actually make it, however. See article in *Die Werkzeugmaschine* (30th January 1915), pp. 21–23.
[3] *Codex Atlanticus*, 381 r.b.; see also 170 v.a.

jecting cylinders as shown, the left-hand one being a portion of the flywheel axle. The right-hand cylinder block is kept firmly against the specimen by means of the turning handle as shown. The cutting tool is held firmly against the specimen by the manipulator of the apparatus.

On the same page as this lathe is also shown a mechanical saw—an obvious machine of utility in the workshop. The design is ingenious. The blade is held vertically, in a wooden frame below which is a horizontal axle. Swivelled to this axle is an eccentric rod operated by a crank mounted on a fly-wheel. The wood to be sawn is fed against the blade, which moves up and down as the eccentric drive is operated below it.

The next refinement of the lathe, at least in current workshop practice, is the screw-cutter. Leonardo devised a separate and special variety of lathe for this purpose.[1] His sketch is shown in Plate 68. The rod into which the required screw-thread is to be cut is mounted on a firm wooden bench in parallel between two lengths of screw-rods. All three terminate in spur-wheels in gear. The centre gear-wheel attached to the specimen to be threaded carries a hand crank. The cutting tool is seen projecting from the centre bearing. The drawing shows that so far about half the length of the rod-specimen has been cut. The centre bearing carrying the tool is advanced by the rotation of the hand crank and the rate of advance which, of course, determines the pitch of the screw-thread being cut, depends upon the gear ratios of the gear-wheels in mesh with the driver-wheel in the centre. In Leonardo's sketch, a series of wheels of varying size are shown on the floor beneath the bench, and any of these can be substituted according to the pitch required. Leonardo's note accompanying the sketch reads as follows: "This is the way to make a screw. You turn the middle wheel, which rests on the screw which you wish to make. If you wish to make screws with greater or lesser inclined threads [i.e. pitch], then remove the wheels *s* and *f* and replace them with the wheels *a* and *b* or the wheels *c* and *d*. Accordingly you push the stirrups *h, e* and *t* farther apart or closer together; also those at the plane *K* [bearing carriage] and the block *g*. The plane is that part which contains the screw-cutting tool which, in being pushed forward, cuts the thread of the new screw."

One cannot but be impressed by this essentially modern design. Whether, in fact, it was brought into practical use by Leonardo is not known. But as a forerunner of the screw-cutting procedures of modern machine-shop practice it is remarkable.

Leonardo paid considerable attention to the design of mechanisms for boring and drilling. There were two angles to this. One was the

[1] MS. *G*, 70 v. See also *Codex Atlanticus*, 14 r.a.

workshop aspect, in respect of which boring and drilling machines were required for such operations as the making of wooden piping for water supply and similar needs; and the other was the external aspect, in which the problem was the normal one of boring down into the surface of the ground.

For the former type Leonardo designed one machine that was horizontal in its action and another that worked vertically. The horizontal type was probably based upon a machine of German origin dating from about A.D. 1430. Leonardo's sketch[1] shows the specimen

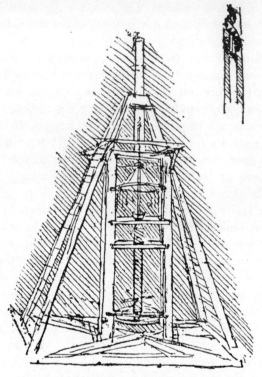

Fig. 84. Vertical boring machine.

to be bored as mounted on a firm trestle along the middle of which is a long screw. This holds the carrier unit which both grips the specimen firmly and carries it slowly forward against a system of four cutting blocks by means of a scheme of geared wheels. More useful and practicable, however, was the vertically acting type of borer, which Leonardo sketched in Manuscript B[2] (Fig. 84). The trunk to be bored is held vertically in a frame as shown and the cutting tool operates from below upwards, enabling the sawdust to fall away harmlessly as fast as it is formed. As the boring tool rotates, the plat-

[1] *Codex Atlanticus*, 393 r.   [2] MS. *B*, 47 v.

form from which it operates is steadily moved upwards. Leonardo writes: "To bore through a tree trunk one must place it vertically and bore it upwards from below, so that the hole is able to empty itself. . . . Make the hole first with a thin borer and then with a thicker one."

As usual, with so many ideas devised by Leonardo, we find the earliest reference to a borer of this type propounded by the Dresden engineer Peschel in the year 1798.[1] Yet Leonardo's sketch dates from A.D. 1500, almost three hundred years earlier.

Finally, as additional items of operational equipment for the ideal machine-shop of the late fifteenth century, we should describe briefly Leonardo's design for mechanical rollers for producing sheet tin, and his "drawing frame" for producing copper strips.

Leonardo's drawing of his mechanical rollers[2] (Plate 69) is the first

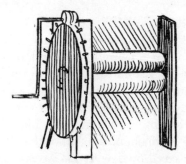

Fig. 85.   Mechanical rollers.

of its kind. Yet it is all simple enough. His note reads: "The art of making a thin and even tin-plate. These rollers should be made of bronze in order that they may be harder; and they are supplied with iron axles so that they cannot wear out. Whilst the one turns the other round, they stretch out a plate whose width is half a yard." The rollers are, in fact, as shown in the drawing, supported by counter-rollers below to prevent bending. This machine was also used for lead sheeting such as was required for roofing and for organ-pipes. Another design by Leonardo of mechanical rollers intended for rolling gold or lead is shown in the *Codex Atlanticus*[3] (Fig. 85).

In the same class of machine-shop equipment we must include an interesting design of a mechanism for stretching and rolling copper strips into equal lengths and thinness suitable for their use, after polishing, for the making of mirrors. Leonardo's drawing[4] is of un-

---

[1] There is, however, in the Deutches Museum in Germany a model of a vertical cannon borer the original of which is claimed to have been in the Royal Foundry in Berlin in 1774.
[2] MS. *J*, 48 v.
[3] *Codex Atlanticus*, 370 v.b.
[4] MS. *G*, 70 v.

usual interest because it gives both plan and elevation, a feature only too rarely to be found throughout his notes (Plate 70). Leonardo describes his machine as follows: "The wheels below have a diameter of one yard, and there are 36 teeth to each yard. But when the powers are less one must exchange the second wheel for another one, smaller by half, and place it on the same axle. The teeth are to be made of very strong iron. And if you wish to know how long the time takes for the shaft (which receives the metal band) to turn itself, then you must multiply the number of teeth thus: 36 times 36 equals 1296. The winch of the first motor will thus make 1296 rotations, whilst the other winch with one turn will receive half a yard of the metal strip." In the elevation drawing below the hand winch which supplies the motive power is lettered *abc*, with a note that reads: "*a.b.c*, the winch should be replaced by a water-wheel".

7. THE CIVIL ENGINEER AT WORK

The apparatus of machine-shop practice which we have so far described relates to what we might call indoor engineering. But, as we have seen, much of Leonardo's work as an engineer was out-of-doors. There he concerned himself with many of the aspects of the civil engineer of today—on schemes of canal construction, the draining of swamps, on projects for road and town planning, on dredging, on problems of bridging, and so on. For all of these his fertile imagination and his quick brain combined with his artistic skill to produce ideas and designs and sketches that are impressive in their range and ingenuity. We can, as before, but quote one or two characteristic examples.

We consider first the day-to-day mechanisms of necessity, common to all engineering activities, both indoors and on outside sites—namely,

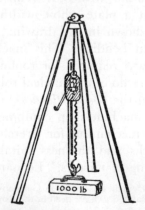

Fig. 86. Rack and pinion mounted on
shear legs.

lifting mechanisms. Leonardo designed a variety of these—pulley tackle, lifting jacks, cranes and so forth. We have already discussed his differential pulley blocks and sheaves (p. 266), and Fig. 86 illustrates one of his devices using the rack-and-pinion combination mounted on sheer-legs.[1] He speaks of it as a "double-lifting jack". The diagram is self-explanatory. Another lifting device, also mounted on sheer-legs, is shown in Plate 71.[2] Here the sheer-legs are designed to raise either a column which has to be fixed on to its pedestal or perhaps a piece of ordnance to be fitted into position on its carriage. The column is held in a long inverted U-shaped grip from which a long screw-bar projects. The lifting is done by turning the capstan at the top. When the column is raised to its required position, the cross-ties are dismantled and removed, and the whole mechanism is drawn to one side by means of the tackle and rope shown on the bottom left of the drawing.

Shown on the same page is an interesting drawing of a sort of tall travelling crane (Plate 72)—a neat device of a lifting mechanism seemingly travelling on an overhead scheme of guide-wires and mounted by a pivot on a small carriage on wheels.

This leads us naturally to Leonardo's use of travelling cranes as part of his equipment in such operations as canal construction, or for the raising and transport of large blocks of stone. In this group of devices he frequently used a system of twin cranes, either in harness at the same level (Plate 73) or with one crane working at a higher elevation than the other. In Plate 73 the winch on the left is seemingly for the purpose of dragging the whole plant forward on its heavy rectangular base as the large mass of stone, which is being cut and removed block by block, is depleted. Clearly, while one crane is being loaded with one block, the other crane is swung round to enable another block to be lowered and removed.

In canal construction there are two well-known drawings (Plate 74 and 75) by Leonardo of cranes working in double-harness. Plate 75 calls for special comment.[3] It will be seen that the structure is mounted on a system of three parallel rails, and the central column carries two derrick cranes, one mounted above the other. The canal-digging operations, as seen on the right, proceed at two levels and at each a series of receptacles or bins are placed at intervals. As these are filled the cranes swing them up and away, to be heaped at the side as shown. As the digging operations proceed, the whole structure is moved forward by the winch mechanism seen projecting from the central rail on the right.

[1] *Codex Atlanticus*, 40 r.a.; see also 359 r.c.   [2] Ibid., 49 v.a.
[3] Ibid., 1 v.b.

It is convenient at this stage to refer back to our reference to Leonardo's boring devices. On p. 280 we described the workshop type of apparatus used by the mechanical engineer for boring into tree-trunks to make piping suitable for water supply. A corresponding boring machine is used out-of-doors by the civil engineer for drilling into the ground. An ingenious design for this, based upon the cork-screw principle, was described by Leonardo in Manuscript B^1 (Plate 76). It was of a type subsequently brought into practice by the famous Bernard Palissy about the year 1580. The simple framework carries the screw-cutter, and Leonardo remarks: "To make the hole, you must rotate the handle *mn* with the right hand and the screw will then penetrate to wind into the ground. To withdraw the borer, hold the handle *mn* tightly and now rotate the handle *fg* in the opposite direction with the left hand. Thus the screw will be withdrawn and will bring the soil up with it."

Against another design in the *Codex Atlanticus*[2] (Plate 77) is shown the brief note: "A borer to drill into the ground to find water."

Allied in a distant sense to the operation of boring to bring up soil is the problem of clearing harbours and waterways of their accumulation of mud and sludge. For these dredging operations Leonardo found varied solutions. One of these, which he describes as an "Instrument for excavating the earth"[3] (Plate 78), is a mechanism, held on a pole between two barges, the bottom of the pole being sunk into the bed of the channel at the point of operations. Mounted on an axle is a toothed wheel *f*, operated by the crank or winch *n*. This causes a battery or "cross" of four receptacles (perforated to release the water from the sludge) to rotate and, in succession, to pick up a load of sludge which is carried round and discharged into the receiving barges on the left. A stake *m* holds the barges in position by a cord fixed to one barge at *b*. The other end is wound round the pole at *f* and, presumably, as the swamp is cleared, the rope is kept taut, pulling the mechanism forward to its next position of operations.

To another design (Plate 79)[4] Leonardo gives the following description: "This is how to dredge a harbour. The plough *mn* (see bottom right of drawing) has spikes in front of it shaped like ploughshares and knives, and this will be used to load a large cart with mud. The cart has its back perforated in the manner of a net so that the water may not be shut within the box. The plough is moved along above the place where the mud is to be dug out, and with it a barge; and when it has reached the bottom the windlass *b* will draw it beneath the windlass *a*, and windlass *a* will lift it up when it is full as far as its beam, in order that there will be room for the barge to go underneath

---

[1] MS. *B*, 65 r.　　[2] *Codex Atlanticus*, 9 v.b.　　[3] MS. *E*, 75 v.　　[4] *Codex Atlanticus*, 307 r.b.

it and receive the mud from the plough; and so this plough will be able to dislodge the mud from the bottom and unload it upon the barge which is placed underneath it."

From the excavation of mud and sludge by dredging to the reclamation of marsh and swamp land by drainage is but one step. Leonardo's *modus operandi* for this was by suitable pumping mechanisms. We have already commented upon his intense interest in all matters appertaining to water, both static and in motion, and he devised a variety of pumps in the course of his career. The normal function of a pump is to raise water from one level to another, and therefore in many of Leonardo's sketches no question of originality of principle is involved. The pump was a well-known mechanism in his day and had been used in one form and another from the times of the Archimedean screw onwards. But Leonardo, as may be expected, added his own characteristic touch in the variety of his sketches. Plate 80[1] shows a delightful group of these taken from the *Codex Atlanticus*. On the right, we see an arrangement of two Archimedean screws (with a characteristic linkage system at the junction of the two) for bringing water in two stages to the top of a tower. Again, to the left of the Archimedean screws is drawn an intriguing pump with twin cylinders. Their pistons are weighted. The motive power to raise them alternately is provided by winches.

We can, however, reasonably claim for Leonardo that he devised a form of hydraulic screw which was, in effect, a forerunner of the water turbine. The steam turbine was already well known in principle. Hiero of Alexandria had used it in his well-known "aelopile" and we have already seen how Leonardo had incorporated it in his apparatus for an automatic roasting spit (p. 249). His hydraulic screw is sketched in the Arundel manuscript. Plate 81[2] is a reproduction of this sketch. In America a working model has been successfully reconstructed from it. The water power is converted to mechanical power by the transmission to a horizontal axis of the rotary motion imparted by the running water to the turbine screws below.

One of his most interesting contributions to the problems of marsh drainage was the application of the principle of the centrifuge to produce a centrifugal pump. Marsh drainage had been carried out by methods other than by pumping for a long time—from the dumping of large quantities of soil, previously described by Leon Battista Alberti, and discussed by Leonardo himself in Manuscript *F*,[3] to the proposal, in his later years[4] to drain the stagnant waters of the Pontine Marshes by first deepening and regulating the bed of the adjacent

---

[1] *Codex Atlanticus*, 386 r.b.
[2] *Codex Arundel*, 63 v.
[3] MS. *F*, 17 r. and v.
[4] In 1514—see MS. *E*, 5 r.

River Martino, to be followed by cutting an additional artificial outlet to the sea, thus channelling out the surplus waters of the Marshes. Leonardo's proposals were, in fact, carried out some years later by an engineer named Fra Giovanni Scotto, of Como; and the consequential appearance of large stretches of arable soil produced a host of rival claimants of proprietorship from people who had hitherto no interest in the former marshland. The many court proceedings that followed almost literally re-bogged up the whole area, and the operations (and the litigations) were ultimately abandoned.

Actually, Leonardo's use of the centrifugal pump, of which he was very proud, was intended to serve as a supplementary device "for drying up the swamps which border on the sea". The mechanism was based upon his observation that "if the hand be turned in a vessel half filled with water, an artificial whirling is set up which exposes

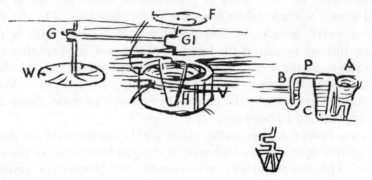

Fig. 87.   Leonardo's centrifugal pump for swamp drainage.

the bottom of the vessel (at its centre) to the air; and when the force that produces it is no longer applied, the whirl continues to be produced but with diminishing speed, until the impetus given by the force ceases". (The reader will note here another example of the application of the doctrine of inertia.)   The sketch of Leonardo's pump is shown in Fig. 87.[1] The small diagram on the right is intended to depict the nature of the operation. In this diagram the vessel A depicts the "sea", whose water level is higher than that of the vessel B, representing the "pond" or "marsh" to be drained. The two are separated by the "wall" C. A pipe P leads from the one to the other, and by an artificially produced water-whirl the water is pumped from the pond across the intervening "wall" to the sea. The pump detail is shown in the larger sketch. The whirling "hand" H is supplied within the vessel V by a piece of shaped wood or similar substance, linked by the crank $G1$ to the axle of the fly-wheel F. The motive power is supplied

[1] MS. F, 13 r.

by the turbine wheel W, linked with the crank $G1$ by the crank G. The function of the flywheel F is, of course, to produce a regularity of movement. Says Leonardo: "The vessel (V) is to be closed everywhere except for a hole in the bottom where the water enters from the swamp, to be transmitted by means of the siphon." The siphon effect becomes possible because of the different levels of the "sea" and "pond".

Much of Leonardo's work in the sphere of civil engineering was concerned with the planning and construction of canals, including the provision of weirs and lock-gates essential to the control of water flow with which all such schemes are necessarily concerned. The device of the canal as an amenity of improvement of the water system of a countryside had been known and progressively developed through the centuries, though the device of the lock-gate, probably of Dutch origin, was not introduced until the fifteenth century. Leon Battista Alberti, to whose engineering projects we have referred from time to time, was one of the pioneers in Italy of the control of the drop in water levels in canals. He suggested the provision of double sets of lock-gates to hold a controlled basin of the canal waters between them, and these began to appear in the second half of the fifteenth century. This was, in fact, a period of considerable activity in canal construction in Europe, especially in Italy, France and the Netherlands.

Leonardo's interest was natural and we have already discussed some aspects of the constructional work involved in our references to Leonardo's cranes (p. 283). We have seen that all problems relating to water flow fascinated him, and we know (Chapter III) that from time to time he was officially consulted about them. We referred, for example (p. 91), to his large-scale project for a canal to link Milan to the sea. This was laid out by him in a detailed drawing which he labelled: "The canal of San Cristoforo, Milan, May 3, 1509". It showed a system of six locks in three pairs, one above the other.

One of his chief contributions to lock design was his invention of the mitred gates within the doors of a lock, to allow the water in the basin to rise to its appropriate level smoothly—a device which was actually to be used in France some fifty years later. A particularly neatly-finished drawing of his in the *Codex Atlanticus*[1], dated about 1475 to 1480, shows a portion of a canal with two locks, each with two sets of doors and three weirs. Boats are shown both inside the locks and between them, and the lock-keeper's house is also shown. To the left of the main picture are shown details of the systems of gates, in pairs, within the doors (Plate 82). The note above these sketches reads: "The winch is turned until its shaft has wound up the whole chain on

[1] *Codex Atlanticus*, 33 v.a.

which the sluice-board hangs. When it is wound up and the sluice-board touches the shaft, the latter is used as a lever."

Another sketch showing a canal lock-gate is seen in Plate 83.[1] Leonardo's drawing is intended to indicate how the water pressure is relieved by the opening of a sluice, and it will be noticed that there is a view in the plan below showing the water streaming through the lock-gate; and in yet another sketch (Plate 84)[2] the gates are operated by a trap-door whose movement is controlled by an oblique draw-bar.

We turn next from canal construction to bridge-building since this, of course, is another of the activities that fall within the ambit of the civil engineer. Since there was no conceivable aspect of constructional work that Leonardo seems to have omitted from his notebooks, the reader will have anticipated that he did indeed interest himself in bridge design. Nevertheless, it must be stressed that bridges were almost as commonplace in Leonardo's times as were streets and buildings. There was a long tradition and history in their construction, reaching back to the timber *Pons Subilcius* over the Tiber, that was defended, it will be recalled, by Horatius in "the brave days of old". This bridge was later to be rebuilt in stone (in 109 B.C.) by Aemilius Scaurus, with arch spans varying from 51 to 79 feet. Trajan was one of the great Roman bridge-builders. He built one in Spain, at Alcantara, of a total length of 670 feet, and its height above the stream was 210 feet. The Alcantara bridge had six arches.

The materials, right up to medieval times, were usually of stone and often with timber superstructure. The Benedictine monks of the twelfth century included in their organisation an order known as "The Brothers of the Bridge", and these were responsible for a number of bridges, mainly in France and England; and later the architects of the Renaissance paid considerable attention to bridge-building. Most of the medieval bridges were narrow, with excessively steep gradients that were more or less determined by the general use of semi-circular and pointed arches. Housed bridges were not infrequent— the Ponte Vecchio (1367) at Florence and the famous, but much later, Rialto at Venice, being noted examples in Italy; but our own London Bridge (1209) and the Pont Notre-Dame in Paris (1507) were similarly cluttered up with houses and shops. As these were built of timber, the danger from fire was very serious and became a reality from time to time.

Bridge building is, in these days, a precise matter of applied science. Hooke's Law that strain is proportional to stress so long as the elastic limit of the material employed is not exceeded was first propounded in 1678, and it was not till 1744 that Euler published his formulae for

[1] *Codex Atlanticus*, 240 r.c.   [2] Ibid., 7 v.b.

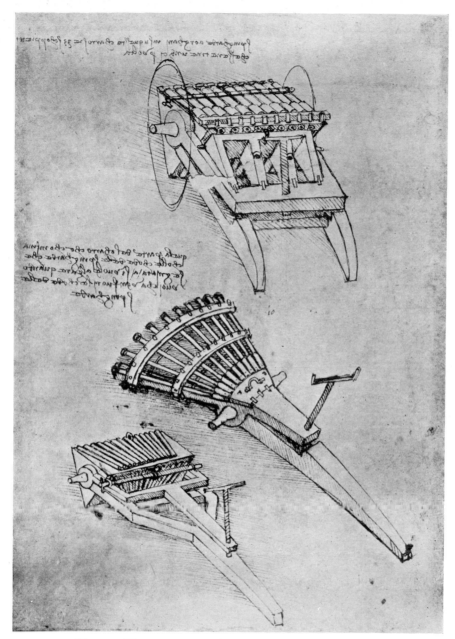

Plate 93—Three types of multi-barrelled guns (C.A. 56 v.a.).

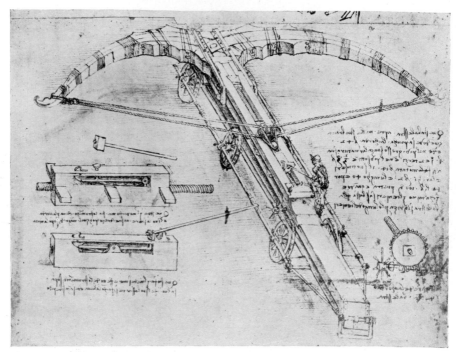

Plate 94—The Giant Bal-
lista—an enormous cross-
bow mounted on six
wheels in three pairs
(C.A. 53 v.b.).

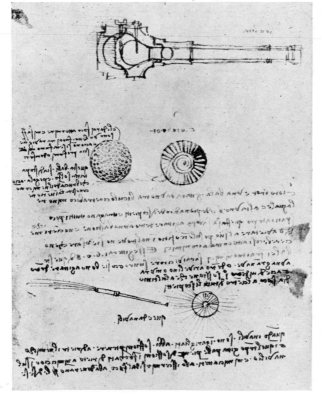

Plate 95—Leonardo's
shrapnel-loaded fire-ball
(MS. B. 31 v.).

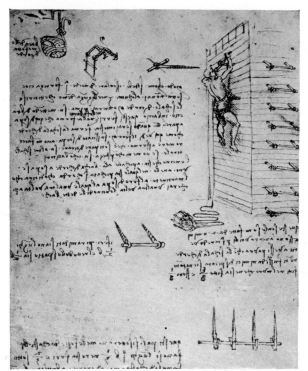

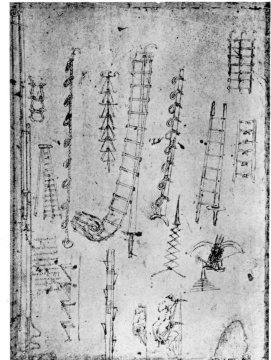

Plate 99—Double-hulled boat "for safety in time of war" (MS. B. 11 r.).

Plate 98—Device for diver and boring apparatus to sink a hostile ship (C.A. 333 v.a.).

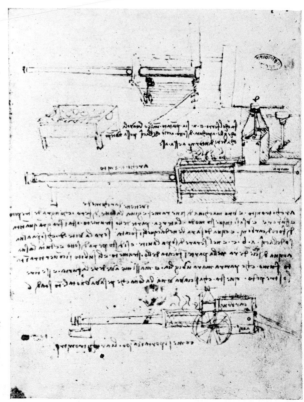

Plate 100—Drawings of Leonardo's "Architronito", or steam gun (MS. B. 33 r.).

the strengths of columns and struts. All early bridges were therefore empirical designs, carrying forward the experience gained by previous failures and successes to promote newer and better designs. But we have noted that Leonardo da Vinci had himself carried out many experiments on the strength and stiffness of columns, struts, beams and wires, and that he therefore appreciated the need for a specific scientific approach to the design of structures. One of his sketches shows a method of investigating the strains on the supporting walls of a loaded arch. The view held in his day was that the direction of the stress follows the swing of the arch, so that at its extremities, where it meets the vertical supports, this stress was considered to be purely vertical—whereas Leonardo was able to show that there is, in fact, a specific horizontal component. It was on this basis that Leonardo proposed his plan, in 1502, for a single-span bridge across the Golden Horn between Pera and Constantinople. He was, at the time, in the service of Cesare Borgia, and his proposals were in response to a delegation sent to Rome by the Sublime Porte, (as the Turkish government of the day was called) of Beyaazid II. An existing wooden bridge, built on heavy barges, dating from the time of Mahomet II, had outlived its usefulness. Leonardo's plan[1] carried the following note: "Bridge from Pera to Constantinople. Width forty braccia, height above water seventy braccia, length six hundred braccia, that is four hundred above the sea and two hundred resting on land, thus forming abatements to itself" (i.e. provided its own supports). To quote a recent authoritative view on this: "No single-span masonry arch of such great size has ever been constructed or is likely to be."[2] It remained a paper curiosity.

Bridge design remained a source of fascination for Leonardo, nevertheless. The reader will recall the paragraph in his famous letter to Ludovico Sforza (p. 22), which reads: "I have a process for the construction of very light bridges, capable of easy transport . . . and of others more solid, which will resist both fire and sword, and which are easily lowered or raised."

There is to be seen in the *Codex Atlanticus*[3] a delightful and imaginative series of three different swing-bridge designs spanning a winding stream (Plate 85). The upper one is a rope-bridge on four columns, the swing mechanism operating from the right; and the lower one a bridge of boats. The middle design is, of course, the more interesting, and Plate 86 shows a model which has been constructed from Leonardo's drawing. The purpose of this bridge is for connecting an island fortress with the mainland so that, operating from the capstan (shown

[1] MS. *I.*, 66 r.
[2] S. B. Hamilton in Singer's *History of Technology*, vol. iii, p. 433 (Oxford, 1957).
[3] *Codex Atlanticus*, 312 r.a.

T

on the right in the original sketch), it can be swung to the island side
when not required for normal use, thus denying passage to an enemy.

Another ingenious example of Leonardo's fertility of ideas in bridge
design is to be seen in Manuscript B (Plate 87)[1] in which is drawn
an N-type bridge at two levels—an upper one for pedestrians and a
lower one for vehicles—a proposal which, in these days of traffic
congestion problems, must have a special appeal.   Plate 88 shows a
model reproduction from Leonardo's drawing.

This general problem of traffic congestion was much in Leonardo's
mind in a more general sense. It will be recalled that during the great
devastation caused by the plague in Milan in 1483 he worked on plans
for the building of a new township with streets "as wide as the universal
height of the houses",[2] and with the roads planned on two levels
(Plate 89). His note read thus: "The high-level roads are six braccia
higher than the low-level roads, and each road should be twenty
braccia wide and have a fall of half a braccio from the edges to the
centre, and in this centre at every braccio there should be an opening
of the width of a finger one braccio long, through which rainwater
may drain off into holes made in the lower-level roads. And on each
side of this road there should be an arcade six braccia broad resting
on columns. . . . The high-level roads are not to be used by wagons or
like vehicles but are solely for the convenience of the gentlefolk. All
carts and loads for the service and convenience of the common people
should be confined to the low-level roads. . . . The privies, stables and
noisome places are emptied by underground passages situated at a
distance of three hundred braccia from one arch to the next, each
passage receiving light through openings in the street above, and at
every arch there should be a spiral staircase. . . . At the first turn there
should be a door of entry into the privies and this staircase should
enable one to descend from the high-level to the low-level road. . . .
The site should be chosen near to the sea, or some large river, in order
that the impurities of the city may be carried far away by water."

Clearly, Leonardo thought of everything!

8. LEONARDO'S MILITARY GADGETRY

From the time when Leonardo first left Florence for Milan onwards
throughout his career, we know that he was intermittently consulted
on a variety of military projects. For these he had clearly prepared
himself, as witness the wide range of the claims to military gadgetry
set out from paragraph to paragraph in his famous letter. And, on
the whole, his notebooks bear full testimony to them—so much so
that we can here only indicate a few representative examples.

[1] MS. B, 23 r.   [2] Ibid., 36 r.

One of the best known of his pen-and-ink cartoons is the fine study (see Frontispiece)[1] of an interior scene of an arsenal store, depicting a large cannon being raised on to a gun-carriage. There is little in this arresting drawing from the point of view of engineering originality. What it does convey to us is something of the best in the current hauling and lifting procedure[2]—the use of sheer-legs, of heavy pulley tackle, of powerful levers; and in the background the neatly stacked spares for future use or delivery. But, above all, it depicts the artistry of life and power and the rhythm of team-work. The picture pulsates with energy.

Nevertheless, there is ample evidence in the notebooks of a deep interest in the design and construction of arms and armament. Military technology had undergone a virtual revolution with the advent of gun-powder and the application of pyrotechnics to weapons of war. The manufacture of fireworks, an Islamic innovation, had reached Europe late in the thirteenth century, and gunpowder was being used in firearms early in the fourteenth. The use of bamboo tubes, filled with gunpowder, was soon to be followed by hand and mechanical grenades. Next came the gun with its barrel of metal, filled with charges of powder and projectiles (stones, broken porcelain and bullets) and fired off from a row of touch holes. By the middle of the fourteenth century cannon had become a normal element in warfare. They were not at first cast but were made from what was called *cuprum*, which was sometimes copper and sometimes brass or bronze, the seams being sealed by riveting, brazing or welding. Then came casting from cuprous metal, followed by the larger built-up forged gun. And with these the size and weight increased from about 150 lb in A.D. 1350 to as much as 600 lb by the beginning of the fifteenth century. Meanwhile, not only was a knowledge developing of the explosive power and of the proportioning of the ingredients of gunpowder, but the processing and purifying of these ingredients—saltpetre, sulphur and charcoal—was being better understood.

Leonardo had his own prescription for gunpowder. It read as follows: "One pound of charcoal, eleven ounces of sulphur, five pounds of saltpetre. And mix it well and moisten it with good brandy and dry it in the sun or at a fire. Then pound it until one cannot see a speck of sulphur or saltpetre, but it is all black and uniform and fine, and moisten it again with the brandy and keep it so. Dry it in the sun in grains and crush just as much as can be placed upon the hole, and this will be sufficient."[3]

The normal method of gun construction was to build up the barrel in the form of a series of wrought-iron bars arranged round a core.

---

[1] Windsor Royal Library, No. 12,647. [2] I.e. at about 1455–1458. [3] MS. *L*, 4 v.

These were then welded together and the core was then removed. Next the end was blocked and a series of iron hoops was shrunk along the length of the piece to strengthen it further. Finally, the barrel was mounted on a wooden stock fitted with wheels for portability.

Let us now see what Leonardo did about it. He had gained some experience in the art of gun casting while working with Verrocchio in Florence, and drawings of guns and ballistas soon found their way into his notebooks. Many of these were clearly inspired by the work of the military writer Roberto Valturio,[1] but later he gave full rein to his imagination and, characteristically, some of his drawings went clearly beyond the range of practicability. He cast his military "net" wide. To quote one writer: "He invented machine-guns and breech-loading guns, armoured cars and mechanical bows capable of hurling flaming projectiles."[2] A miscellany of these, including mortars and cannon, forms the subject of a sheet of pen-and-ink studies at the Royal Library at Windsor (Plates 3 and 90)[3]. The reader will not fail to note the fearsome mortar (at the bottom of the picture) being fired from a boat on the water.

The various stages of the construction of the barrel of a gun were clearly shown by Leonardo in a series of five sketches in the *Codex Atlanticus*,[4] beginning with the laying out of the bar-lengths in the first picture to the provision of a series of iron hoops in the fifth (Plate 91).

In later designs, however, he used bronze or copper, and the barrel was formed either by building up round a core, as already described, or, alternatively, by boring into a solid casting. Leonardo's instructions included relative dimensions for the bore in relation to the length, according to the overall size of the ordnance. Light guns were designed to have the longer barrels in relation to bore. Leonardo also included wheel-lock devices for breech-loading, one of which is illustrated in Plate 92.[5] The breech of the gun is closed by a bronze circle which is advanced by the rotation of a screw connected through gearing with the handle. Details of the breech mechanism are shown in detail in the figure.[6]

The device of the machine-gun had its fascinations for Leonardo. Three types of these multi-barrelled guns are shown by him in one page of his notes (Plate 93).[7] The uppermost of the three mounted on wheels has three tiers of twelve barrels each. The scheme of opera-

---

[1] *De re militari* by Valturio was a standard book in Leonardo's possession (p. 92).
[2] Irma A. Richter, *Selections from the Notebooks of Leonardo da Vinci* (Oxford, p. 296).
[3] Windsor No. 12652 r.
[4] *Codex Atlanticus*, 19 r.b.
[5] MS. *B*, 24 v. Note the design for a movable tower below the breech-loading gun.
[6] The attribution of the wheel-lock invention to Leonardo da Vinci is ably discussed in a recent paper—"A Note on the Early History of the Wheel-Lock", by Claude Blair. (Journal of the Arms and Armour Society. March, 1961.)
[7] *Codex Atlanticus*, 56 v.a.

tion was that while one tier was being fired a second was being loaded, whilst the third was cooling down after firing.

But perhaps his most ambitious design is of a giant *ballista* (Plate 94).[1] This was an enormous cross-bow mounted on six wheels in three pairs. The loading is effected by turning a windlass connected through a worm-gear with a long screw. Details of this gearing are shown separately on the right of the main drawing. The actual capstan and gearing is seen in the main mechanism to the left of the human figure just ahead of the rear pair of wheels. The projectile is released either by striking a pin with a hammer or by tripping a latch with a lever. Details of both these devices are shown to the left of the main drawing. The probability is, however, that this design was beyond the workshop capacity of the times (about 1485–1488).

Turning from the weapon to its ammunition, let us note a characteristic example of Leonardo's shrapnel-loaded fire-ball. This is well-illustrated in a page of notes (Plate 95).[2] Below an equally interesting sketch giving a cross-sectional view of a breech-loading gun with a screw-locking device, we see two drawings of a bomb, the second in cross-section. Leonardo describes the bomb thus: "As this ball reaches the ground the canes which are bound at the top with ignited linen cloth are driven into it, thus igniting the powder which surrounds a piece of tow that has been soaked in turpentine, the rest of it being wrapped up in hemp, also soaked in a mixture of turpentine, oil of flax and pitch. The wrappings should be thin in order that the flames may reach the air, for otherwise it will not work."[3]

A bigger and more vicious example of fire-ball is described thus: "This ball should be made of melted pitch, sulphur and tow of hemp rubbed together so that when it burns the enemy may not carry the ball away. It should be two and a half braccia in height and filled with tubes which should be coated with pitch so that they do not fall. The tubes should be a braccio in length and made of pasteboard after the manner of spokes, and the space between them should be padded with plaster and wadding. The ball should be thrown upon the bastions by means of a mangonel. At the centre of it will be placed a cannon-ball to which the tube serves as good epaulets . . . with its circumference perforated so that the fire is able to penetrate to the tubes; and the ball should be all tied up on the outside except for a hole which serves as a passage for the fire."[4]

It need hardly be said that, apart from guns and ammunition, Leonardo had numerous ideas, illustrated by characteristic sketches, for fortifications,[5] for the offensive scaling of walls both by ladders

---

[1] *Codex Atlanticus*, 53 v.b.   [2] MS. *B*, 31 v.   [3] MS. *B*, 4 r.   [4] MS. *B*, 37 r.
[5] *Codex Atlanticus*, 41 v.a.

(Plate 96)[1] and by portable "pitons" and rope-ladders (Plate 97),[2] or, in the converse case of defence, for repelling scaling-ladders by a simple mechanism, operating within the defensive walls, that jerked the ladders violently away from the fortress walls,[3] of chariots armed with scythes,[4] and so on.

Let us turn, however, to some of his ideas appropriate to naval warfare. Leonardo was full of schemes of all kinds, mainly offensive, whereby enemy ships could he holed and sunk. Note, for example, the fearsome underwater spear-head mechanism in Fig. 88[5] project-

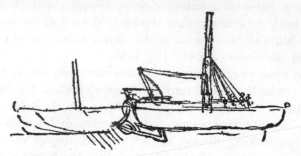

Fig. 88.   Combat at sea—holing the enemy.

ing from the forepart of the attacking ship and operated by the crew through a series of linkages and a set of pulley sheaves carrying a heavy weight at the masthead. Says Leonardo with regard to this, under the caption "How to stave in the Bows of a Ship": "It is necessary to ensure that they be engaged together in such a way that when the enemy ship goes to the bottom it will not drag yours with it. Let this be done as follows: draw a weight up to a height and then release it. As it falls it will give such a blow like a pile-driver; and in so falling it will draw back the head of a beam which is in equilibrium when upright; and as the head of the beam comes back the projecting end that is below lunges forward and staves in the bow of the ship. But see that the beam has a cutting edge so that as it rushes to give the stroke the water does not offer resistance to it. And above all see that the chains which hold the ships fastened together are such as can be severed at your will from your side so that the enemy's ship, when it sinks, may not drag you down with it."

Another device of naval warfare described by Leonardo in Manuscript *B* was the fireship (*Zepata*), the chief feature of which was a fire-brand projecting from the prow. This comprised, first, "some wood a braccio above the water, then tow, then powder, then tiny faggots and so gradually larger ones; and put iron wires and burning

[1] *Codex Atlanticus*, 316 v.a.   [3] *Codex Atlanticus*, 49 b.   [5] MS. *B*, 90 v.
[2] MS. *B*, 39 r.   [4] MS. *B*, 10 r.

rags on the top; and when the wind is as you want it direct the rudder. And as the fire spreads in the ship it will set fire to the powder and do what is necessary. It is also useful for setting fire to bridges at night, but make its sail black." [1]

In yet another note Leonardo describes a scheme for a diver (Plate 98) (he sketched many devices for divers' suits and for provision to breathe while submerged) to approach a hostile vessel and to stay submerged for a sufficient time to fasten suitable boring apparatus to spring a leak by forcing out one of the planks, and then to withdraw. [2]

One other device of naval warfare should be mentioned. In Manuscript *B* there is a sketch of a partially submersible boat, and below this a cross-sectional view of a double-hull[3] which, Leonardo suggests, should be provided for ships generally "for their safety in time of war", so that in the event of damage to the outer hull by the enemy the inner hull should still enable the vessel to remain afloat (Plate 99).

It will be obvious that examples of Leonardo's versatility of ideas and mechanical tricks of warfare abound beyond the limits of further enumeration in this work, and we will therefore conclude this section by referring the reader once more to the contents of the famous letter to Ludovico for a summary of claims, of which it may be said that all were quite specifically further elaborated in one notebook or another.

9. PRIME MOVERS—WAS LEONARDO A PIONEER OF THE STEAM ENGINE?

In Section 12 of Chapter VII we referred in some detail to Leonardo's notes on the expansive power of steam and we described some of his experiments designed to measure the amount of this expansion. Leonardo was quick to realise the potentialities of force behind this expansion and the interesting query has been posed quite recently by Dr. Reti as to how far this appreciation went. Did Leonardo in fact know that in steam power there was to be found a "prime mover", i.e. a source of energy that was capable of being harnessed to useful purposes? It is appropriate in our survey of Leonardo's work as an engineer that this should now be reviewed.

As a preliminary link with the foregoing section on the military aspects of Leonardo's notes, Manuscript *B* (which, as the reader will have realised, is considerably concerned with military matters) includes a series of drawings of a steam-gun known as an "architronito" (Plate 100).[4] Its principle was ascribed by Leonardo to Archimedes. As pictured by Leonardo, it is constructed of thin copper, and is designed to shoot iron balls with great violence, using the expansive power of steam suddenly applied. Virtually there are three elements

---

[1] MS. *B*, 39 v.   [2] *Codex Atlanticus*, 333 v.a.   [3] MS. *B*, 11 r.   [4] MS. *B*, 33 r.

to the mechanism—a lower fuel chamber for the burning of the char-coal fuel, a water chamber above it for the production of steam, and the gun-barrel containing the ball-ammunition. Screw valves are provided to control the sudden ejection of the steam jet to impact violently on to the cannon-ball.

Actually it is difficult to accept that this weapon was an invention of Archimedes, and the grounds for Leonardo's own statement on the subject are unknown. There is a possible link between Archimedes and the much later Hiero of Alexandria through Ctesibius, approxi-mately contemporary with Archimedes. Ctesibius was the inspirer of many of Hiero's inventions, one of which was the aelopile. The whirling aelopile was the toy predecessor of the modern steam tur-bine and was a device containing water, the boiling of which produced jets of steam which caused the vessel, delicately mounted on a pivot, to rotate rapidly against the resisting air in the direction opposite to the jets, in accordance with the law of reactions.

Reti, in his important paper,[1] concludes that the Architronito is in fact a genuine invention of Leonardo's, and this may well be the case. It was clearly the sort of device characteristic both of his brain and his pen, but nevertheless it is strange that he should go out of his way to attribute it to someone else.

Reti's thesis generally is that Leonardo da Vinci knew and com-mented upon the use of steam as a source of mechanical power and that he directly and positively influenced the subsequent trend of events leading to the evolution of the steam engine as we know it today.

The basic point is the re-stated Aristotelean truism that "nature abhors a vacuum" and the special application of this doctrine to the case of the vacuum that may be created by the condensation of steam. "When the air is condensed into rain," writes Leonardo on this point, "it would produce a vacuum if the rest of the air did not prevent this by filling its place, as it does with a violent rush; and this is the wind which rises in the summer, accompanied by heavy rains."[2] There are numerous other references to the same end in the *Codex Atlanticus* and elsewhere. Fifty years later both Cardan (the younger) and della Porta made similar statements (although both were somewhat hazy in regarding steam as something akin to air), and Reti suggests that both were influenced by Leonardo. Since in the case of Cardan this may well have been the case on a number of other matters, it may have been so on this matter also, with della Porta, who is generally accepted as a pioneer in the story of steam power.

---

[1] L. Reti, "Leonardo da Vinci nella storia della macchina a vapore" (*Rivista d'Ingegneria*, Milan, 1956–1957), pp. 21 et sq.
[2] MS. *E*, back cover.

The next figure in the story of the evolution of the steam engine is Salomon de Caus, a French engineer and landscape gardener. He specialised in the creation of fountain effects, and these he accomplished by contrivances acting under steam pressure. Reti makes two points of significance with regard to de Caus—firstly, that these water-column devices were later to be taken up by the Marquis of Worcester and Thomas Savery, thus getting us nearer to the engines of Newcomen and Watt; and secondly, that there is a remarkable similarity, amounting to more than a matter of chance or coincidence, between de Caus' published pronouncements[1] in 1615 and some corresponding notes by Leonardo da Vinci a hundred years or so earlier. A series of such notes, by de Caus and by Leonardo, printed side by side in Reti's paper, certainly impress with their similarity of content.

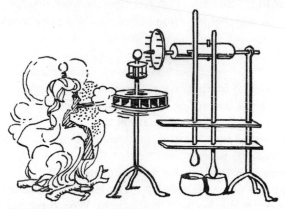

Fig. 89.   Branca's forerunner of the steam turbine.

Next we come to Giovanni Branca, a native of Loretto, and his picturesque steam turbine of 1629. His scheme, as shown in Fig. 89, is that of the impinging of a jet of steam from a boiler designed in the figure of a man (note the filling plug on the man's head) on to a horizontal wheel fitted with vanes. By suitable mechanism this is made to gear with a horizontal drum, and the power thus transmitted is applied to a variety of useful purposes—e.g. in the figure, to the mechanical stirring of the ingredients in the bowls at the base of the apparatus. The germs of the steam turbine are here, but at the time the idea was incapable of development.

We come here to the next point in Reti's argument. The distinguished scientist Arago, discussing the history of the steam engine, with a firm bias in favour of de Caus as its true inventor, suggested that Branca was not original in his conception of the impulse turbine, and that he must have acquired the idea from some unknown source.

[1] S. de. Caus, *Les Raisons des Forces Mouvantes* (Frankfurt, 1615).

That source, suggests Reti, must definitely have been Leonardo da Vinci. And, indeed, there is at least a striking resemblance to the basic feature of a steam jet issuing from the mouth of a cauldron in the shape of a human torso in several pages of the *Codex Atlanticus*,[1] of which Plate 101 is an excellent example.

Additionally, we should again remind the reader of Leonardo's application of the steam-turbine principle to a device for an automatic roasting-spit (Plate 45).

But steam was not the only fluid prime mover that interested Leonardo da Vinci. We know, of course, that for a long time both wind and water power had become a familiar sight in the countryside through the medium of windmills and water-wheels, and one example of the design by Leonardo of a water turbine has already been described (Plate 81). But the *Codex Atlanticus* also presents us with an excellent scheme for the provision of power, using compressed air as the prime mover[2] (Plate 102). Twin jets of compressed air are created by the use of mechanically operated bellows and are seen in the drawing impinging on a turbine wheel whose rotations are transmitted by a series of toothed wheels in gear with each other as shown.

Clearly, therefore, we must accord to Leonardo a specific appreciation of *all* forms of fluid prime movers and, very definitely, from our immediate point of view in this section, of the importance of steam as a source of useful power.

But, following up further the orthodox story of the evolution of the steam engine, we come, following some further constructive work by Edward Somerset, the Second Marquis of Worcester, and his "water commanding engines" of 1628 and 1663, and by Jean Hautefeuille of Orleans, who in 1678 proposed the substitution of alcohol for steam as the working fluid, to the great Dutch scientist Christian Huyghens (1629–1695) and his French collaborator Denis Papin. Huyghens had conceived the possibility of substituting the explosive force of gunpowder for steam and, additionally, of introducing the device of a piston working in a cylinder. His scheme, which brings us for the first time to anything really approaching the principle of the engine of today, is shown diagrammatically in Fig. 90. Working in a cylinder A is a piston B attached by a rope passing over a pulley C to a counterweight W. D and D' are two outlet pipes fitted with check valves, and H is the gunpowder chamber at the base of the cylinder. The action is very simple. On the explosion of the charge in H the piston B is forced up and the weight W moves down, the air above B being expelled through D and D'. The products of ex-

---

[1] *Codex Atlanticus*, 80 r.b., 388 v.a. and 400 r.a.
[2] Ibid., 13 r.b.

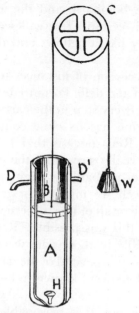

Fig. 90. Huyghen's forerunner of
the internal combustion engine.

plosion below the piston now cool and accordingly contract. This
causes a reduction in pressure below the piston, and the superior
atmospheric pressure above forces the piston down again. As a result,
the weight W moves up, thus performing useful work.

In effect, we see here the first specific case of an engine in the real
sense of the term—i.e. a mechanism for the actual *performance of useful
work*.

Denis Papin, who had moved from France to England, picked up
Huyghens' important pattern of a piston and cylinder, but wisely
reverted from gunpowder to steam as the prime mover; and his first
designs much resembled those of Huyghens', externally. In effect,
he substituted a small quantity of water for the gunpowder at H in
Fig. 90, and used a charcoal fire beneath it. The rapid expansion
of the steam thus produced would lift the piston and so enable *useful
work to be performed*.

Here again, however, Reti draws attention to a parallel experiment
proposed by Leonardo da Vinci 170 years earlier[1] (Plate 103). Here
also we have a scheme of piston and cylinder, but in this case the
weight to be lifted is below the cylinder. Leonardo's note reads thus:
"To lift a weight with fire, like a cupping glass. And the vessel should
be one braccio wide and ten long, and should be strong; and should

[1] MS. *F*, 16 v.; see also *Codex Atlanticus*, 5 r.a. and 7 r.a.

be lit from below like a bombard, and the touch-hole rapidly closed and immediately closed on top. You will see the bottom rise, which has a very strong leather like a bellow; and this is the way to lift any heavy weight."

Here, then, are a succession of instances to which Reti has drawn attention. From Cardan and della Porta to de Caus, Branca, Huyghens and Papin, we find that every step in the earlier history of the development of the steam engine has its close counterpart in the pages of Leonardo's notebooks. Reti suggests that to accept these as a series of mere coincidences is really stretching the claims of coincidence too far. The mathematics of probability might perhaps be applied here, but if we accept—as well we might—the inference that Leonardo's work was known to some or all of this succession of workers, the mystery still remains as to how this was possible. Reti suggests that the notes must have been accessible to those who were interested in them and he pertinently reminds us that several of the notebooks have disappeared completely and that others were known to have passed from one hand to another.[1]

Whether this be so or not, it is reasonable to speculate upon what may have happened at least during the fifty years of the custody of the notes by Francesco Melzi until his death in 1570. Was this a period of complete prohibition against the legitimate curiosity of interested persons? It is difficult to believe that of the many who had known that here were treasures of learning in store, none were permitted a peep. Vasari, for instance, who wrote *The Lives of the Painters*, visited Melzi in 1566, and may have inspected them. In a recent study of Leonardo's Flying Machines one writer declares: "It is not regret but castigation we must reserve for the loyal but stupid Francesco Melzi."[2] But we have seen that *his* heir and successor, Orazio Melzi, was not so particular, and both inspection and dispersion began.

We cannot therefore rule out the likelihood that occasional men of science would have had opportunities for the examination of some of the notes. They may not have been able to decipher the caligraphy, but so many of the sketches, as we know, speak for themselves and could well have conveyed valuable ideas to the inspired examiner.

Bearing these slender factors in mind, it still remains doubtful if the *direct* influence of Leonardo's notes could be traced in the matter of steam power right through from Cardan (from whose lack of principle anything was possible in the use of other people's intellectual material without acknowledgment) to Papin—a period of 150 years

---

[1] See also Chapter X.
[2] C. H. Gibbs-Smith, *The Flying Machines of Leonardo da Vinci—a New Appraisal* (London, 1954).

or so. If we concede that occasional coincidences are possible—even to such pictorial similarities as Branca's torso-turbine and Leonardo's counterpart—can we say that five in 150 years are improbable?

That is the crux of the interesting and important problem posed by Reti.

10. LEONARDO AS PRODUCTION ENGINEER—A MISCELLANY OF MECHANISMS AND GADGETRY

There are very many instances of Leonardo's wide inquisitiveness and ingenuity over a wide range of mechanical matters that, on the whole, do not fall pertinently into any of the sections already discussed in this chapter; and we conclude this survey of Leonardo's engineering and practical mechanics with but a selected few, some of which belong properly to what in these days we refer to as "production engineering". Generally speaking, there was hardly any branch of practical activity of his day that he did not enrich with fertile suggestions of mechanisation. Take, for example, the staple Italian industries of wine and vegetable oil production. Leonardo's sketch of an oil press is shown in Plate 104. The olives are contained in two press-baskets, the lower one fixed and the upper one held by a screw operated through a suitable gearing to the power applied at the extremity of the long handle (Leonardo suggests a horse). A receptacle below the baskets catches the escaping oil. Leonardo describes the working thus: "Each time you wish to give the screw a direct turn take away the transverse which is above the press-baskets, and turn the screw in such a manner that you press the two baskets as firmly together as possible. Then you replace the transverse, tie a horse to the large lever, and let it go round. I promise you that the olives will be pressed so firmly that they will look as if they are dried. But understand that such a press will have to be made much stronger than the others which are in use, in order that it may not be overpowered by the strength of the horse, but will withstand a sufficient resistance."[1]

Another example of the application of pressure, though obviously on a much smaller scale, relates to Leonardo's sketch of a printing press[2] (Plate 105). Although the art and practice of printing had made very rapid strides, the presses in general use had to be hand-fed. Leonardo's contribution was to introduce a method of automatic feed. The platen carrying the type is moved up and down by the operation of the handle, which rotates a large screw of steep pitch. The gearing of the spindle of this screw to the large toothed wheel above it, and the smaller wheel and spindle behind the platen are clearly shown. The action of the press is as follows. The sheet to take the printing is placed

[1] *Codex Atlanticus*, 14 r.a.   [2] Ibid., 358 r.b.

on a flat-bed. This is arranged on small wheels to run down an inclined path simultaneously with the raising of the platen (which, of
course, contains the type), thus automatically presenting the printed
sheet for removal and replacement by a fresh sheet. The flat-bed is
now, by a swing of the handle, drawn back again up the incline and
under the platen, which is brought down on to it for the next imprint;
and so on indefinitely as required.

Other industrial activities for which Leonardo devised machines
of one kind and another included textile manufacture—a very lively
industry in Lombardy in his day—rope-making, needle-manufacture,
mirror-making, the designing of lamps, and the making of musical
instruments. It is neither possible nor necessary to include examples
of all these and of his other mechanical activities. We have already
referred to Leonardo's spinning machine (Plates 58 and 59) in the
section on "The Transmission of Power", but, additionally, Leonardo
designed numerous machines to substitute mechanical drives for the
more costly process of cropping by hand. In one such design[1] (Plate
106) four shearing tables are shown, with the driving mechanism at the
back. The cloth is wound on rollers and is drawn tightly over cropping
benches on the tables. Two cutters—worked by wires which are
jerked tight by the action of the gearing behind—run quickly over
the rough cloth surfaces and shave them smooth. At the same time,
the cropping benches are made to slide backwards to present the
cloth at a pace in tune with the shearing operation, which is carried
out in a succession of evenly timed jerks. This is done by the main
horizontal shaft at the back, which is jerked round by the action of
the vertical pin engaging the main vertical wheel on the left, cog
by cog.

As with so many others of Leonardo's designs, there is no record
of its use in practice—but some 150 years later a similar design made
history in Nottingham, where its introduction into a factory scared
workers (who thought they saw unemployment ahead from machines
that could be worked by one man instead of four or more) into violence
in which machines were smashed and the factory burnt.

Leonardo's designs for a rope-making machine are also in the *Codex
Atlanticus*.[2] There are two drawings, the first being of a machine
for the spinning and twisting of a rope of three strands; and the second
a more complex arrangement for the spinning and twisting of no less
than fifteen strands. An exceptional feature of the first drawing is
that it includes a simple screw device for the adjustment of the tension
in the belt which drives the spindles—an innovation of the times characteristic of its designer.

---

[1] *Codex Atlanticus*, 397 r.a.; see also 356 r.a.   [2] Ibid., 2 r. and 2 v.

Leonardo's needle-grinding machines, one of which is shown in Plate 107,[1] were designed for the purpose of mass production, a phrase that seems strangely out of keeping with his times. The needles are made to revolve, 400 at a time, between the inner surfaces of a range of five revolving leather belts and are carried against a large wheel treated with a suitable abrasive. Leonardo writes against one of these designs: "Tomorrow morning on January 2nd, 1496, I will try out the broad belts. A hundred times in each hour 400 needles make 40,000 per hour, and in 12 hours 480,000. But let us say 400,000, which at 5 soldi for each thousand gives 20,000 soldi, that is in total 1,000 lire per day for one man's work; and if one works for 20 days in the month, the yearly total becomes 60,000 ducats."[2]

Before we leave the purely engineering aspects of Leonardo's gadgetry, we should refer briefly to his sketches of mechanically propelled boats. These are mainly to be seen in the *Codex Atlanticus* and in Manuscript *B*.[3] Common to all is the use of paddle-wheels, in which the paddles are shovel-shaped. In the earlier and smaller types these are manipulated by hand (Plate 108)[4], but in larger vessels more mechanism is introduced (Plate 109). The simple outline sketch at the top-right of the figure shows a scheme of paddle-wheels working on a crank-shaft with two cranks separated by a central flywheel, which, of course, gives stability and steadiness to the working of the vessel. The paddle-boat shown in the main drawing (*Codex Atlanticus*, 344 r.b.) is operated by a pair of treadles. As these are alternately depressed and raised they operate a belt round a central drum which is geared to toothed wheels in the manner shown. Ratchets incorporated in the gear-wheels ensure that the paddles always revolve in the same direction.

Turning finally to one or two examples among Leonardo's many devices for all conceivable purposes, we should note first his "way-wiser" or hodometer, used by surveyors for measuring distances (Plate 110). Two types are drawn, the one on the right being based on an earlier type described by Vitruvius. The improved design on the left is described by Leonardo in the following note: "If the wheel of a cart is to have a circumference of 10 braccia . . . it will have measured 10 braccia of the way (i.e. in one revolution), which is the three-hundredth part of a mile (miglia) . . . and the wheel *m* will have only moved one tooth further. This has 300 teeth, so that the cart will have just covered a mile when the wheel has made a complete revolution; but then the wheel *f* will only have moved one tooth, and

---

[1] *Codex Atlanticus*, 31 v.a.; see also 25 r.b., 318 v.a., and 341 r.a.
[2] Ibid., 318 v.a.
[3] E.g. *Codex Atlanticus*, 319 v.a., 344 r.b., 374 v.b., 384 r.b.; and MS. *B*, 83 r.
[4] MS. *B*, 83 r.

the wheel *n* has done the same—this tells, by means of one indicator, each mile covered, instead of the hour as in the case of a watch. On the other hand, the wheel *f*, instead of reading by a pointer, can cause the ear to hear a sound by means of a small stone which is allowed to fall into a vessel suitable for emitting a note when struck."[1] (This refers to the one-wheeled type, of course.)

The third drawing, on the right of the two hodometers, is of a pedo-meter, working on the same principle but registering the number of steps, for example, made by a man or horse as he moves, by means of the pendulum resting on his thigh.

These examples of measuring instruments are based on a uniformity of movement, and therefore upon a uniformity of time intervals. Odd sketches here and there show instances of his thinking regarding the use of pendulum devices,[2] usually in connection with the regulating of the movements of other mechanisms. Sometimes it takes the form of a simple weight unwound from a winch or winder, mounted at a high elevation; and sometimes it takes the form of a weight suspended from an elongated bar or rod, from the upper end of which a ratchet is geared to a wheel whose rotations are controlled on a time basis, so that a succession of impulses are given to set up the swing of the pendulum (Plate 111).

A particularly ingenious invention intended as a mechanism for clock-springs is described in Manuscript *B*,[3] accompanied by a very rough sketch, a modernised version of which is shown in Fig. 91.

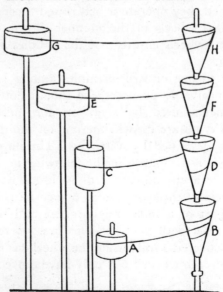

Fig. 91.   Clock-spring device.

[1] *Codex Atlanticus*, 1 r.a.   [2] Ibid., 257 r.a. and 348 v.a.   [3] MS. *B*, 50 v.

Plate 101 — Leonardo's steam-jet. Compare with Branca's device in Fig. 89, p. 297 (C.A. 80 r.b.).

Plate 103—Lifting a weight by the expansion of steam (MS. F. 16 v.).

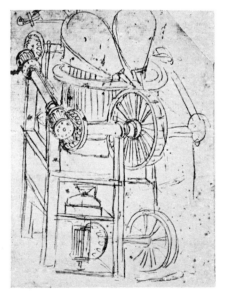

Plate 102—Leonardo's device for a turbine using compressed air (C.A. 13 r.b.).

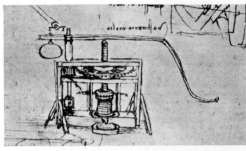

Plate 104 — Leonardo's Oil Press (C.A. 14 r.a.).

Plate 105—Leonardo's sketch of a printing press (C.A. 358 r.b.).

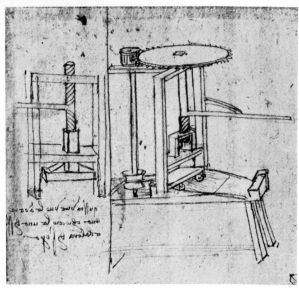

Plate 106—Leonardo's mechanical cloth-shearing machine. (C.A. 397 r.a.).

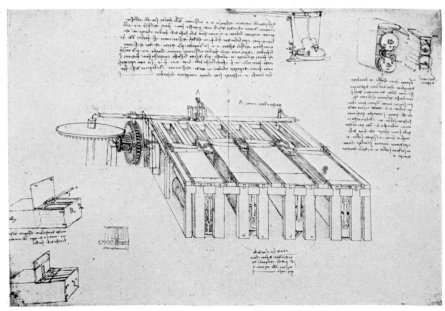

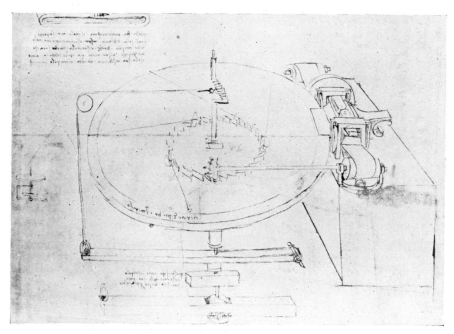

Plate 107—One of Leonardo's needle-grinding machines, designed for mass production (C.A. 31 v.a.).

Plate 108—Hand-manipulated paddle-boat (MS. B. 83 r.).

Plate 109—Treadle-operated paddle-boats (C.A. 344 r.b.).

Plate 110—Sketches of hodometers, and (right) a "pendulum-type" pedometer (C.A. 1 r.a.).

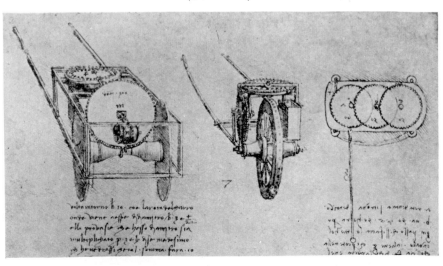

The note reads: "Four springs for a clock in such a way that when one has completed its run, the other begins. During the revolution of the first the second remains fixed. The first fastens itself upon the second by means of a screw, and when it has screwed itself quite firmly, the second spring takes up the same movement, and so on with the remainder."

It is actually not easy to follow the detail of the mechanism. The object is evidently to design a scheme which will operate for a long time without the necessity for rewinding. *ACEG* are a series of four spring drums, mounted obliquely one above the other, and each is connected by means of gut with a conical "worm" working on a worm-shaft. Possibly beginning from the bottom, the pull of the gut by the spring drum *A* gradually rotates the cone *B* on the right, and in so doing screws it into the cone *D*. As the spring in *A* uncoils, its pull naturally decreases—but this is compensated for by the increased tension in the gut as it winds round the progressively wider diameters of the cone. As soon as *B* finally engages tightly with the next cone *D*, the spiral spring in the drum *C* comes into operation, now winding the worm-shaft *D* into the next cone *F*, and so on progressively until the whole cycle of springs and drums have completed their operation. Whether this design was practicable enough to be brought into use is doubtful, but there is no doubt whatever about the ingenuity of the idea behind it.

One other time device is worthy of mention, if only as an illustration of the lighter side of Leonardo. This was his somewhat hilarious version of the modern alarm clock, intended for the reluctant early morning riser (Plate 112). This was a sort of domestic clepsydra, arranged a little in front of the sleeper's bed. A measured amount of water was placed in the upper receptacle (fitted with an orifice at its base) so that the trickle flow would just suffice to fill the lower vessel at the time required to awake the sleeper. This lower vessel was so poised that, when full, its weight would then just suffice to tilt it forward and so manipulate a lever which would push against the sleeper's feet. To accentuate the effect, there is also a water-container on the right which discharges into the left, so that the overbalancing drop releases a substantial force. "This," his note says, "is a clock for the use of those who watch carefully over the use of their time. And it works thus: When as much water has been poured through the funnel into the receiver as there is in the opposite balance, the balance rises and pours its water into the first receiver; and this being doubled in weight jerks violently upwards the feet of the sleeper, who is thus awakened and goes about his business."[1]

The reader will appreciate that the mechanisms and devices so far described are but a selected few of those to be found within the thousands of pages of Leonardo's notes. Our purpose has not been, however, to record a mere enumeration or catalogue of these but rather to attempt, through a systematic survey of the various aspects of engineering activity that interested him, to understand his attitude towards them and to appreciate his methods of dealing with them. Very many devices have therefore been omitted from our survey—some of them of considerable importance and all of them of considerable ingenuity. Whether it be in the domestic scene, for which he devised such amenities as a revolving cowl for the chimney, an improved form of oil lamp fitted with a lamp glass, a ventilator, modern latrine conveniences; or in the field of musical recreation, with his mechanical drums and other instruments; or both in and on the water, for which he devised diving suits, breathing apparatus, life-belts, floating shoes, webbed gloves, and the like; or alembics and crucibles and ovens for the alchemical laboratory; or such apparatus for meteorological needs as the hygrometer, the anemometer, and the like; or some extremely original ideas for mechanical transport, such as armoured cars and tanks; or plans for military fortifications and a host of other military devices additional to those we have already discussed—it can confidently be said that whatever the need and the occasion, at some time or other in his career, Leonardo da Vinci gave it some thought and produced for it some solution.

Nevertheless, it is hoped that what has been said in the various sections of this chapter will have convinced the reader that the truly great artist whom we showed in the previous chapter to have been also a truly great man of science was additionally a great engineer. There is one other aspect of his life, however, we have yet to explore. It touches both his science and his engineering and was born probably with his art. It concerns his life-long dreams of artificial flight, and it is to this concluding study of Leonardo da Vinci that we next proceed.

IX

ARTIFICIAL FLIGHT AND THE FLIGHT OF BIRDS

1. THE PERIOD OF LEGEND

There is a well-known piece of malicious gossip attributed to the mathematician Jerome Cardan regarding Leonardo da Vinci. "Leonardo," he wrote, "also attempted to fly but misfortune befel him from it. He was a great painter." Apart from the uncharitable phrasing of this comment there was really little basis for Cardan's remark. It will be recalled that his father was a personal friend of Leonardo's, and we must accept that the Cardan household could claim some first-hand knowledge of him. The inference was that Leonardo, who had undoubtedly studied deeply the problems of artificial flight, did more than write about them, and perhaps had tried to carry out actual flight tests. But while there is a remote possibility that this was true, there is no evidence that it was so in the sense that Leonardo actually mounted a full-sized flying machine of his own design and that he attempted to fly it. He was, of course, somewhat secretive about his actual experimental work. "Close up with boards," he writes, "the room above [a loft of some kind?] and make the model [i.e. the machine] large and high, and you will have space upon the room above —if you stand upon the roof at the side of the tower the men at work upon the cupola [of the neighbouring cathedral] will not see you." But to read into this that he both made and tried out a flying machine would be mere wishful thinking. So, too, a more specific note to the effect that "tomorrow morning on the second day of January 1496 I will make the thong [soatta] and the attempt" *might* be construed to refer to a try-out of a large-scale model, but it is virtually certain that no such actual attempt was made on that day. And, indeed, it is certainly as well that this was the case, because such records, either factual or apocryphal, as have been handed down to us, from the legendary fatal flight of Icarus onwards, tell of a sequence of failure and disaster to all who had attempted to master the air in artificial flight.

Aeronautics is no longer the very young science that it was in the early years of this century. The movement of aircraft and their controlled flight in the skies are a commonplace of daily experience. Yet it was only at the beginning of the present century, in the early morning of the 17th December 1903, that the brothers Wright flew the first mechanically-powered man-carrying airplane on a series of four short flights, the best of which lasted 59 seconds. Actually, the small number of onlookers on that occasion—five to be exact—were the fortunate participators in a remarkable historical experience. They were the witnesses of a culminating point in man's age-old aspiration. Dreamers of air conquest pass before us throughout the panorama of the past. To all of these it was but natural that the tantalising spectacle of the ease of bird flight should have constituted a perpetual challenge; and so from time to time we meet with stories, mainly legendary but occasionally with some background of fact, of men hazarding their lives for the slender fortune of an idea and a dream and, whether in legend or in fact, usually with the same result. In the language of Cardan, "misfortune befel them from it".

From the range of legend we should certainly recall the classical story of Dædalus, the Athenian, because in an alleged scope of achievement he might well have been regarded as a sort of mythological version of Leonardo da Vinci. He was reputed to have been the most ingenious artist of his age, even to the sculpturing of statues that were so perfect that they seemed endowed with life and movement. But it is also said of Dædalus that he invented the wedge, the axe, the wimble (a delightful name given to a sort of large-sized gimlet or augur), the level, and a host of other mechanical contrivances. He was also concerned with the idea of using sails for ships, and from that it was but one step to the conception of wings for human flight.

But we must not press this alleged parallelism with Leonardo any further. Dædalus was not a very pleasant sort of person. He had murdered one Talus, of whose competitive prowess in mechanical invention he was jealous, and then fled to Crete. Here he incurred the displeasure of King Minos, who imprisoned him with his son Icarus. It was in order to escape from this confinement that the famous flight of legend occurred. The story has it that he made wings of feathers and wax and carefully fitted them to both his own body and that of his son; and then, in the language of modern aeronautics, they "took off". But Icarus made the mistake, it seems, of flying too high. Now this is a curious and interesting point, because throughout the development of the modern era of flight it has always been a dictum of the "safety first" campaigns of the air that "high flying is safe flying". If anything goes wrong the pilot has just that much more room and time to enable him to restore control over his aircraft.

Leonardo da Vinci was quite clear himself about this. In his notebook *On the Flight of Birds*[1] we read: "The movement of the bird" (and it should be interpolated here that Leonardo frequently referred to his proposed artificial aircraft as a bird) "ought always to be above the clouds to avoid the peril of wind revolutions among mountain gorges, which are always full of whirlings and turnings of the winds. Beyond that, if the bird should turn somersault you would have more time for righting it with the directions already given before it reaches the ground."

And in a later passage from the same notebook he also says: "The said bird ought, with the assistance of the wind, to rise to a great height *and that will be its safety*; even should it experience all the above-mentioned revolutions, it has time enough to recover its balance provided its limbs be very strong so that they may safely resist the fury and vigour of the descent."[2]

But, reverting back to Leonardo's mythological predecessors, it is curious that, in spite of the dictum above referred to, it was just because Icarus flew high that he was killed. The explanation in the traditional story is that this very high flying, so much above the altitude of his notorious parent, angered the sun, causing it, by way of punishment, to accentuate its heat. This melted the wax and lost Icarus the aerial support of his wings—another example of impetuous youth refusing to accept the dictum that "father knows best"! Icarus fell into what has ironically since been called the Icarian Sea, and was drowned.

During the years that followed there were, of course, other legendary and factual predecessors to Leonardo, none of whom would have been known to us but for the disasters that befell them—for of such was the material of early aeronautical fame!

There was, for example, the short-lived flight of Simon Magus, who was helped by demon colleagues and ended with a broken neck! And of Abaris and his flight round the world on a golden arrow—a variant of the "Old Mother Shipton" theme. Later, there was the more circumstantial story of the Saracen of Constantinople who staged his project with no less an illustrious onlooker than the Emperor Comnenus. His idea was to fly round the local Hippodrome at Constantinople. Wearing a long, white robe braced with rods to catch the breeze, he mounted to the top of a tower and leaned into the wind. Quite probably he had his qualms about starting but the crowds below became impatient, as crowds do. They voiced their feelings loudly and so he felt impelled to "take off". The records tell us that "the weight of his body having more power to drag him down than the artificial wings had to sustain him, he broke his bones, and his evil plight was such that he did not long survive".

---

[1] *Sul Volo degli Uccelli*, 7 (6) v.   [2] Ibid.

But perhaps the outstanding figure of the pre-Leonardo period was Roger Bacon—whom we have already seen to have been the creator of a minor Renaissance of his own. Among his many remarkable writings was his thirteenth-century prophecy that: "An instrument may be made to fly withal if one sit in the midst of the instrument and do turn the engine, by which the wings, being artificially composed, may beat the air after the manner of a flying bird. . . ."

This prophecy, so remarkable and so characteristic of its author, has been regarded by some as implying the use of mechanical power. More probably the implication was of the mechanical *transmission* of muscular power. Either way, it was neither more nor less than a forecast. On the other hand, as we may have expected, Leonardo really did carry out experiments and tried to produce models.

More or less contemporary with Leonardo himself, we meet several instances of alleged practical interest and attempted achievement in artificial flight. One was in far-off China—the land of kite-flying and kite-flyers—where Wan-Hoo is said to have attempted a sort of rocket-aircraft.[1] He fixed a saddle between two large kites, tied forty-seven rockets to them to provide the "take-off" impulse, boarded his "machine" and gave the signal to forty-seven waiting coolies. These ignited the rockets more or less simultaneously, after which, to quote Gibbs-Smith, "this intrepid Chinese departed to his ancestors to the accompaniment of much noise and smoke".

Closer home to Leonardo, the distinguished astronomer Regiomontanus, to whom we have already referred (p. 139), is alleged to have made in his workshop at Nuremberg a sort of artificial "fly" which, "taking its flight from his hand, would fly round the room" and would then "home" back to its master's hand; and also an artificial eagle which he sent out in flight to greet the emperor's approach to the city. What is more probable is that he was known to be interested in clockwork and that he fashioned a clockwork contrivance which, as much by good luck as by design, was able when released to mount upwards a short distance.

More reliably we have also the story of the mathematician Giovanni Battista Danti of Perugia, who in 1490 attempted a flight from a tower in the city. Like his predecessor the Saracen of Constantinople four hundred years earlier, he probably had artificial wings strapped on to him by means of a rigid frame, with which he was intended to glide "through the air with the greatest of ease". But his attempt went the usual way and he crashed and was badly injured—and no doubt lucky to have escaped with his life.

Finally, we should note John Damian, an Italian alchemist and

[1] C. H. Gibbs-Smith, *A History of Flying*, p. 47 (London, 1953).

physician. He was very much of a wanderer before finally settling down to become the Abbot of Tungland. In 1507, while he was in Scotland as court physician to James IV, he made an attempt to fly from the walls of Stirling Castle—and broke his thigh-bone for his temerity.

2. LEONARDO'S HEEL OF ACHILLES

And what of Leonardo himself? There is ample evidence that the dreams of air conquest were with him all through his adult life. It fascinated and held him. It impelled him to thoughts which rose superior to the many crudities of expression with which his notes abound. So he writes, as the concluding note in his studies *On the Flight of Birds*: "The great bird [referring again here to his flying machine] will take its first flight on the back of the great bird and filling the world with stupor and all writings with renown and bringing glory to the nest where it was born."

The "back of the great bird" and the "nest where it was born" were evidently his word pictures for a hill situated near Fiesole, from the summit of which he hoped one day to be able to take off. The obvious fervour behind these words was genuine. He wrote them in 1505 when he was fifty-three years old—surely a sober enough age. Yet we meet with his discussions on the subject as early as 1488, when he was living in Milan, and as late as 1514, when he was in Rome.

The conquest of the air was his dream and his obsession—and so were the birds whose freedom of the air he wanted to emulate. He loved them and hated to see them in captivity. He would buy birds in their cages, not to take home but to return them to their own world. As a child he had had a vivid dream of a great bird hovering over him and then descending to brush his mouth with its tail. This affected him profoundly. He never forgot this dream and we must relate his years of study and note-taking to it.

It is interesting to observe how, as the years went by, Leonardo continued to return to the theme either of bird studies or of artificial wing studies. The over-all period was of some twenty-five years. Apart from the *Codex Atlanticus*, whose notes are a composite over the years, his earliest work was in Manuscript *B*, which he started in 1488 at the age of thirty-six. Here he plunged immediately into his totally impracticable designs for flying machines. As against this, his best work was from the years 1505 onwards. It was in this year that he wrote his *Codice Sul Volo degli Uccelli (Manuscript on the Flight of Birds)*— a small notebook of some thirty pages which is now in the Royal Library of Turin; but notes on bird flight are also to be found in several of the other notebooks, notably in Manuscript *E*, written much later, in 1514. In this notebook his flight studies are to be found in folios 21 v. to 23 v. and thence from 35 v. to 54 v. The little pocket note-book *K* has such notes from folios 3 to 13 and from 58 to 60; and others are in Manuscript *G* (which includes notes on insect flight as well as on bird flight) on folios 41 v. and 42 r., 63 v. (on bats) and 64 and 65 (on insects); and in Manuscript *L*, the dates of whose notes range from 1499 to 1502, notes occur from folios 53 to 62. Additionally, some odd notes are to be found in Manuscript *F*, dated 1508.

As we shall see, however, whilst these notes show a considerable understanding of a bird's behaviour in relation to gliding and soaring, Leonardo did not apply this understanding to his treatment of the problems of artificial flight by man. Here he was entirely obsessed with the feeling that the solution lay in the direction of flapping flight. Not only were the various fantastic drawings of his proposed flying machines based on the ornithopter principle, but his many experiments in the methods of overcoming the resistance of the air were all in terms of flapping wings.

This was most unfortunate. To simulate soaring and gliding would have meant designing flying machines with fixed wings. But Leonardo's "heel of Achilles" was, however, this obsession with flapping wings. Now this required the basic assumption that man's muscular system was adequate enough for him to produce sufficient power both to set up and to maintain the flapping. Unfortunately, this simply is not true, and therefore Leonardo was on the wrong track. His designs remain as mere freaks of curiosity, created by him fruitlessly before he embarked on the long series of scientific studies and observations on soaring flight which might so well have led him to more fruitful and practical results. To quote Gibbs-Smith: "It was the vital mis-conceptions which he allowed to possess him in his early work which retarded his aeronautical evolution so that, in old age, he was only reaching towards the more valid conclusions which he could easily have achieved in his early and middle life."[1]

It is, of course, basic that since birds fly and men do not, the obvious procedure if man is to achieve flight is that he must somehow imitate the bird. Hence, deduced Leonardo, its study would reveal the true secrets of flight. "A bird," he writes, "is an instrument working according to mathematical law, an instrument which it is within the capacity of man to reproduce with all its movements, though not with a corresponding degree of strength, for it is deficient in the power of maintaining equilibrium. We may therefore say that such an instru-

---

[1] C. H. Gibbs-Smith, *The Flying Machines of Leonardo da Vinci—A New Appraisal* (Shell Aviation News—London, August 1954). This is an accurate and convincing critical analysis of Leonardo da Vinci's work on flight.

ment constructed by man is lacking in nothing except the life of the bird, and this life must needs be supplied from that of man."[1]

But, unfortunately, this comparison between birds and man left out of account, as Gibbs-Smith has pointed out, the relative disparity of muscular power between the two species in relation to overall weight. Leonardo's flying machines were designed to be worked by the muscles of the pilot's arms and legs—a muscle power of from a fifth to a quarter of his total weight. But in the case of the bird, the flying muscles account for as much as up to half the total weight; added to which, the instinct of the species is to get into and use the air, whereas the instinct of man is to keep his feet firmly on the ground. But when, added to this already formidable handicap, we add the dead load of the weight of the artificial wings and the rest of the machine which the would-be flyer must add to his own weight, the handicap of flight by muscular human power becomes overwhelming. The only thing that saved Leonardo da Vinci from heading for a fall was almost certainly the fact that he never went further than designing his projects—or, at best, if he did build up a machine from his projects, that he never tried it out in practice.

There was one other error of observation of which Leonardo was guilty. This was his assumption that a bird in flight beats its wings downwards and backwards, comparable with a man swimming. "A bird makes the same use of wings and tail in the air as a swimmer does of his arms and legs in the water," he writes.[2] And again, "The second method employed by birds at the commencement of their flight is when they are descending from a height: they merely throw themselves forwards and, at the same time, spread their wings high and forwards and then, in the course of their leap, lower their wings downwards and backwards, and so, using them as oars, continue their slanting descent."[3]

We give yet one more quotation to make it clear that this erroneous view was no mere passing fancy of Leonardo's. "The birds which fly swiftly," he writes in Manuscript L, "keeping at the same distance above the ground, beat their wings downwards and behind them; downwards to the extent needed to prevent the bird from descending, and backwards according as it wishes to advance with greater speed."[4]

But, in fact, the true movements of the wings of small birds in flapping flight are forwards and downwards, and upwards and backwards. With all the keenness of sight that we may well concede Leonardo to have possessed, the rapidity of vibration of the wings of the smaller birds would have been quite beyond him to follow in detail—and even

[1] *Codex Atlanticus*, 161 r.a.
[2] *Sul Volo degli Uccelli*, 11 (10) v.; see also MS. *M*, 83 r.
[3] MS. *G*, 64 r.
[4] MS. *L*, 59 v.

the slower motion of the bigger birds, such as the kites and eagles, would still have been too fast (and too far off) for him to detect. In these days of rapid and accurate bird cinematography, and the capacity to reduce these to the visual analysis of slow-motion study, such movements are susceptible of analysis. But not so in Leonardo da Vinci's day.

Unfortunately, however, it was upon this completely wrong assumption that Leonardo based his schemes for flying machines. But as Gibbs-Smith reminds us: "A bird does not, and cannot, beat backwards on the downstroke; such behaviour would practically capsize the creature at every wing-beat and it would proceed through the air rather like a bucking bronco."

A quick note on the normal structure of a bird's wing may not be inappropriate. It is boned on a distant similarity with that of a man's

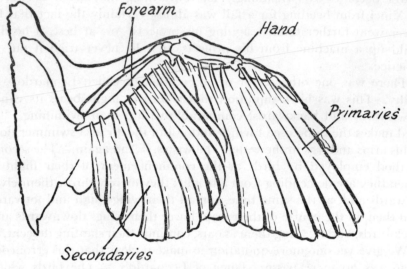

Fig. 92. The structure of a bird's wing.

arm—the upper humerus (Fig. 92), the radius and ulna, from elbow to wrist, from which the *secondary* feathers depend; and a much less comparable "hand" extremity, from which come the primaries. The bony structure and articulation of the joints are such that rotation at the "wrist" is impossible. There is an essential element of rigidity to ensure that the stiff primary feathers can resist being twisted out of alignment with the rest of the wing through gusts. When the wing is folded, its three sections lie in a compact Z formation against the body. On the other hand, in flight the extended wing presents an uninterrupted edge to the wind. Each of the three sections of the wing bears a set of feathers differing in both shape and quality from the others. The primaries and secondaries together constitute the flight feathers. The function of the primaries, appropriately stiffened to bear the greatest resistance, is to *propel*, and they move, of course, in a wider arc than the others. The less rigid and differently-shaped secondaries act as a *sustaining* area or parachute; whilst the tertiaries provide the link between the wing and the body. The relative lengths of these three main wing elements—the "hand", the "forearm", and the "upper arm"—differ from species to species, according to the special flight needs. Birds that are vigorous flapping-fliers have a dominant "hand" section and a shortened "upper arm", whilst gliding and soaring birds, that need more sustaining power, have a dominant upper arm and forearm. And with these shifts of emphasis go also differences in the size, shape and quality of the feathers. The total number of actual flight feathers also varies from type to type—from sixteen to fifty or so—but the variation is always in the *arm* section. On the hand section most birds have either nine or ten primary feathers—so that the variation in "secondary" feathers of the arm becomes from six or seven (e.g. in humming birds) to forty (in, e.g., the albatross).

In action each of the flight feathers is over-lapped by its neighbour. On the downstroke they are forced together into an airtight composite and thus meet with a maximum of air resistance. During this downwards beat, in the case of the smaller "flapping" birds, the four or five outer primary feathers flex into a propeller-vane sequence, producing a rapid forward propulsion effect. On the upstroke, the wing is partially flexed to turn and separate the primary feathers slightly, providing slots through which the air streams to reduce resistance. The upstroke involves the bird in far less exertion not only on this account but also because it has the advantage of the momentum provided by the greater effort of the downstroke.

A word should be said regarding the muscle control of these two strokes in flapping flight. The downstroke is accomplished directly by the "depressor" muscles attached to the under-part of the breastbone but the "elevator" muscles raise the wings by a sort of pulley action, slipping the tendons up and over the humerus at the shoulderjoint. An advantage of this is to concentrate the centre of gravity of the bird below the supporting wing area; otherwise the bird would tend to be top-heavy.

We may now finally turn to the main reason why Leonardo's obsession with flying machines based upon the ornithopter or flappingflight principle was doomed to failure. The speed at which a bird flies is a composite of many factors—wing-shape, wing area in relation to overall weight, rate of wing-beat, angle of "attack"—so far as the bird itself is concerned; and the obvious influence of the air conditions, so far as the medium of flight is concerned. Any surface may be sustained in the air *if it moves fast enough*—not alone by the supporting air pressure on the *under* side of the "wing" surface (which, in fact, is the lesser factor) but also by an upwards "suction" effect on the upper surface, where the air-flow sets up a partial vacuum. Although Leonardo knew nothing of this upper-surface "suction" lift—which, in fact, provides about twice as much lift as the more obvious upwards pressure exerted on the underside of the wing—he did have *some* vague ideas regarding a differentiation of pressure conditions above and below the wing. Thus we read: "Because the air underneath flying things is thicker than it is above them, and thicker in front than it is behind. . . ."[1] But even more significantly, in another notebook, he says: "When the heavy substance descends in the air, and this air moves in a contrary direction in order to fill up continuously the space left by this heavy substance, the movement of the air is a curve, because when it desires to rise by the shortest line it is prevented by the heavy substance which descends upon it and so, of necessity, it is obliged to bend and then to return above this heavy substance and fill up the vacuum that has been left by it. And if it were thus, the air would not be compressed beneath the speed of the heavy substance, and, this being so, the birds would not be able to support themselves upon the air that is struck by them; *but it is necessary to say here that the air is compressed beneath that which strikes it and it becomes rarefied above in order to fill up the void left by that which struck it.*"[2]

It requires the developing of sufficient initial speed to create enough lift to equal, and therefore to sustain, the weight of the bird or aircraft. This minimal velocity is the take-off speed—and it makes for harder work for some bird types than others. Obviously the heavier the bird, the faster it must fly, since it must set up more "lift" than is required by a smaller and lighter bird. Theoretically, for example, if the unfortunate ostrich were to fly at all (which it cannot do) it would need a speed of a hundred miles per hour to be "air-borne".

Wing shape, of course, matters very much. A long, narrow, flat wing is faster than a broad, cambered (i.e. arched from front to back) wing of the same area, since in the latter case there is less "suction effect" upwards from the upper surface. The slow fliers and glider birds have the wings of greatest camber.

On the whole, therefore, the factor of "wing loading", i.e. of the relation between the wing's surface to the total weight carried, becomes critical. Curiously, and perhaps unexpectedly, the heavier birds usually have proportionately smaller wing spans than the lighter and smaller birds, who usually have more wing span than they really need. But wing

[1] MS. *E*, 45 v.   [2] MS. *F*, 87 v.

span is a matter of two dimensions, whereas weight involves three—so that although span increases as the square of the linear dimensions, the weight involves a cubic increase. Mathematically, therefore, we see why the larger birds have to look more to soaring and sailing flight than to flapping flight. The inference as to flying machines is immediate. The wise solution—as time has shown—is for the fixed wing aircraft which soars, whereas the successful flapper aircraft is yet to be seen—even with powered flight-aids such as were not available to Leonardo da Vinci. Yet it was specifically to the ornithopter or flapper type of flying machine that Leonardo directed all his practical efforts. He could, alas, never get away psychologically from his life-long dream. It is interesting to recall that, just over 160 years after his death, the Italian mathematician Giovanni Alfonso Borelli, in his treatise *De Motu Animalium*, calculated in 1680, by comparing the bulk and weight of the muscles used by birds in flapping flight (which he computed to be one-sixth of its total weight) with those of men (which he said was less than one hundredth), that flapping flight for man was simply impossible, "whatever the apparatus is used". Yet even today the challenge goes on.

3. LEONARDO'S EXPERIMENTS WITH WINGS

True to form, Leonardo attacked the problems of design for his various types of flying machines in the true manner of the experimental scientist. What resistances had the would-be pilot to overcome? What sort of forces would he have to exert? What was the best shape for his wings? Of what materials were they to be made? These and many other relevant questions he clearly posed to himself, and his notes and sketches give us some idea of the trend of his thoughts and experiments.

We have seen that he was basing his schemes on the pattern of the bird in flapping flight. But he recognised, of course, that the problem also involved a study of the medium in which flight occurs—namely, the atmosphere. "To attain to the true science of the movement of birds in the air," he writes, "it is necessary to give first the science of the winds, which we will establish by means of the movements of water. This science will be a means of arriving at the knowledge of the winged creatures in the air and in the wind."[1] Then he speaks of the hub of his problem—the wing. "You will study the anatomy of the wings of a bird," he says, "together with the muscles of the breast which are the movers of these wings. And you do the same for man in order to show the possibility that there is in man to sustain himself in the air by the flapping of [artificial] wings."[2]

Did Leonardo understand what we speak of today as the "drag"

[1] MS. *E*, 54 r.   [2] *Codex Atlanticus*, 45 r.

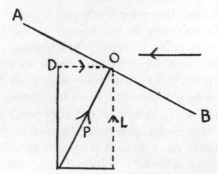

Fig. 93.   Lift and drag.

and "lift" components of the slanting air pressure P exerted against an advancing inclined surface AB? (Fig. 93). Readers will know that the air pressure created by the forward movement of the surface is at right angles to its plane AB and that this is resolvable into its two equivalent components at right angles, the upwards *lift L* sustaining the gravity of the surface, and the forward *drag D opposing* the motion of the surface; and that it is the problem in aeronautics to supply the requisite artificial power (an engine today; but a man's arm- and leg-muscles in Leonardo's day) to overcome the drag and to maintain the lift.   In Manuscript G we meet a passage which tantalisingly hints that Leonardo had some sort of appreciation of this.   Thus we read: "Every slanting movement made by a heavy substance through the air divides the gravity of the movable thing in *two* different aspects, one of which is directed to the place towards which it moves and the other to the cause that restrains it."[1]   Perhaps this is another of those many cases in which the well-wisher is tempted to read more into the difficult phraseology than Leonardo intended, whilst the sceptic prefers the more cautious view.   It is, however, more clear that this passage deals with the conception of drag than it does with lift.

Be that as it may, however, Leonardo had to find some practical basis for the design of his artificial wings.   What was to be his model?

Fig. 94.   The bat's wing.

[1] MS. G, 74 v.

Leonardo decided upon the bat. "Dissect the bat," he says, "and concentrate on this, and on this model arrange the machine."[1] And in his notebook *On the Flight of Birds* he sketches the bat (Fig. 94) accompanied by a note which reads: "You are to remember that your bird [i.e. flying machine] ought not to imitate anything but the bat, because the membranes form an armour or liaison to the armour, that is to say, strength to the wings. And if you imitate the wings of the feathered birds, the wings are more powerful in bone and nerve through being pervious; that is to say, the feathers are disunited and permeable to the air. But the bat is aided by the membrane which binds the whole and is not pervious."[2]

In effect, his idea was that a bat's wing behaves something like a sail, whereas a feathered wing could not so behave. This was sound advice and finds its final expression in modern aviation design. It is but a small step from the impervious membrane of a bat's wing to the fabric of the modern aeroplane wing. Yet how far did Leonardo follow this advice himself? Here was a line of attack upon his practical problem which, in the light of modern developments, would appear to have contained the germs of some possible success, particularly if he could have realised the advantages of the fixed type of wing over the flapping type. Yet in fact he appears to have neglected it and it is disappointing that the sketches and notes in his manuscripts show Leonardo, as we shall shortly see, to be occupied chiefly with the idea of the substitution of "jointed" oars for wings. An almost isolated exception occurs in one notebook in which we meet with a sketch of an artificial wing (Fig. 95), obviously modelled after the wing of a

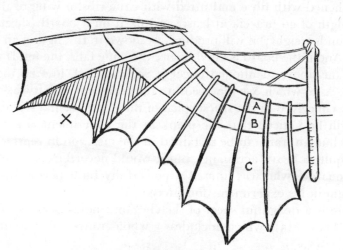

Fig. 95. Construction of an artificial wing.

[1] MS. *F*, 47 v.   [2] *Sul Volo degli Uccelli*, 16 (15) r.

bat. Against the shaded portion *X* he writes: "Make the meshes
of this fibre one-eighth in. width." Further details of construction are
given with reference to the letters *A, B* and *C* in the diagram as follows:
"*A* will be of blades of deal, which has threads [?] and is light. *B* will
be of fustian, on which will be glued the feathers, so as not to be easily
pervious to the air. *C* should be of starched light silk and, in order to
test it, you may make it of thin pasteboard."[1]

A most interesting development in wing design recorded by Leonardo
was his device (Plate 113), comparable to the clack valve of the
modern wing, in which a sort of flap opened on the upstroke (remember
Leonardo's error in thinking that birds open their wings on the upstroke to relieve air resistance) and closed on the downstroke. Leonardo's note reads: "Device so that when the wing rises up it remains
pierced through, and when it falls it is all united. And in order to see
this it must be looked at from below."[2]

Presumably Leonardo abandoned this type of wing as impracticable.
Possibly he may have concluded that the wind resistance created by
such an expanse of wing surface was far too much for the muscular
energy of the human frame to cope with, but if this had been the case,
one would have supposed the scientific alternative would have been to
have reduced the area of surface accordingly. It seems certain that
Leonardo attempted some experiments with a mechanical wing, the
object being to study the relationship between wing surface and wind
resistance. Thus we meet with a sketch of a man operating a mechanical
wing (Plate 114) accompanied by the following explanatory note: "If
you wish to see the true test of the wings, take some pasteboard
strengthened with fibre and fitted with cane ribs, a wing of the width
and length of 20 braccia at least, and fix it on a board (sheet-pile) of
200 pounds weight;[3] it will produce, as shown in the figure, an effective
force. And if the board is lifted before the wing falls, the test is good . . .
and if the above-mentioned effect is *not* obtained, lose no more time
on it." As to which, we may venture the comment that it was excellent
advice, conceived in the truest spirit of the experimental scientist.

It will be noticed that the plank in the experiment is a substitute
for the human frame to be sustained in the air. 200 lb represents 14 st
6 lb—quite a heavy aeronaut—but it would nevertheless be in keeping
for Leonardo, who was himself a powerfully built person, to provide
a margin in his experiments for safety.

There is a delightful sheet of sketches and notes in the *Codex Atlanticus*[4] (Plate 115), which includes a whole range of experiments on

---

[1] MS. *B*, 74 r.
[2] MS. *B*, 73 v. and 74 r.
[3] Sketches explanatory of these parts are shown in MS. *B*, 77 v.
[4] *Codex Atlanticus*, 381 v.a.

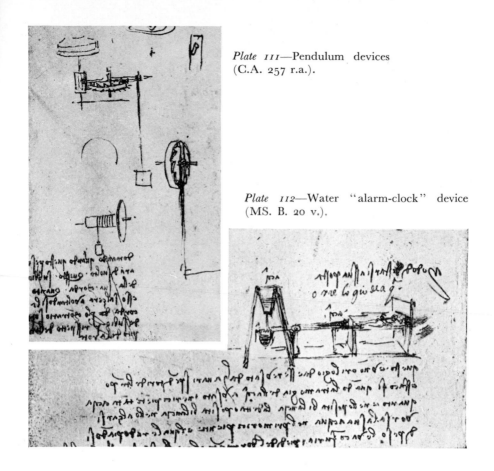

Plate 111—Pendulum devices
(C.A. 257 r.a.).

Plate 112—Water "alarm-clock" device
(MS. B. 20 v.).

Plate 113—Design for a "flap" valve comparable with the
clack-valve of the modern wing (MS. B. 73 v.).

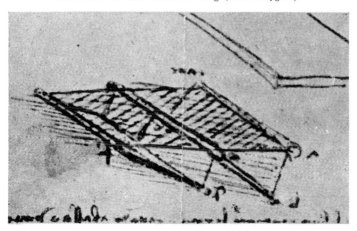

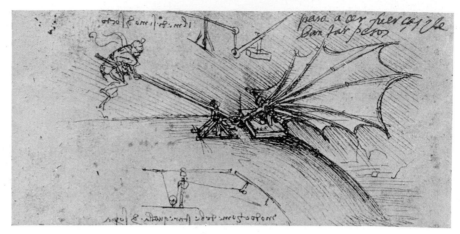

Plate 114—Man operating an artificial wing (MS. B. 77 v.).

Plate 115 —Page of notes and sketches on artificial flight (C.A. 381 v.a.).

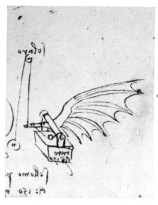

Plate 116—An artificial wing rigged for testing (C.A. 307 r.b.).

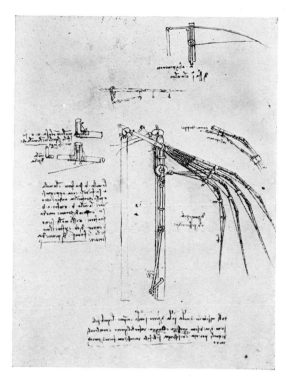

Plate 117—Mechanism for "articulated-joint" type of artificial wing (C.A. 308 r.a.).

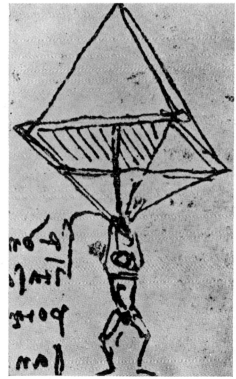

Plate 118—Leonardo's design for a parachute (C.A. 381 v.a.).

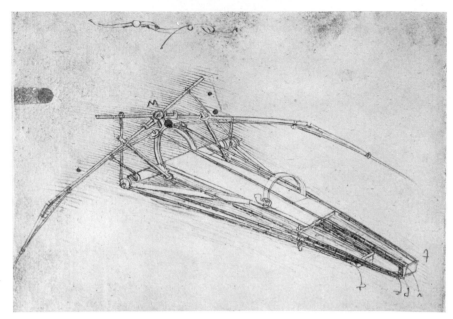

Plate 119—Design for prone-type flying machine (MS. B. 74 v.).

Plate 120—Design for improved prone-type flying machine, with rudder section.

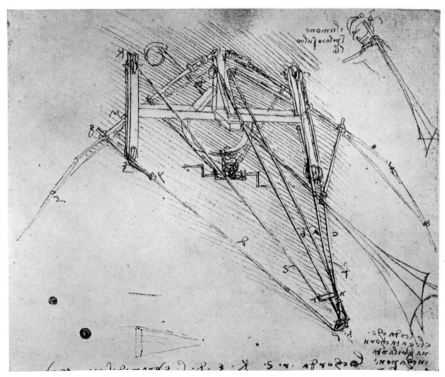

wing surfaces. In one, the experimentor is sitting in one scale of a balance, operating the wing under test, and in others one sees a range of pulley and other transmission designs for the proposed manipulation of pairs of wings.

Equally interesting is the sketch (Plate 116) in the *Codex Atlanticus*[1] of an artificial wing rigged for testing. The power is applied by a weight at the end of a cord passing over a pulley wheel and linked to the loaded block from which the wing projects.

These are naturally of qualitative rather than quantitative interest. But perhaps the best and clearest of all sketches of this type is one shown in Plate 117[2] of the proposed power transmission scheme for a flapping wing of the type in which the manipulator is in a vertical position. An important feature of this design is that it shows Leonardo to have departed from the "bat's-wing" type in favour of an articulated joint scheme. This obviously offers greater flexibility and variety o control. The transmission mechanism for operating the wing from the eccentric crank handle is clearly shown.

Finally, we should note a characteristic entry in notebook *H*, which reads: "In constructing wings one should make one cord to bear the strain and a looser one in the same position so that if the one breaks under the strain the other is in position to serve the same function."[3]

4. LEONARDO DA VINCI'S FLYING MACHINES

The general conclusion to which one is led from the notes, sketches and experiments to which we have referred, is that, on the whole, Leonardo came to no settled decisions as between the use of the "bat's wing" surface and the "jointed oar" type of wing, but that he did cling closely to his obsession for the ornithopter type of machine. This is particularly unfortunate (and not a little strange) having regard to the fact that most of his later studies on the flight of birds were concerned with soaring and gliding flight. On the other hand, we must remember that most of his designs (there are some fourteen in all) were drawn in his earlier years before the full implications of his later studies were emerging in his mind.

That there was a link between gliding surfaces and human flight is clear from a fascinating "corner" of sketches (Fig. 96)[4] in which we see five successive views of a fluttering leaf falling in zigzag fashion and, below these, four views of a man suspended from a plane surface in "glider" flight. It is an extraordinary and fascinating thought that here, tucked away in an odd corner of a hotchpotch of notes, are miniature sketches that portend, for the first time in history, the coming of the glider aircraft. Yet here was something of the

---

[1] *Codex Atlanticus*, 307 r.b.   [2] Ibid., 308 r.a.   [3] MS. *H*, 29 v.   [4] MS. *G*, 74 r.

wizardry of the man who sketched them. What a pity that he did not pursue the idea further to evolve a fixed-wing type of aircraft.

In just one related sense, however, he can be said to have developed the idea further, for one of the specific inventions of proved practical utility that we must concede to Leonardo da Vinci was that of the parachute. Referring back to Plate 115, with its curious collection of wing experiments, the passage of notes at the top reads thus: "An object offers as much resistance to the air as the air does to the object."[1] (Note here a specific example of Leonardo's appreciation of the law of reactions.) "You may see that the beating of its wings against the air supports a heavy eagle in the highest and rarest atmosphere, close to the sphere of elemental fire"—a reference, of course, to Leonardo's

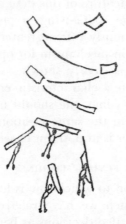

Fig. 96.   The first conception
of gliding flight.

acceptance of the classical conception of the outer universe. "Again, you may see the air in motion over the sea fill the swelling sails and drive heavily-laden ships. From these instances, and the reasons given, a man with wings large enough and duly connected, might learn to overcome the resistance of the air and, by conquering it, succeed in subjugating it and rising above it."

Here, clearly, we have the principle of the parachute, and Leonardo's small drawing of a man suspended from it (Plate 118) is seen below and to the right of the passage. Against the sketch he writes: "If a man have a tent of densely woven linen twelve braccia broad and twelve braccia high, he will be able to let himself fall from any great height without danger to himself." Here, then, is something quite specific and quite true. While there is no evidence that Leonardo backed his notes and his convictions with a full-scale demonstration, the note and

[1] *Codex Atlanticus*, 381 v.a.

the idea was real enough, and it is almost certain that he made a working model for himself.

There is evidence that in 1595, i.e. nearly a century after da Vinci's invention, Fausto Veranzio, a Venetian, working from a marine analogy, used a square sort of sail, extended by four cords attached at the corners, in a drop from the top of a tower.[1] More authentically, as a matter of history, it was not until 1783, nearly three hundred years after, that Lenormand made the first successful parachute descent from the observatory of Montpellier.

The parachute, of course, is the main safety "stand-by" in modern aviation. But it is quite clear, nevertheless, that Leonardo did *not* devise the parachute as a safety measure. His development of the idea was entirely independent of any other line of thought concerning his flying machines. For him it was just another idea of a device that could be air-borne.

So far as safety measures are concerned, he had other and, on the whole, cruder suggestions—apart from the sound advice we have already met as to flying high. All that these amounted to was that the aviator should carry "shock-absorber" equipment—mainly wine-skin bags. There is a rough sketch in the notebook *On the Flight of Birds* showing these strung together, and the accompanying note reads: "Bags, where a man falling from a height of six braccia would not injure himself, falling either on water or on land."[2] There is a further note which advises: "If you fail, see that you strike the ground with the double wine-skin under you."

And so we turn to Leonardo's various designs for his flying machines. As we have seen, the materials for his wings were cane and fustian and starched taffeta; and he also used cords of well-greased oxhide and springs made with bands of iron or strips of cow's horn. His general principle was that when equipped with wings "a man should be free from the waist upwards in order to balance himself as he does in a boat in order that his centre of gravity and that of his 'instrument' [i.e. his machine] might be capable of adjustment when necessity required it, according to the change in the centre of its resistance"[3] (see p. 332–5). Not all his designs, however, quite conformed to this principle.

Leonardo's various designs occur over a span of some sixteen years, from about 1483 to 1499. It may be said that, on the whole, they are of little scientific importance. They are curiosities and fascinating

---

[1] Veranzio described his parachute in his work *Machinae Novae*, published *c.* 1620. See the chapter on "The Origins of the Parachute" in Gibbs-Smith's *The Aeroplane: An Historical Survey*, pp. 165–168 (London 1960).

[2] *Sul Volo degli Uccelli*, 17 (16) r. and v.

[3] Ibid., 6 (5) r.

illustrations of mechanical genius running amok with his dreams, his hopes and his ambitions. They display, in their aggregate designs, few of the separate factors that we know from his many notes to have been familiar to him as requirements that should be incorporated in any successful design. In practically every case Leonardo visualised a mechanism of wings worked by man-power alone, using the muscles of the arms, legs and, sometimes, of the neck, to manipulate artificial wings by a sort of rowing movement.

It is not easy to trace consecutively his steps from one design to another. Presumably, following historical tradition, his first idea was somehow to attach a pair of wings directly to the human body—but he must have abandoned this plan fairly soon. So he turned to devices in which the operator lay anchored in a prone position, with face

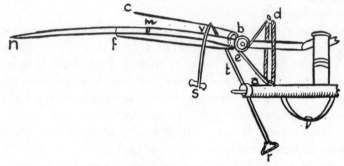

Fig. 97.   Design for a flying machine.

downwards, and extended at full length in the manner of a boy manipulating a coasting sled.

In Manuscript *B*, for instance, there is a sketch showing one half only of the design for a machine. We must presumably imagine that the wing (not shown) is attached to the "oar" or articulated span *mn*. The pilot's head is held in the saddle below, with his hands gripping the handles *s* and his feet the stirrups *r* (Fig. 97).[1] The action is not too clear, but according to the note accompanying the sketch the oar *mn* with appended sail or wing is raised by the mechanism marked *abc* and lowered by *def*. *rt* lowers the wing by means of the foot (by stretching the leg), and *vs* raises the wing by the hand and "turns it".

Another picturesque design is described in the same manuscript[2] (Plate 119). The aviator is lying on a plank across the front of which is a sort of pole or axle. Fitted to the centre of this axle is a rounded iron shank through which the head of the prone pilot protrudes, and his body is held by another such shank or belt midway along the plank.

The pointed oars carrying the wings are attached to the top of the

[1] MS. *B*, 73 v.   MS. *B*, 74 v.

head-shank at *m*. The wings are operated by the feet by means of stirrups at *c* and *d*, the right foot lowering the wings and the left raising them. The design is not easy to follow, but *a* is intended to twist the wing and *b* to turn it in some way.

Leonardo must have had great hopes of this design, which was somehow intended to give a variety of controlled movement. For example, he envisaged using both legs together instead of alternately, holding that "the downward movement with the two feet is always stronger than with one foot; it is true, of course, that the movement in this case is slower". And he goes on to say: "If the wings are to be raised, it must be done by the force of a spring or, if you wish, with the hand; or, better still, by drawing the feet towards you, which is better because it leaves your hands more free." But he also says: "The action of lowering should be done by the force of the two feet at the same time so that you can regulate the movement and preserve your equilibrium by lowering one wing more rapidly than the other, according to need, as you may have seen done by the kite and other birds." All of which makes the action and the intention very difficult to follow. Leonardo spoke of an intention to test this machine over a lake, adding the prudent advice that: "You should carry a long wineskin as a girdle, so that in case you fall you will not be drowned."

The next aircraft, again of the "prone" type, to which we must refer, follows on the next page of Manuscript *B*[1] (Plate 120). Although in general it is very similar to the previously described design, it shows two very specific improvements. One is in the easier hand manipulation afforded by the provision of two crank handles to which the wing mechanism is linked. The other, and the more interesting and significant, is the attachment of a *tail* or rudder section, the manipulation of which is to be controlled by the muscles of the head and neck. A special band or loop attachment is provided for this purpose. The tail section is seen to the right of the lower extremity of the main machine and the head loop is shown ahead of the "oars". The detail of this "head and tail" element is also separately shown on the top right of the main drawing. A close inspection of this "tail" unit is fascinating. It appears to comprise both horizontal *and* vertical elements and must therefore be regarded as a quite remarkable vision of the future. Four hundred years later, in 1895, Otto Lilienthal incorporated a similar device –for the first time in the history of flying—in a machine of his own design, though it does not appear to have met with much success. Leonardo's idea was, presumably, for the operator to steer the aircraft with his head, leaving his hands free to turn the cranks. The note reads: "The rod [shaft] is to have its centre of rotation at the neck." Thus, if

[1] MS. *B*, 75 r.

he turns his head to the left, the rudder swings to the right, and vice-versa. It is curious that this is the only drawing, among so many, in which this idea of a tail unit is used, especially when one realises that his many notes on bird flight make frequent reference to the tail as an essential factor in flight manœuvre.

As Leonardo's sketches pass progressively from one design to another, it is clear that he is more and more concerned with means to ensure better comfort for the operator combined with more efficient means of propulsion. Thus, a few pages on from the design just described, we see one (Plate 121)[1] in which, while the operator may still be described as having to adopt a prone position, the general posture suggests greater ease and a minimum of strain. Further, the operator appears to be provided with a windlass mechanism which is operated, presumably, both by the feet and the hands. The sketch is very rough and the detail is difficult to follow, but obviously the legs are used alternately. Another feature of interest in this sketch is the apparent provision of a double set of oars. The note accompanying the sketch reads thus: "This can be made with one pair of wings and also with two. If you wish to make it with one, the arms will raise it by means of a windlass, and two vigorous kicks with the heels will lower it, and this will be useful. And if you make it with two pairs, when one leg is extended it will lower one pair of wings and, at the same time, the windlass worked by the hands will raise the others, helping also very much those that fall, and by turning the hands first to the right and then to the left you will help first the one and then the other."

Gibbs-Smith, in the paper previously quoted,[2] refers to this model as a transitional stage from the "prone" type of flying-machine design to the "vertical" or standing type. On the very next page[3] Leonardo has decided to place his operator in a vertical position. "I conclude," he tells us, "that the upright position is more useful than face downwards because the instrument [i.e. the machine] cannot get overturned and, on the other hand, the habit of long custom requires this."

This sketch has a number of features completely absent from previous designs. The pilot (Plate 122) is more or less comfortably seated at his "controls". Again, there are twin sets of wings, alternately operated by a capstan type of mechanism housed in a bowl-shaped container. "This man," he writes, "exerts with his head a force that is equal to two hundred pounds, and with his hands a force of two hundred pounds, and this is what the man weighs. The movement of the wings will be crosswise after the manner of the gait of the horse.

[1] MS. *B*, 79 r.   [2] See footnote p. 312.   [3] MS. *B*, 80 r.

So, for this reason, I maintain that this method is better than any other."

But the novelty of design goes further. The bowl-shaped fuselage of the machine is kept above ground level by an undercarriage device of two ladders. The pilot mounts one of the ladders and enters the aircraft through a hatchway, shown clearly in the sketch above the right-hand ladder. Moreover, in a later sketch[1] (Plate 123) some interesting and important features of this undercarriage are clearly seen. At the base of each upright of the ladders there is a rounded spring to act as a shock-absorber, and once the pilot is in position (and presumably after he has "taken off"(?)) the undercarriage is retracted by means of a cord or wire manipulated by the crank mechanism above the base-board. The sketch shows the ladders in the lowered position below, and nicely stowed in the retracted position above.

Accompanying this drawing is a note that reads: "Make the ladders curved to correspond with the body. When the foot of the ladder a touches the ground it cannot give a blow to cause injury to the instrument because it is a cone which buries itself and does not find any obstacle at its point, and this is perfect.

"Make trial of the actual machine over the water so that if you fall you do yourself no harm. These hooks that are underneath the feet of the ladder act in the same way as when one jumps on the points of one's toes for then one is not stunned as is the person who jumps upon his heels. . . . When you have raised yourself draw up the ladders as I show in the second figure above."

Paradoxically, we find that the more Leonardo incorporates what, in modern aircraft, we would regard as common-sense essentials, the more hopeless becomes his overall design as an object of practical achievement. Gibbs-Smith expresses this with picturesque bluntness thus: "The chimerical flying-saucer . . . at whose all-up weight one can only shudder—is pure fantasy and totally alien to all Leonardo's normal processes of scientific thought."[2] Perhaps, however, we may partially retrieve some hopes for rational ideas in the later example of a da Vinci proposal for a flying machine, to which we now turn.

This is a design seen in the *Codex Atlanticus*[3] (Plate 124), and is remarkable because it incorporates a scheme for the use of *mechanical* power as a supplement to the muscular power of the operator. And although, as usual, the device was unworkable, the fact that this is the first instance in history of a specific proposal of harnessing of mechanical power for the purposes of aerial flight is sufficient to justify

[1] MS. *B*, 89 r.
[2] C. H. Gibbs-Smith, *The Flying Machines of Leonardo da Vinci—A New Appraisal*, p. 6 (Shell Aviation News, Sept. 1953).
[3] *Codex Atlanticus*, 314 r.b.

its place in the history of aviation. Even Roger Bacon's famous reference to "one turning an engine by which the wings, being artificially composed, may beat the air after the manner of a flying bird" was almost certainly intended to imply a contrivance propelled by man-power alone—and the subsequent ingenuous confession that although neither he nor anyone else had seen it, he did "well know by name the learned man that invented the same" may be taken as "third-hand" imaginative table gossip.

From Leonardo's drawing it will be seen, firstly, that there is only one set of wings and, secondly, that these are powered by two bow-like springs to which they are linked by a sequence of pulley wheels. The springs as shown are obviously compressed "ready for action", and in a separate lower sketch we see the detailed mechanism for winding the springs preliminary to "take-off" (wishful thinking, alas, and we must agree with Gibbs-Smith in wondering what Leonardo thought might happen both to pilot and craft if the springs became completely unwound during flight!). But, after all, let us not forget that for years the open spaces of the countryside have been the scene of countless model aeroplanes taking off successfully, powered by the spring action of elastic bands. If Leonardo continued to be obsessed with his dreams of ornithopter flying machines, we still must pay tribute to those elements within his dreams that history showed to have a factual foundation.

It is generally conceded, for example, that this device of the mechanical power supplied by a wound-up spring was successfully applied by Leonardo da Vinci, for the first time in history, in his famous fore-runner of the modern helicopter—the first example of a machine capable of vertical movement by using a helical screw.[1] Leonardo's sketch is shown in Plate 125,[2] and accompanying it is a note which reads: "Let the outer rim of the screw be of steel wire, as thick as string, and let the distance from the outer circumference to the centre be eight braccia. I find that if this instrument, made with a helix, be well made, that is to say, of flaxen linen, of which the pores have been closed with starch, and is turned with great speed, the said helix will make a screw in the air, and will climb high. Take the example of a wide and thin ruler whirled rapidly and violently into the air; you will see that your arm will be guided by the line of the edge of the said flat surface.

"The framework of the above-mentioned linen should be of long, stout cane. You can make a little model of this of pasteboard, whose

---

[1] But see Appendix D regarding a recent claim that the helicopter principle was already known and used in children's toys.
[2] MS. *B*, 83 v.

axis should be of thin steel wire, twisted with force; on freeing this, it causes the helix to turn."

Here, then, beyond doubt, we have the first successful helicopter; and it is curious to reflect that, only in very recent years, it was first successfully applied a long time after fixed-wing aircraft had become a commonplace experience in our daily lives.

We return finally to a single instance in which Leonardo showed some break in his perpetual proclivity for a flapper-type aircraft in terms of the fixed-wing designs which might have been so much more fruitful in his hands. In the *Codex Atlanticus* there are two drawings[1] (Plate 126) of a machine that is clearly a combination of a fixed-wing with an ornithopter extension. In other words, there is a rigid centre-section having an area of fixed wing on either side of an aperture for the pilot, and hinged to this, at a long single hinge lying parallel with the line of flight, we see a flapping panel unit.

There are one or two unique features in this design that call for comment. There is first of all the fact that the fixed wing implies an appreciation of the soaring and gliding possibilities that we know Leonardo to have studied subsequently in his observations on the flight of birds; and we have already referred (Fig. 96) to his significant thumb-nail sketches below a falling leaf, of a man gliding with a plane surface. The second feature is a consequence of the nature of the hinge link between the fixed section and the flapping unit. It had hitherto been a persistent (but erroneous) feature of Leonardo's designs that his flapping wing would "row" through the air downwards and backwards. In this design only an up-and-down movement was possible. There are, unfortunately, no notes accompanying the drawings, and there is no evidence that Leonardo followed up this line of thought further. In fact, it constituted an anticipation of a device for a semi-ornithopter by Lilienthal four hundred years later, even to the way in which the machine is attached to the pilot at the opening in the centre section. The pilot hangs in a harness similar to that of the modern parachute.

There are numerous other sketches and notes relating to wings and artificial machines among Leonardo's notes, but the more important have now been described. It is curious that they should all have been thought out before Leonardo's systematic studies of the scientific principles underlying soaring flight, and that there should seemingly have been no further modifying designs on a more rational basis. So the flying machines of Leonardo da Vinci must remain a dream and an anomaly—the price of a life-long obsession.

Before we pass to a formal consideration of Leonardo's studies on the

[1] *Codex Atlanticus*, 309 r.a. and v.a.

flight of birds, we should consider briefly, even if only to dismiss the matter, whether he was aware of the possibilities of "lighter-than-air" flight. It has been suggested that Leonardo knew of the hot-air balloon —normally linked in history with the names of the Montgolfier brothers. The grounds for this are flimsy—mainly a "hearsay" reference in Vasari's *Lives of the Painters* to the statement that he fashioned very thin hollow animal figures from a sort of wax-paste, "blowing into which he made them fly through the air." In fact, however, no human breath would be anywhere near hot enough for this to be possible. What is much more likely, as Gibbs-Smith has suggested[1], is that Leonardo cut out and made to fly tiny kites shaped as animals. These would keep aloft in the wind, but would fall to the ground when the wind dropped.

5. LEONARDO'S STUDIES ON THE FLIGHT OF BIRDS

There were certain fundamental ideas which clearly guided da Vinci through the whole course of his investigations. We have already in-dicated that, of these, the most important was the time-old view that the imitation of the bird was the right line to adopt and that its study would reveal the true secrets of flight. "A bird," he writes, "is an instrument working according to mathematical law, an instrument which it is within the capacity of man to reproduce with all its move-ments, though not with a corresponding degree of strength, for it is deficient in the power of maintaining equilibrium. We may therefore say that such an instrument constructed by man is lacking in nothing except the life of the bird, and this life must needs be supplied from that of man."[2]

He had no illusions as to the comparison between a bird using its own living members and accessories and a man using wings and accessories which have no life in themselves. Thus he goes on to say: "The life which resides in the birds' members will, without doubt, better conform to their needs than will that of man which is separated from them, and especially in the almost imperceptible movements which preserve equilibrium. But since we see that the bird is equipped for many obvious varieties of movements, we are able from this experience to deduce . . . that he will to a great extent be able to provide against the destruction of that instrument of which he has himself become the living principle and the propeller."

Another fundamentally sound principle laid down by Leonardo should also be noted, namely, the need for study of the medium in which flight is carried out. So he writes: "To attain to the true science

---

[1] "The Flying Machines of Leonardo da Vinci—A New Appraisal", C. H. Gibbs-Smith, p. 8, *Shell Aviation News No.* 194, August 1954.
[2] *Codex Atlanticus,* 161 r.a.

of the movement of birds in the air it is necessary to give first the science of the winds, which we will establish by means of the movements of water. This science will be a means of arriving at the knowledge of the winged creatures in the air and in the wind."[1]

Leonardo's propensity for ordered classification was as evident in this field as in all others that interested him. Thus he wrote: "I have divided the treatise on birds into four books: the first treats of their flight by flapping their wings; the second treats of flight without flapping their wings and with the help of the wind; the third treats of flight in general, such as that of birds, fishes, animals and insects; the fourth of the mechanism of this movement."[2]

In yet another notebook we meet with a somewhat different plan of classification. Here he says: "To speak of this subject you must explain in the first book the nature of the resistance of the air, in the second the anatomy of the bird and of its wings, in the third the method of working of the wings in their various movements, in the fourth the power of the wings and of the tail at such time as the wings are not being moved and the wind is favourable, to serve as a guide in different movements."[3]

As we shall see, for Leonardo the problems of bird flight were the problems of mechanics, and at the outset he recognised the role of centres of gravity as being fundamental. Early in his *On the Flight of Birds* we read that "mechanical science is very noble and useful beyond all others, for by its means all animated bodies which have movement perform their operations; which movement proceeds from their centre of gravity. This is situated at the centre, except with unequal (distribution of) weight."[4]

Later in the same notebook[5] we meet with a little sketch of a "bird" suspended from a bracket by means of pulleys, together with the note: "This is done to find the centre of gravity of the bird without which this instrument would have but little value."

Da Vinci clearly realised that both movement and manœuvre were matters of the controlled relationship between the *internal* force exerted by the bird through its wings and the *outside* pressure variations of the wind.

He poses his practical problem in this way: for a bird to be sustained in the air during horizontal flight there must be an upwards pressure supporting the moving-wing surface. Is this pressure, he asks, in effect spread uniformly along the under surface of the wing? Or does it vary? And, if it varies, what is the effect of the variations, and how can the bird by its muscular action *induce* such variations for the pur-

[1] MS. *E*, 54 r. [3] MS. *F*, 41 v. [5] Ibid., 16 (15) v.
[2] MS. *K*, 3 r. [4] *Sul Volo degli Uccelli*, 3 r.

pose of controlled manœuvre? Developing his theme further, he continues: "All bodies which do not bend, whatever their size or weight, exert equal pressures on all the supports that are equi-distant from the centre of gravity, this centre being at the middle of the substance of such a body."[1] In the *Codex Atlanticus* he discusses this matter further. "The properties of the air are such that it may become condensed or rarefied," he says.[2] He realises clearly that support must come from air condensation below the wing. "Unless the movement of the wing which presses the air is swifter than the movement of the air so pressed, the air will not become condensed beneath the wing, and in consequence the bird will not support itself above the air. . . . That part of the air which is nearest to the wing which presses on it will have the greatest density."

In effect, therefore, he calls for a quick wing movement to trap, and so to compress, the air cushion to provide increased upwards pressure and therefore increased lift. In his sketch he shows how the elevation of the shoulders at *m* and *o* do this. Thus he writes: "When the bird

Fig. 98.   Wing movement to induce lift.

shall be in the position *anc* [Fig. 98] and shall wish to rise, it will elevate the shoulders *m* and *o*, and will thus be in the position *bmnod*, and the air will be pressed between the sides and the point of the wings so that it will be condensed and cause an upward movement and give rise to an impetus in the air, which impetus of the air will push the bird upwards by its condensation."[3]

One of the most important aspects of the "heavier-than-air" theory is that concerned with the relationship between centre of gravity and centre of pressure. Leonardo's treatment of the relationship between the centre of gravity of a bird in flight and the centre of pressure of the wind pressing on the wings of the bird, must not be pressed too closely in terms of their accurate, present-day significance. It is, in fact, quite extraordinary that any conception of these two factors, even in their broadest terms, was known to him at all at this time. What quite clearly emerges from a study of Leonardo's notebooks is that he understood, firstly, that while the centre of gravity was a fixed point in any

[1] *Sul Volo degli Uccelli*, 4 v.   [2] *Codex Atlanticus*, 161 r.a.   [3] *Sul Volo degli Uccelli*, 13 (12) r.

given body, such as a bird in flight, the centre of pressure (he called it the centre of resistance) shifted according to circumstances; and secondly, that this shift of the centre of pressure in relation to the fixed centre of gravity produced an immediate change in the nature of the flight of the bird. This, of course, is one of the fundamentals of elementary aerodynamics. The centre of pressure actually shifts with the varying angles formed by the wing surface to the direction of the air opposing it—and nowadays its position can be calculated for any given angle and for any given amount of wing surface.

Although Figs. 99 and 100 are perhaps over-simplifications of what can happen to an aircraft in flight, they will serve to show the nature of this relationship between the centre of gravity and the centre of pressure. It should first be noted that (*a*) The centre of gravity of the

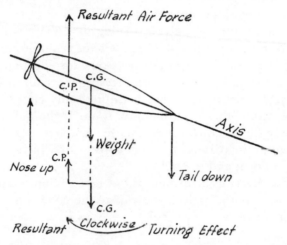

Fig. 99.   Centre of pressure in front of centre of gravity.

aircraft (Leonardo would call it the bird) is a fixed and unalterable point. It belongs, so to speak, to the machine or bird and is the point within it (regarded for convenience as being situated on the longitudinal axis of the machine) at which the weight of the machine can be considered to be concentrated. The weight, of course, acts vertically downwards, as shown in both figures. (*b*) The centre of pressure, on the other hand, is external to the machine, but, like the centre of gravity, is the point (again on the longitudinal axis) through which the total lifting forces of the moving air may be regarded as being concentrated. This lifting force is really a complicated and varying quantity, but its resultant effect is upwards, just as the resultant weight effect of the aircraft is downwards. To be more accurate, however, the lifting force is not necessarily quite vertically upwards but nearly so; and, to be more precise, what we are really concerned with is the vertical component of this nearly upwards lifting force.

If then these two forces, the internal downwards weight of the aircraft, acting through its centre of gravity, and the external upwards lifting force, acting through its centre of pressure (or, as Leonardo called it, its centre of resistance), are equal to each other in amount, and if they both pass through the same point on the axis, they would just balance each other and the thrust of the propellers would smoothly carry the aircraft along in the direction of the longitudinal axis.

But what if they do not pass through the same point on the longitudinal axis of the aircraft? Suppose, for example, that through any cause the centre of pressure moves along the axis say towards the nose, as in Fig. 99. It will be obvious in that case that the two forces, i.e. the weight W downwards, acting through the centre of gravity, and the effective wind pressure P upwards, acting through the centre of pressure, will set up a clockwise turning movement which will tend to bring the nose up and the tail down. Changes of this kind frequently occur during flight, and indeed are necessary for effective manœuvres, but so long as they are controlled changes they are all to the good.

Conversely, as seen in Fig. 100, if through any cause the centre of pressure moves the other way, namely, towards the tail, then the two forces, the weight W downwards and the wind pressure P upwards, now create an anti-clockwise turning movement which would tend to bring the nose down and the tail up.

Leonardo da Vinci clearly knew about this, though naturally, in the absence of exact mathematical knowledge, he could only deal with it in a very general way. Nevertheless here, as in so many other cases,

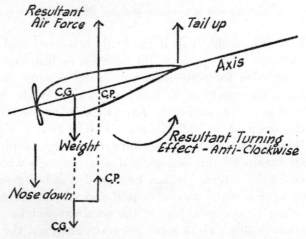

Fig. 100. Centre of pressure behind the centre of gravity.

his combination of accuracy of observation with scientific intuition was quite remarkable. Consider the following passage, for example: "When, without the assistance of the wind and without beating its wings, the bird remains in the air in the position of equilibrium, this shows that the centre of gravity is coincident with the centre of pressure. When a bird which is in equilibrium throws the centre of resistance of the wings behind the centre of gravity, then it will descend with its head downwards. A bird which finds itself in equilibrium will have the centre of pressure of the wings more forward than the bird's centre of gravity; and such a bird will fall with its tail towards the earth."[1]

Or, looking at the matter from the point of view of manœuvre, we read: "When the bird sinks, then the centre of gravity is outside the centre of resistance; as if the centre of gravity were on the line *ab* [Fig. 101(A)] and the centre of resistance on the line *cd* and if the bird

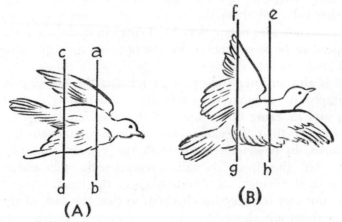

Fig. 101.   Relation between centre of gravity and centre of pressure in bird flight.

wishes to rise, then the centre of gravity remains behind the centre of resistance as if the centre of gravity might be *fg* and the centre of resistance would be *eh*" (Fig. 101(B)).[2]

And now let us see what Leonardo had to say about the function of the tail of a bird in flight. Naturally, in this particular matter, it is not easy to make comparisons with the modern aeroplane, since while in the case of the bird there is merely a tail, manipulated by muscular control, in the case of the aircraft there are both tail plane and fin, each with separate functions, to say nothing of the rudder. On the other hand, there is the interesting physiological fact that a bird can so adjust the flexure of the constituent components of its wings as to enable it to vary the relative positions of the centres of gravity and

---

[1] *Sul Volo degli Uccelli*, 8 (7) v.   [2] Ibid., 16 (15) v.

pressure.[1] It was once thought that this control was aided by the air sacs which birds have as supplementary to their wing supply, but this view has now been abandoned. This undoubtedly provides the bird with a mechanism for stability and control that is denied to the artificial machine without the carefully designed additions of the tail, fin and rudder.

But let Leonardo speak for himself on the use of the tail in bird flight (note once again his familiar use of the analogy of a ship and its sails): "Beginnings of things are often the cause of great results. Thus we may see a small imperceptible movement of the rudder turn a ship of marvellous size and loaded with a very heavy cargo and that, too, amid such weight of water as presses on its every beam, and in the teeth of the impetuous winds enveloping its mighty sails. So, in those birds which can support themselves above the course of the winds without beating their wings, a slight movement of wing or tail, serving them to enter either below or above the wind, suffices to prevent their fall."[2]

And we should also note a very brief entry in notebook L that reads: "The speed of birds is checked by the opening and spreading out of the tail."[3]

There is also an interesting passage relating the function of the tail to the important manœuvre of landing. This is how it reads: "The opening and lowering of the tail and the simultaneous spreading out of the wings to their full extent, arrests the swift movement of birds. When birds, in descending, approach the ground and the head is below the tail, they lower the tail, spread it wide open and take short strokes with the wings: as a consequence, the head becomes higher than the tail and the speed is checked, so that the bird alights on the ground without any shock."[4]

What, in effect, this means is that the bird *induces*, by both spread of tail and the strokes of the wing, an appropriate shifting of the centre of pressure to set up the necessary *clockwise* turning effect that will bring the nose up and the tail down.

We turn next to the subject of soaring flight—that is to say, flight without the beating of wings—in so far as it was developed by Leonardo da Vinci. In this, more than in any other branch of the study of natural flight, Leonardo excelled in the care and accuracy of his observations. It was known to Leonardo that the power of birds in keeping poised in the air for long periods with apparently very little effort is aided to

[1] This is discussed in detail by J. B. Pettigrew, *On the Physiology of Wings*, trans. of the Royal Society of Edinburgh, vol. 26 (1871), p. 365; see also Blanche Simpson, *Wings*, pp. 133 and 142-3 (London, 1955).
[2] *Codex Atlanticus*, 308 v.b.
[3] MS. *L*, 5 v.
[4] Ibid, 58 v.

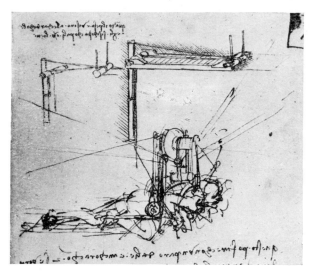

Plate 121 — Prone-type flying machine with windlass mechanism and twin "oars" (MS. B. 79 r.).

Plate 122 — Flying machine with pilot upright. Note the undercarriage device and twin "wings" (MS. B. 80 r.).

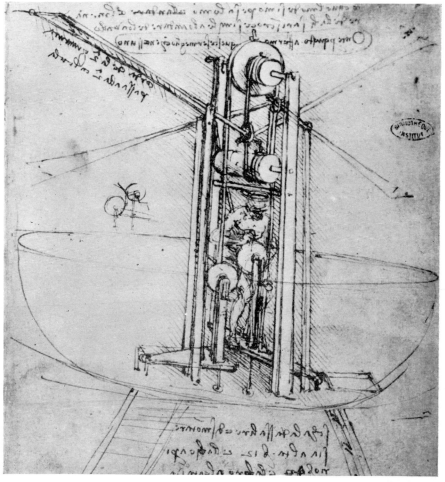

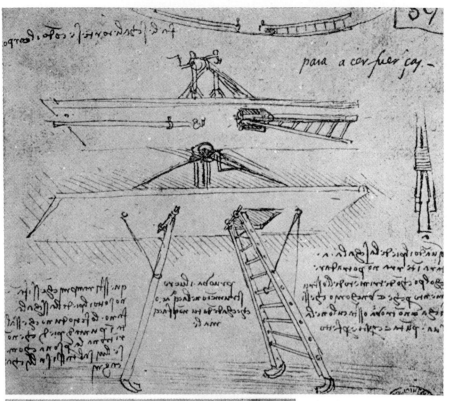

Plate 123—Detail of undercarriage features (MS. B. 89 r.).

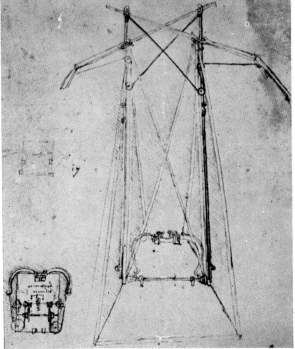

Plate 124—Design for flying machine with supplementary spring-operated power (C.A. 314 r.b.).

some extent by the existence of varying air currents at different levels. "The imperceptible fluttering of the wings," he writes, "without any actual stroke keeps the bird poised and motionless amid the moving air."[1] He also knew that some of the features of the flight and buoyancy of birds are due to their instinctive knowledge and utilisation of air movements which normally appear almost too fine for detection. Thus we read: "The kite and other birds that move their wings very little seek the air currents, and when the wind is blowing high up then they will be seen at a great height and if the wind blows low down they remain low down. When there is little wind the kite beats several times with its wings during flight so that it may rise and obtain impetus, with which impetus descending a little, it goes a long distance without beating its wings; and when it has dropped somewhat it repeats the movements and so successively; and this drop without beating the wings serves as a means of repose in the air after the fatigue of the said beating of the wings."[2]

It is known that air currents are influenced by ground obstacles, such as hills and woods. That da Vinci was to some extent aware of this influence of ground contour on air currents is evident from the following passage: "Nature has so provided that all the large birds can stay at so great an elevation that the wind which increases their flight may be of straight course and powerful. If their flight were low, among mountains where the wind goes wandering and is perpetually full of eddies and whirlwinds they would be unable to find any spot of shelter by reason of the fury of the icy blasts among the narrow defiles of the mountains, nor would they be able to so guide themselves with their great wings as to avoid being dashed upon the cliffs and high rocks and trees, and this would sometimes prove to be the cause of their destruction."[3]

We turn finally to some of the problems of manœuvre and control in bird flight which da Vinci included in his notes. We have of necessity already met with some examples of manœuvre and control in discussing the functions of the tail, but there are of course others. As an instance, let us consider the manœuvre of turning. The necessity for "banking" was well known to da Vinci, who tells us that "when the bird wishes to turn to the right or the left by beating its wings then it will beat lower with the wing on the side to which it wishes to turn [Fig. 102] and thus the bird will turn the movement behind the impetus of the wing which moves most."[4]

In another note he returned to his familiar device of a comparison with a boat on the water. His note reads: "The bird beats its wing repeatedly on one side only when it wishes to turn round while one

[1] *Codex Atlanticus*, 308 v.b.
[2] *Sul Volo degli Uccelli*, 6 (5) v.
[3] *Codex Atlanticus*, 308 v.b.
[4] *Sul Volo degli Uccelli*, 6 (5) r.

Y

Fig. 102. Banking on a turn.

wing is held stationary; and this it does by taking a stroke with the
wing in the direction of the tail, like a man rowing in a boat with two
oars, who takes many strokes on that side from which he wishes to
escape, and keeps the other fixed."[1]

In the notebook *On the Flight of Birds* there is a special reference to
the manœuvre of sudden turning, in which Leonardo makes use of the
principle of inertia. This, as we have already noted (p. 211), is one of
the fundamentals of Newtonian physics, which Galileo first discussed
in the year 1638. Leonardo's note referring to the principle of inertia
is extremely lucid. It accompanies a sketch of the type of Fig. 103
and reads: "When a bird wishes to turn itself suddenly on one of its
sides, then it quickly pushes the point of the wing on this side towards
its tail and, because all movement tends to maintenance, or rather all
moved bodies continue to move as long as the impression of the force
of their motors remains in them, the movement of such a wing thrust
with violence towards the tail reserving still at the end a part of the
impression, not being able by itself to follow the movement com-
menced at first, will move all the bird with itself, until the impetus
of the moved air may be consumed. The tail pushes with its face and

Fig. 103. Manœuvre of sudden turning.

[1] MS. *K*, 7 r.

the wind struck by it makes the bird move suddenly in the contrary direction."[1]

We conclude this survey of Leonardo's discussions on bird manœuvre with a reference to his treatment of gusts. Leonardo frequently refers to the conscious varying of the extent of the wing surface a bird presents to the wind as a method of maintaining control and equilibrium. Against a diagram of the type shown in Fig. 104, he writes:

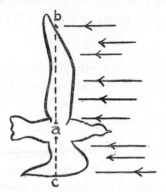

Fig. 104. Wing control in a gust.

"When the wind strikes the wing, then such a bird will turn itself, with its spine to the wind, and if the wind were more powerful below than above, then the bird would turn upside down if it did not immediately take care to draw in the wider wing and stretch out the upper wing. In this manner it rights itself and returns to the position of equilibrium. The proof is thus: Let *ac* be the wing withdrawn under the bird, and *ab* be the extended wing, I say that the forces of the wind that strike the two wings will have the same proportion as that of their extensions, that is to say, as *ab* to *ac*."[2]

[1] *Sul Volo degli Uccelli*, 13 (12) r.　　　[2] Ibid., 9 (8) v.

X

THE PROBLEM OF LEONARDO'S
INFLUENCE ON SCIENTIFIC PROGRESS

We have confined ourselves in this theme of flight, as in our earlier discussions on Leonardo's physical and mechanical science and engineering, to but a few examples from his notebooks, characteristic of many. They suffice, however, to show how he matched the keenness of his observations on birds with the application to them of the fundamental principles of mechanics. To Leonardo da Vinci there was no difference in principle between the problems of co-ordination and control in bird flight and those of co-ordination and control in mechanisms. But how unfortunate it was that, in telling us that "a bird is an instrument working according to mathematical law . . . which it is within the capacity of man to reproduce", all his attempts at such reproduction were in vain. The order of his effort was at fault. His intense activity in aircraft design, based uselessly on ornithopters, came first, and his wiser discussions on soaring flight came after. But perhaps by then it was too late for him to apply these discussions to the safer logic of rigid-wing aircraft. He was approaching the end of his life and his health was none too good. Nevertheless, the quotation above-mentioned remains true, not merely as an inspired prophecy but also as a statement of fact. Moreover, Leonardo had contributed the principles of the parachute and the helicopter. These were positive achievements indeed; and even though they had to be discovered afresh by subsequent investigators, they remain as the specific creations of a great investigator.

And this brings us back to the frustrating question (previously referred to in Chapter VI), of *why* Leonardo's work should have been so completely lost to the world for so long, and why later workers in the scientific field should have been denied the knowledge of his valuable contributions to their respective specialities.

It seems almost inconceivable that during Leonardo's active lifetime there was no informed knowledge of what he was doing scientifically. Yet almost certainly, apart from some inevitable gossip, few people could have been involved in his experiments, even as onlookers, let alone collaborators. In the world of science Leonardo on the whole played a lone hand. The only avowed collaborators on record, as we have seen, were Pacioli the mathematician, and de la Torre, the anatomist. Scrappy notes refer to others fleetingly but the links seem of little consequence other than in the matter of borrowing a few books, with perhaps some occasional discussion. Yet Leonardo nevertheless moved and lived in centres of scholarship.

In the scientific field, however, the fifteenth century on the whole contains few names of note. It was, as Burckhardt has stated, a period of "many-sided men"[1] a few only of whom were "all-sided". Of these few, none reached the stature of Leon Battista Alberti, and he was as far below Leonardo as was the *dilettante* to the master. The relatively great men of science of the calibre and stature of Toscanelli, for example, who might have had creative links with da Vinci, were elderly when Leonardo was a youth, and were of a generation that knew not Leonardo the investigator. It was more a world of letters than of science and, as we have seen (p. 27), Leonardo lacked the classical culture and the inclination to share this world.

The patrons of learning who so largely determined the atmosphere of culture in fifteenth-century Italy, were the men of power—the Medicis, the d'Este, the Sforzas, the great Popes like Nicholas V, republican heads like Francis Barbaro of Venice, the great Alphonso, conqueror of the Kingdom of Naples, and so on. Their courts were thronged with scholars, but the main trend of their scholarship was letters—philosophy and science had no great share in their professions. This was characteristic, too, of the universities and the lycea. Florence in particular was a centre of distinction in the study of Greek and Latin literature. Other university centres of the times in Tuscany included Pisa, Arezzo and Siena, in each of which a strong legal school had developed.

Medicine, more as an art than as a science, continued amid all this, somewhat lost among the traditions of the great Arabic doctors whose books dominated both the training and the practice of the medical profession. A few among the medieval scholars of the fifteenth century attained some reputation above the common level. Such included Nicholas Leoniceno, author of a natural history; his friend and rival Poliziano; Ugo Benzi of Siena, who held medical chairs in a number of universities; and the surgeon Agliacozzi of Bologna, whose reputation appears to have been founded on the art of restoring a large piece of lost nose to a deformed countenance!

In the mathematical field we have already mentioned Pacioli as the outstanding representative of his day and one of the few known

[1] J. Burckhardt, *The Civilisation of the Renaissance in Italy*, p. 85 (London, 1944).

collaborators with Leonardo. Tuscany was one of the first countries which taught algebraical operations, introduced earlier from the Arabs by the Pisan Fibonacci, and Pacioli became its great exponent. Also, bearing in mind that mathematics was the essential instrument of astronomy, we should recall that Copernicus was himself a fifteenth-century student in Italy in the University of Bologna, his teacher being the distinguished astronomer (and astrologer!) Domenico Maria Novara of Ferrara (1454–1504). When Copernicus completed his studies in Bologna he went to Rome to teach astronomy there in his turn.

Other names in the mathematical and astronomical field of those days included William Becchi, Bishop of Fiesole, who dedicated his observations on comets to Cosimo de' Medici in the year 1456; Goro di Saggio Dati and his brother, Fra Leonardo, who wrote of the movements of the celestial bodies in heroic verse (a method of scientific writing that was almost a vogue); Guilliano Bellarti, famous as an astrologer, who reasoned ingenuously on the irregularity of the solar and lunar movements; Lorenzo Buonincontri, astronomer, astrologer, poet, historian and very much a wanderer.

Amid all these, the Florentine Paolo Toscanelli (b. 1397) stands out boldly with a level of scholarship far ahead of his contemporaries. He scorned the side-tracking lure of astrology, cultivated both Greek and Latin literature, particularly in the fields of medicine and natural philosophy, studied mathematics under Brunelleschi, and so passed on to astronomy and geography. His construction of the great gnomon of the sun-dial of S. Maria del Fiore is a lasting tribute to his memory. He lived to a ripe old age of eighty years, and although he left little in the way of writings, his fame was world-wide. We have already referred to the extent to which he was consulted by the scholars of many countries, and for us it is important to recall that he directly influenced Leonardo da Vinci in his early days. As we have also mentioned, Toscanelli's authority and advice was a great spur to Christopher Columbus in his famous voyage of discovery.

With this reference to Columbus we should also record that Amerigo Vespucci, whose later voyage gave the name of America to the new continent, was also a Florentine.

Also, too, we have the relatively shining star of Leon Battista Alberti —less erudite perhaps than Toscanelli in the specialist fields with which the name of the latter is associated—but brilliant nevertheless in his many-sided activities. Born in 1404, he must have been something of a prodigy in "drawing-room" accomplishments and outside sports as well as in early intellectual promise. He studied canon law in Bologna, became a priest, and was a Florentine canon at twenty.

Poet, Latin scholar, scientist, architect (his Ten Books of Architecture
—*de re Architectura*—written in elegant Latin and translated in many
languages, gave him the title of the modern Vitruvius), he was also an
experimenter and an inventor. He died in 1472, when Leonardo was
but twenty years of age; and as we have seen, Leonardo at all times
showed great interest in his writings and experiments.

Other names worthy of mention as more immediately contemporary
with Leonardo were Giovanni Battista Capuano of Manfredonia
(fl. *c.* 1475), Allesandro Achillini of Bologna (1463–1512), and Agus-
tino Nifo (1473–1538) in the field of mechanics; and the fifteenth-
century encyclopaedist, Raphael Maffei of Volterra. Maffei was born
in 1454, two years later than Leonardo, and became well versed in
both Latin and Greek. He wrote a *Commentaria Urbana*, a sort of
magazine of general knowledge extending to thirty-eight volumes,
covering geography, history, the rudiments of the arts, the scientific
knowledge current in his day (as he understood it), and a record of the
voyages of the great navigators.

Such then was the standard and range of scholarship in Leonardo's
Italy in the fields of mathematics and science. The standards of literature and art were much higher and wider, but these lie outside our
province. So too does the field of politics, whose illustrious representative
Macchiavelli was, in fact, an acquaintance, if not a friend, of Leonardo.
What we have to consider is whether, in such a contemporary company,
there was any possibility that Leonardo's own work and interests—
apart, of course, from his art—could have been known to, let alone
have influenced, those about him in his own lifetime. The whole
weight of probability is against this. In his earlier years he met many
men of intellect and erudition, particularly during the period of his
training with Verrocchio; but he was then the listener and the learner.
Later, when he became the master, his labours were carried out in
solitude and his records were kept in a form difficult to decipher. His
duties, both ceremonial and military, naturally involved him in many
contacts but they were not of the type that could materially help to
disseminate his many important theories and discussions in the scientific
field. The one great type of intellectual organisation in which his
talents and his contributions might have found a medium for consideration, the Florentine Academy, was a Platonic institution in which
he found no place and from which he was effectively excluded. The
later and more specifically scientific Florentine Academy was not to be
created for another two centuries.

We must not, however, get this matter out of perspective. Leonardo
was a man of acknowledged distinction in art and engineering, whose
services were eagerly sought after by the rulers and leaders around him.

And, as a matter of general gossip, everyone knew that he was actively interested in problems of science covering a very wide ground. But clearly, outside his art and engineering, he was left to himself in the pursuit of these manifold activities.

There is one somewhat rare element in this story. Almost invariably in history those who have an absorbing and expert interest find others of similar interests with whom they can discuss and argue, agree or disagree—men who can stimulate each other and help to develop their mutual interests and researches further. But in the case of Leonardo's science, at any rate, there is no evidence or record of such mutual influences. His friendship with Pacioli, for example, was somewhat one-sided in the sense that Leonardo himself was fundamentally no mathematician. He appreciated the importance of mathematics completely, but it was not in him to advance the subject in any way himself. On the other hand, his friendship with the young anatomist, de la Torre, was one in which the two could, and probably did, work together, but de la Torre himself unfortunately died at a very early age.

We must accept, therefore, that when Leonardo died in 1519, with his work fully recorded in his many notes, very little was known regarding their contents, and very little curiosity was expressed about them. So we come to the relatively long period from 1519 to 1570, during which the notebooks were in the care of Francesco Melzi, to whom Leonardo had bequeathed them; and the suggestion has been generally accepted that they were treated by him as secret matters to be kept rigorously from inquisitive eyes. The historian of aeronautics, Gibbs-Smith, speaks of Melzi's attitude towards his duties as executor as one of "culpable stupidity"; and certainly he would seem to have acted in a misguided way over his charge. Melzi had been a faithful companion to Leonardo long enough to know that the master had all along intended publication "sooner or later", and also that the notes must have included much material of great originality and worth. Moreover, they had become his own personal property, and there was therefore no question of withholding them from posterity on behalf of some other owner. He should, at least, have sought advice and guidance as to the wisest way of dealing with the notebooks. But he did not do so, and the consequences were enormous.

But fifty years is a long time. It is incredible to think that over this period there were no curious or importuning eyes cast at the "hidden store". There simply must have been at least intermittent informed gossip about the notebooks and it is very probable that from time to time Melzi would have shown them to interested visitors, even if he persistently refused to part with them. Cardan the elder, for instance (1444–1524), to whom we have already referred as a lawyer of repute with a serious interest in optics was a personal friend of Leonardo who had had opportunities to appreciate the value of his work; and his less scrupulous son, the younger Cardan, is known to have acquired and used some of Leonardo's material (see below).

There were, of course, during the period covered by Francesco Melzi's custody of Leonardo's notebooks, a number of scholars of some repute in the scientific field who, although perhaps late contemporaries of Leonardo da Vinci, were nevertheless too young in da Vinci's old age to have been directly influenced by him. Such, for instance, were the mathematician Niccolo Tartaglia, who was born at Brescia, near Milan, in 1500, and therefore was a youth of nineteen when Leonardo died; Geronimo Cardan, born in Milan in 1501—a youth of eighteen in 1519; Petrus Apianus (1495–1552), a cosmographer; and Raphael Bombelli, who was probably born at the beginning of the sixteenth century. Bombelli's memory rests chiefly on his reputation as a sixteenth-century algebraist. His treatise on this subject was published by him in 1572, shortly before his death. But he was also known to be very greatly interested in hydraulics and in those problems of marsh drainage that held such fascination for Leonardo da Vinci; and he was, in fact, employed for such work by Alessandro Rufini, Bishop of Melfi. Nevertheless, there is no evidence whatsoever that he was either aware of, or influenced by, either similar work and procedures by Leonardo, or by any of Leonardo's notes on the subject.

The case of Geronimo Cardan, on the other hand, is different, if only because his father *did* know Leonardo personally. Amid a stormy but brilliant career, the younger Cardan may well have found means to acquire some inkling as to the contents of occasional loose notes from Leonardo's collection; and he may well have used such information without either scruple or acknowledgment. Yet even here there is no direct evidence of such influence on Cardan's work of the type that might have advanced the world's knowledge in the material way that could have been possible with so many of Leonardo's scientific discoveries.

One other sixteenth-century man of science should finally be referred to, namely, Simon Stevin (latinised to Stevinus), because, although not an Italian, his fruitful work traversed so many of the subjects that had similarly interested Leonardo. Stevinus earns a very high place in the records of science for his distinguished researches in both mathematics and mechanics. He was born in Bruges in 1548 and probably had no contacts, either directly or indirectly, with Italy or Italian philosophers. But he was a man of remarkable attainments whose studies in many ways paralleled those of Leonardo. He was interested in the problems of forces and their effects, he studied pulley systems, he used (but did not formulate formally) the principle of the parallelogram of forces and its converse, and he carried out a series of brilliant investigations on the forces acting upon a body on an inclined plane that were later most fruitfully followed up by Galileo. In mathematics, too, Stevinus made notable contributions. He introduced the idea of decimal fractions, and developed the theory of equations.

Stevinus was definitely a man of the Renaissance. Yet not only was he after Leonardo's day, but all his writings were in Dutch. His main work on statics and hydraulics was published in 1586, which brings him midway between Leonardo da Vinci and Galileo. Yet his work, based on Archimedes, showed no Italian influences. It may well have been that he was aware of possible Italian work in the same field, but the whole trend of his arguments show them to have been based fairly and squarely upon the writings of Archimedes. It is worth a thought to consider how much farther he might have gone (since, after all, when Simon Stevin's works were published in 1586 Orazio Melzi, Francesco's brother, had not only inherited the manuscripts, but had well set in train the general dispersal of the notebooks in the manner described in Chapter V—a dispersal that scarcely embraced those who, like Stevinus, were specially interested in science and technology) if, instead, the notebooks had been freely available to those who could usefully have used them.

In an earlier chapter, however, we referred to Giambattista della Porta as a material contributor to the story of the evolution of steam power and as a possible example of the few who may have been directly influenced by Leonardo's notes (p. 296). Here indeed we are on more plausible ground. A Neapolitan (1535(?)–1615), he both read and travelled widely. As a youth he showed considerable precocity; and as a man of ingrained scientific curiosity he wandered everywhere among libraries, book stores and workshops, and mixed freely with all sorts and conditions of men. Not surprisingly, therefore, he could be somewhat superficial in his own prolific thinking and writing. For example, in the field of optics he published a book in 1558 called the *Magia Naturalis* (*Natural Magic*), which gained considerable popularity. Yet a far better man of science, Francesco Maurolycus (born of Greek origin at Messina in Palermo in 1494), who lived variously at Naples, Rome and back again at Messina, where he taught mathematics until his death in 1575, had gained far less popularity with a far better work, the *De Refractione*. (Actually, his best optical book, the *Photisini*, was not published until 1611. This has been regarded as one of the ablest optical works of the Renaissance.)

Della Porta wrote on all sorts of topics, and he claims that the scientific work previously referred to, the *Magia Naturalis sive de mir-*

aculis rerum naturalium (*Natural Magic, or Miracles of the World of Nature*), was begun by him at the age of fifteen. It was a queer hotch-potch that found its way on the *Index Expurgatorius* of the Catholic Church. But amid all the varied levels and standards of his work, his important experiment on the raising of water from one level to a higher with the aid of steam power, which we have previously discussed, and which carried with it the implications of sources of information derived from Leonardo, remains one of the outstanding high-lights of his achievements. With his keen nose for gossip and "information", it may well have been possible for him to have acquired some knowledge of Melzi's store of notes upon which to base an idea or two for his own experiments.

But let us return to Melzi himself and note what attention was in fact being paid to his treasures. One writer has suggested that "in order to enhance the fame of his master, Melzi permitted copies to be made of various manuscripts and, with some restrictions, allowed various artists and scientists to use the collection".[1] As a matter of common sense, one feels that over the span of the years this may well have happened from time to time. However reluctant Melzi may have been, he must surely have succumbed to pressure occasionally.

As early as 1523 Alfonso d'Este, Duke of Ferrara, was advised by a visitor to Milan (Alberto Bendedeo): "that a brother of his [i.e. of Melzi's] . . . knows many of Leonardo's secrets and opinions . . . and I believe that he has those little notebooks of Leonardo's and lots of other precious things."

The first reasonably authentic known biography of Leonardo da Vinci was a short one in Vasari's famous *Lives of the Painters*, first published in 1550 in Florence, with a second edition in 1568.[2] Vasari is known to have visited the Melzi household in May 1566 and almost certainly he gained more than a peep at the manuscripts. He writes thus: "Leonardo wrote letters in a rough reversed style with his left hand. He [Francesco Melzi?] has not tried to read them and does not intend to do so as they can only be read with a magnifying glass. A lot of his [Leonardo's] anatomical drawings are in the hands of Francesco da Melzo, a Milanese gentleman who, in Leonardo's time, was a beautiful child and much loved by him; even as today he is a handsome and courteous old man; and he cherishes these drawings along with his happy memories of Leonardo. To anyone who sees these works it seems impossible that this divine spirit could have discussed art, and muscles and nerves and veins, with such diligence in each detail. Again,

---

[1] A. P. Usher, *A History of Mechanical Inventions*, p. 109 (Harvard, 1954).

[2] There was, in fact, an earlier (and shorter) biography by the anonymous "Magliabechiamis", which also includes a reference to the manuscripts. (See Appendix I to J. P. Richter's *Literary Works of Leonardo da Vinci*, 2nd ed., 1939.)

a Milanese painter has some writings of Leonardo, in the same left-hand characters, which discuss design and colour. He came to Florence recently to see me, wishing to have this work printed, and took it to Rome to carry out his plan, with what result I know not."

Since elsewhere Vasari claims that he himself was in possession of some of Leonardo's drawings, there must have been substance in the view that there were leaks in the tightness of Francesco Melzi's hold on his treasures.

The real hunt was up after Francesco's death, and we have already surveyed the broad story of the dispersal of the notebooks and their subsequent study. These happenings, however, were too late to have effected any serious influence upon the work of scientific investigation and research. All that Leonardo had done and achieved remained to be accomplished all over again by subsequent investigators at various times in various places.

A review of the slow story of the dispersal of and hunt for the notebooks and sketches tends to show that those mainly interested were either wealthy collectors or patrons of art. There is little evidence of any specific desire to recover the notebooks for the sake of their scientific content. The public memory is always fleeting. The knowledge in Leonardo's own lifetime that he was a great artist must have been very general. The fact that he was frequently employed as a military and civil engineer was almost certainly less generally known, but this was still a matter of importance and interest to appropriate sections of the community. But that Leonardo was almost continually concerned with matters of science and experiment could only be known in the more distant sense of vague gossip. His views and procedures were far too unorthodox for the acknowledged men of science who, in his day and times, were wedded to classical and ecclesiastical authority and to the orthodox procedures and disciplines of university life and teaching practice.

These were not the ingredients that could help to publicise the scientific work and the importance of Leonardo da Vinci. The "hush-hush" hints of the existence of volumes of notes written in a queer and secret caligraphy could be well understood; but only for the occasional person could these have had any special significance or importance. And with the death of Leonardo and the policy of deliberate reticence of Francesco Melzi, the forces of forgetfulness must have found rapid play. However many people there may have been with any sort of awareness of the nature and quality of Leonardo's writings in his lifetime, their numbers must have diminished very rapidly after his death.

On the whole, therefore, all his work had to be traversed over again. In spite of his many discoveries and inventions, known by the subsequent march of scientific and technological history to have been of major importance, it had to be left to a number of individual workers in many countries and at varying intervals of time to repeat, each in his own way, these separate contributions to the world's knowledge. Yet of what other man in history can we say that as physiologist, anatomist, biologist, architect, engineer or physicist, he was not only in the forefront of his contemporaries but was of a quality that belonged to the future?

And if the world has thus lost something in the pace of development of its scientific story, does this ultimately matter so very much? In the last analysis the records of civilisation must primarily be the concern of human beings *about* human beings. The personal records of civilisation have been forever enriched by the life, the personality, the capabilities and the outstanding achievements of Leonardo da Vinci. These will persist as a treasured memory wherever culture, scholarship and intellectual endeavour are revered as an essential contribution to the strivings of man towards the perfection of his life and his world.

THE PATTERN OF REFERENCES TO LEONARDO'S NOTEBOOKS

A, B, C, D, E, F, G, H, I, K, L, M—the notebooks in the Library of the Institut de France. Published by Ravaisson Mollien, Paris, 1881–1891, and including:

B.N. 2037 and *B.N.* 2038—originally part of MMS. *B* and *A* respectively. (*B.N.* denotes Bibliothèque Nationale, where they were formerly housed. They are now at the Institut de France.)

B.M.—the Arundel MS. Published by the Reale Commissione Vinciana, Rome, 1923–1930.

Codex Atlanticus.—*Codex Atlanticus*, in the Ambrosiana Library in Milan. Published by G. Piumati, Milan, 1894–1904.

Codice *N*—*Codice Sul Volo degli Uccelli* (Codex on the Flight of Birds, etc.) and originally labelled MS. *N*—in the Royal Library at Turin. Published in facsimile by Sabachnikoff, Paris, 1893.

Leic.—Codex of the Earl of Leicester at Holkham Hall, Norfolk. Published by G. Calvi, Milan, 1909.

Oxford—Sheets in the Library at Christ Church College, Oxford. Published by the Reale Commissione Vinciana, Rome.

S.K.M.—I, II and III—The Forster Manuscripts, in the Library of the Victoria and Albert Museum, South Kensington. Published by the Reale Commissione Vinciana, Rome, 1923–1930.

Triv.—*Codex Trivulzi*, formerly in the Trivulzi Palace, now housed in the Castello Sforzesco, Milan. Published by Belrami, Milan, 1891.

V—Sheets in the Academy at Venice. Published by the Reale Commissione Vinciana, Rome.

W—Manuscripts and Drawings *A* and *B* at the Royal Library, Windsor; catalogued by Sir Kenneth Clark, Cambridge, 1935. An earlier publication of these comprised the anatomical drawings and manuscripts in two volumes by Piumati and Sabachnikoff, Fogli *A* (Paris, 1898) and Fogli *B* (Turin, 1901) and the *Quaderni d'Anatomia* in six volumes by Vangenstan Fonahn and Hopstock (Oslo, 1911–1916).

THE CALLIGRAPHY USED BY LEONARDO DA VINCI IN HIS NOTEBOOKS

In his standard book on *The Literary Works of Leonardo da Vinci*, to which we have referred from time to time, Jean Paul Richter summarises the calligraphy of the notebooks by showing the letters of the alphabet and the numerals as Leonardo scribbled them. The reader who is interested may refer to these as necessary.

They are also described in detail by G. Calvi, *I Manoscritti di Leonardo da Vinci* (Bologna, 1925). (Fig. 3—"Prospetto di Carratteri e Segni Vinciani".)

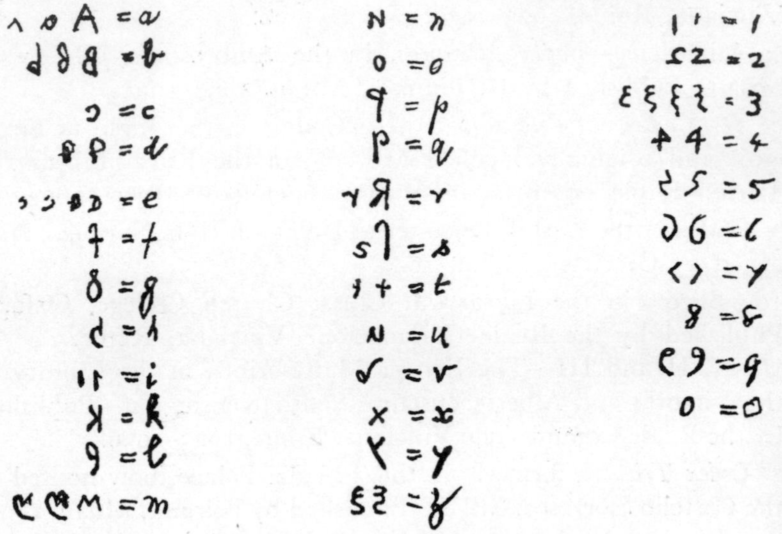

Fig. 105. Leonardo's calligraphy.

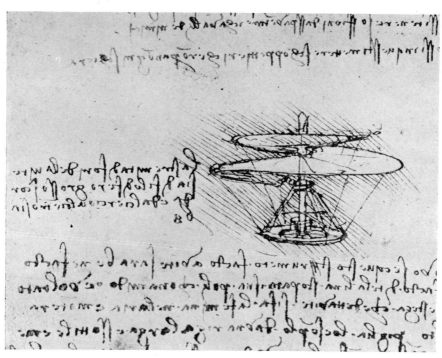

Plate 125—Leonardo's helicopter (MS. B. 83 v.).

Plate 126—Leonardo devises a fixed wing with ornithopter extensions
(C.A. 309 r.a.).

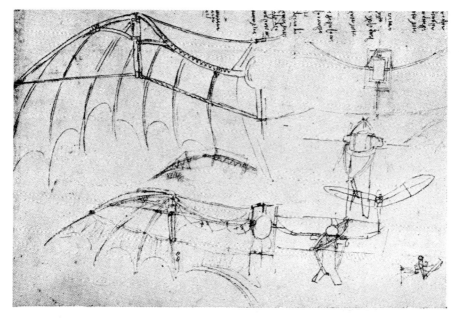

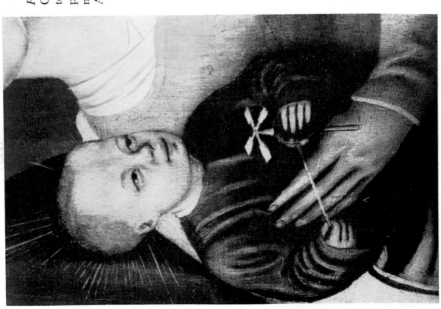

Plate 127 (left)—Christ Child with "whirligig" toy. From a medieval panel picture in the museum at Le Mans. Artist Unknown, c. 1460.

Plate 128 (right)—Portion of a stained-glass window (originally in the Church at Stoke Poges, Bucks., England) showing the Christ Child with a "helicopter" toy.

APPENDIX C

BIBLIOGRAPHY

The purpose of these lists is to provide suitable background reading for the non-specialist general reader.

All the books mentioned below are in English. There are naturally many others of equal competence and authority in other languages. Several have recently been re-issued as "paper-backs".

A. BACKGROUND TO THE RENAISSANCE PERIOD OF LEONARDO'S ITALY

The Ancient World, T. R. Glover. London, 1935.
The Greeks, H. D. F. Kitto. London, 1951.
The Romans, R. H. Barrow. London, 1949.
Rome Beyond the Imperial Frontiers, M. Wheeler. London, 1954.
The "Legacy" Series published by the Oxford University Press and comprising:

> *The Legacy of Greece.*
> *The Legacy of Rome.*
> *The Legacy of Islam.*
> *The Legacy of Israel.*
> *The Legacy of the Middle Ages.*

The Arabs, E. Aliyah. London, 1955.
The Arabs in History, Bernard Lewes. London, 1950.
Islam, E. Denison Ross. London, 1927.
The Emergence of Christian Culture in the West (The Classical Heritage of the Middle Ages), H. O. Taylor. New York, 1958.
Medieval Contributions to Modern Civilisation, Hearnshaw. London, 1921.
The Making of the Middle Ages, R. W. Southern. London, 1953.
Medieval Panorama, G. G. Coulton. Cambridge, 1938.
Medieval People, Eileen Power. London, 1924.
The Dark Ages, W. P. Ker. Edinburgh, 1904.
The Dark Ages, C. Oman, London, 1901.
The Waning of the Middle Ages, J. Huizinga. London, 1924.
Life in the Medieval University, R. S. Rait. Cambridge, 1912.
The Universities of Europe in the Middle Ages, H. Rashdall. Oxford, 1895.
The Wandering Scholars, Helen Waddell. London, 1932.

z

Medieval Man and His Notions, F. Harrison. London, 1947.
A Short History of Italian Literature, J. H. Whitfield. London, 1960.
The Civilisation of the Renaissance in Italy, J. Burckhardt. London, 1944.
The History of Tuscany (4 vols.), J. Browning. London, 1826.
The Renaissance in Italy—Age of the Despots, J. A. Symonds. London, 1897.
The Renaissance in Italy—The Revival of Learning, J. A. Symonds. London, 1906.
Celebrities of the Italian Renaissance, R. dela Sizeranne (Trs. by J. E. Jeffery). London, 1926.
The Renaissance and its Makers. J. D. Symon and S. L. Bensusan. London, 1913.

B. THE PHILOSOPHICAL BACKGROUND

A Sketch of Medieval Philosophy, D. J. B. Hawkins. London, 1947.
Medieval Philosophy, F. Copleston. London, 1952.
Medieval Thought, G. Leff. London, 1958.
The Great Mystics, G. Godwin. London, 1945.
A Short History of Christianity, J. M. Robertson. London, 1931.
A History of Philosophy, C. C. Webb. London (Home University Library).
Aquinas, F. Copleston. London, 1955.

C. THE SCIENTIFIC BACKGROUND

Science in Graeco-Roman Antiquity, A. Reymond. London, 1927.
The Works of Archimedes, T. L. Heath. Cambridge, 1907.
Aristotle, A. E. Taylor. London, 1919.
Life and Work of Roger Bacon, J. H. Bridges. London, 1914.
Plato and Aristotle, J. A. K. Thomson. London, 1928.
Seneca—Physical Science, Clacke & Geekie. London, 1909.
Science and Civilisation, Ed. F. S. Marvin. Oxford, 1923.
Introduction to the History of Science (Vol. 1), G. Sarton. Baltimore, 1927.
The Great Physicists, I. B. Hart. London, 1927.
Science and Literature in the Middle Ages, Paul Lacroix. London (n.d.), Published by Bickers and Son.
From Magic to Science, C. Singer. London, 1928.
History of Science and Experimental Magic (Vols. I and II), L. Thorndike. London, 1923.
Studies in the History of Medieval Science, C. H. Haskins. Cambridge, Mass., 1924.
Six Wings—Men of Science in the Renaissance, G. Sarton. London, 1957.
Short History of Science, C. Singer. Oxford, 1941.
Makers of Science, I. B. Hart. Oxford, 1925.

D. THE TECHNOLOGICAL BACKGROUND

History of Technology (Vols. I, II and III), Singer, Holmyard, Hall and Williams. Oxford, 1956.

A Short History of Technology, Derry and Williams. Oxford, 1961.

History of Mechanical Inventions, A. P. Usher. Cambridge, Mass., 1954.

The Quest for Power, H. P. and M. W. Vowles. London, 1931.

History of Science and Technology in the 16th Century, Wolf and McKie. London, 1947.

History of the Growth of the Steam Engine, R. Thurston. London, 1939.

Man the Maker, R. J. Forbes. London, 1950.

The Great Engineers, I. B. Hart. London, 1927.

Short History of Building Crafts, M. S. Briggs. Oxford, 1925.

Medieval English Industries, L. F. Salzman. Oxford, 1923.

Development of Bridges, W. N. Thomas. London, 1920.

The Sons of Vulcan (Story of Metals), T. Hibben. London, 1944.

History of Flying, C. H. Gibbs-Smith. London, 1953.

Wings (Insects, Birds, Men), Blanche Stillson. London, 1955.

The Aeroplane—An Historical Survey, C. H. Gibbs-Smith. London, 1960.

Engineers and Engineering in the Renaissance, W. B. Parsons. Baltimore, 1939.

E. STUDIES OF LEONARDO DA VINCI

The Literary Works of Leonardo da Vinci (two vols.), J. Paul Richter. Second Edition, Oxford, 1939.

The Notebooks of Leonardo da Vinci (two vols), E. McCurdy. Fifth edition, London, 1948.

The Mind of Leonardo da Vinci. E. McCurdy, London, 1932.

The Drawings of Leonardo da Vinci, A. E. Popham. London, 1947.

Leonardo da Vinci, Kenneth Clark. Cambridge, 1939; London, 1958.

Selections from the Notebooks of Leonardo da Vinci, Irma A. Richter. Oxford, 1952.

Leonardo—A Pictorial Biography, R. Friedenthal. London, 1959.

Leonardo da Vinci (two vols.), L. H. Heydenreich. London, 1956.

Leonardo the Florentine—A Study in Personality, R. A. Taylor. London, 1927.

Leonardo da Vinci, Antonina Vallentin. London, 1952.

The Mechanical Investigations of Leonardo da Vinci, I. B. Hart. London, 1925.

APPENDIX D

A NOTE ON LEONARDO'S
HELICOPTER MODEL

By Charles H. Gibbs-Smith

Just as this book was going to press, a further development of importance arose concerning the validity of the claim that Leonardo invented the helicopter. My friend and colleague, Mr. Charles Gibbs-Smith, has very kindly substituted a new note here instead of the appendix originally prepared by myself.—I.B.H.

Dr. Hart has kindly invited me to contribute this note on Leonardo's helicopter model. Until recently we have all accepted Leonardo as the inventor of the helicopter, either as an idea, or in the form of the helical screw model he drew in Manuscript B, fol. 83v.

Then, late in 1960, my friend Charles Dollfus drew my attention to a painting in the Museum at Le Mans in France, in which the Christ Child is standing on the Madonna's lap, and holding a curious little toy (see Plate 127 in the present work). The picture is by an anonymous artist of the Le Mans area, painted about 1460. The presence of such a sophisticated toy points to such a device already being well known at the time, and dating in essence from long before.

The items beyond dispute are the string wound round the shaft of a four-bladed rotor (which rests in a spherical container) and the child pulling the string to rotate the rotor. Dollfus had assumed that it was a helicopter toy in which the rotor—after a strong pull on the string—was rapidly rotated and rose out of the container and high into the air. The string would have been threaded through the hole seen, and wound onto the shaft, through a carved-out aperture in the other side of the container, as seen in Cayley's similar toy of 1853. I assumed the same sequence of events when I received the photograph. This toy, therefore, would definitely pre-date anything that Leonardo thought of in the helicopter field, and presumably is related to a toy believed to have originated in China.

But Dollfus and I were led to modify our opinions after consulting Miss A. Scott Elliot (Keeper of the Prints and Drawings in the Royal Library at Windsor Castle), who pointed out that whirligig toys were well known at the time, and this was probably one of them. Whirligigs

356

are toys that are spun round and form intriguing patterns by the motion of their arms, or patterns made on a flat surface, etc. Miss Scott Elliot then agreed with me that this particular toy must have been on the helicopter principle, owing to the close analogy with the contemporary windmill sails, and with the little propeller toys already well-known in Europe; it would, we supposed, rise up and then sink down, to rise up again at the next pull on the string. Dollfus also agreed that this was the answer to our problem. A similar toy is shown in a stained-glass window of a little later date, which was formerly at Stoke Poges, and is now lost (Plate 128).

The whole position has now been changed through a discovery by Mr. John Lowe (the authority on stained glass in the Victoria and Albert Museum) who telephoned me to come and see a French panel of glass from Normandy (dated about 1525) which he had placed on exhibition after many years in store. He knew of my interest in these toys, and had found one in this piece of glass. When I saw it, there was one small but vital difference in basic character which immediately convinced me that all these toys were in fact true helicopter models with their rotors rising up in free flight, and not 'captive' whirligigs. The difference may appear small at first but it is decisive. For on the end of the string in the boy's upraised hand is not just a button or knot, but a large handle, like the grip of a sub-machine gun. This can only be for one purpose: to allow the child to get a good grip for a good strong pull on the string; and that can only be to give the rotor a rapid initial rotation to send it spinning upwards.

I am convinced that the Chinese top had found its way from China across the Middle Eastern trade routes many years before, following printing types, gunpowder, the rocket, and many other devices; and that it had been adapted for European toys. I am afraid that this deprives Leonardo of being the first to invent the helicopter in Europe, and will force us to rewrite the history of the origins of the rotating wing aircraft.

z*

INDEX